The Family
Treasury of
Children's Stories

Book Two

The Family
Treasury of
Children's Stories

edited by PAULINE RUSH EVANS

illustrated by DONALD SIBLEY

DOUBLEDAY & COMPANY, INC., *Garden City, New York*

Pauline Rush Evans has had wide experience in working with parents and children. After she received her M.A. in Child Psychology from Columbia, she joined the staff of the Child Study Association of America, where for nine years she edited the magazine CHILD STUDY and served as publications editor of the Association. From 1950 to 1954 she was an assistant editor at Doubleday and was the associated editor of the ENCYCLOPEDIA OF CHILD CARE AND GUIDANCE. Mrs. Evans divides her time between New York City and a dairy farm in Danbury, Connecticut.

Don Sibley is a talented young artist who has had considerable success as a commercial illustrator and has also done work on children's books. He lives in Syosset, New York, and has three children—his most enthusiastic and severest critics.

Acknowledgments

Margaret J. Baker for "The Fairy Who Didn't Believe in Children", originally published in JACK AND JILL. Reprinted by permission of the author. Coward-McCann, Inc. for "Digging for Treasure" from THE BASTABLE CHILDREN by E. Nesbit. Reprinted by permission of the publishers. J. M. Dent & Sons, Ltd. for the Hans Christian Andersen fairy tales, "The Emperor's New Clothes" and "The Wild Swans," translated by Mrs. Edgar Lucas. Reprinted by permission of the publishers. Doubleday & Company, Inc. for "The Elephant's Child" from JUST SO STORIES by Rudyard Kipling, reprinted by permission of Mrs. George Bambridge, Doubleday & Company, Inc., and The Macmillan Company of Canada; "Bingo Has an Enemy" from GAY GO UP by Rose Fyleman. Copyright 1929,1930 by Doubleday & Company, Inc. Reprinted by permission of the publishers. Dodd, Mead & Company for "How Thor Lost and Found His Hammer" from NORSE STORIES by Hamilton Wright Mabie. Faber and Faber, Ltd. for "Macavity: The Mystery Cat" from OLD POSSUM'S BOOK OF PRACTICAL CATS by T. S. Eliot. Harcourt, Brace and Company, Inc. for "The Huckabuck Family and How They Raised Popcorn in Nebraska and Quit and Came Back" from ROOTABAGA PIGEONS by Carl Sandburg, copyright, 1923, by Harcourt, Brace and Company, Inc.; renewed, 1950, by Carl Sandburg; "Phizzog" from EARLY MOON by Carl Sandburg, copyright, 1930, by Harcourt, Brace & Company, Inc.; "Macavity: The Mystery Cat" from OLD POSSUM'S BOOK OF PRACTICAL CATS by T. S. Eliot, copyright, 1939, by T. S. Eliot; "Rufus M" from RUFUS M by Eleanor Estes, copyright, 1943, by Harcourt, Brace and Company, Inc. Used by permission of the publishers. Henry Holt and Company, Inc. for "Some One" from COLLECTED POEMS by Walter de la Mare. Copyright, 1920, by Henry Holt and Company, Inc. Copyright, 1948, by Walter de la Mare. Reprinted by permission of the publishers. Houghton Mifflin Company for "Grizzly Bear" from THE CHILDREN SING IN THE FAR WEST by Mary Austin. Reprinted by permission and arrangement with Houghton Mifflin Company, the authorized publishers. Alfred A. Knopf, Inc. for "The Elephant" from CAUTIONARY VERSES by Hilaire Belloc. Reprinted by permission of the publishers. J. B. Lippincott Company for THE PLAIN PRINCESS by Phyllis McGinley. Copyright © 1945 by Phyllis McGinley. Reprinted by permission of the author; "I Keep Three Wishes Ready" from ALL THROUGH THE YEAR by Annette Wynne. Copyright 1932 by Annette Wynne. Reprinted by permission of the publishers; "The Rarest Animal of All" from THE STORY OF DOCTOR DOLITTLE by Hugh Lofting. Copyright 1920, by Hugh Lofting; renewal 1948, by Josephine Lofting. Reprinted by permission of Josephine Lofting; THE PURPLE COW by Gelett Burgess. Reprinted by permission of Louise Andrews. Little, Brown & Company for "Eletelephony" from TIRRA-LIRRA by Laura E. Richards. Copyright 1918, 1930, 1932 by Laura E. Richards; "The Octopus" from GOOD INTENTIONS by Ogden Nash. Copyright 1942 by Ogden Nash. "The Rhinoceros" from MANY LONG YEARS AGO by Ogden Nash. Copyright 1933 by Ogden Nash. Reprinted by permission of the publishers. The Macmillan Company for "The Hairy Dog" and "The Elephant" from PILLICOCK HILL by Herbert Asquith. Copyright 1926 by The Macmillan Company; "The Skunk" from COLLECTED POEMS by Robert P. Tristram Coffin. Copyright 1937 by The Macmillan Company; "In the Garden" from THE LITTLEST HOUSE by Elizabeth Coatsworth. Copyright 1940 by The Macmillan Company. Frederick Muller, Ltd. for "Dick Whittington", "History of Tom Thumb" from ENGLISH FAIRY TALES by Joseph Jacobs. Oxford University Press, Inc. for "Jonathan Bing" from JONATHAN BING AND OTHER POEMS by Beatrice Curtis Brown. Copyright © 1936 by Beatrice Curtis Brown. Reprinted by permission of the author. A. D. Peters for "The Elephant" from CAUTIONARY VERSES by Hilaire Belloc. Random House, Inc. for chapters from ELMER AND THE DRAGON by Ruth Stiles Gannett, copyright 1950 by Random House, Inc. Illustration by Ruth Chrisman Gannett. Reprinted by permission of the publishers. St. Martin's Press for "The Hairy Dog" and "The Elephant" from PILLICOCK HILL by Herbert Asquith. Charles Scribner's Sons for "The Open Road" from THE WIND IN THE WILLOWS by Kenneth Grahame; copyright 1908, 1933 by Charles Scribner's Sons; "The Duel" from POEMS OF CHILDHOOD by Eugene Field. Used by permission of the publishers. Simon and Schuster, Inc. for "How Bambi Found the Meadow" from BAMBI by Felix Salten. Copyright © 1928, 1956 by Simon and Schuster, Inc. Reprinted by permission of the publishers. The Society of Authors for "Bingo Has an Enemy" from GAY GO UP by Rose Fyleman. The Viking Press, Inc. for "Little Georgie Sings a Song" from RABBIT HILL by Robert Lawson. Copyright 1944 by Robert Lawson; "Cousin Kate From Budapest" from THE GOOD MASTER by Kate Seredy. Copyright 1935 by Kate Seredy. Reprinted by permission of the publishers.

Contents

From the Land of Make-believe . . .

Fairy Tales, Old and New

Remarkable Animals and Astonishing Things . . .

Fun and Fantasy

From the Land of Make-believe . . .

Fairy Tales, Old and New

The Emperor's New Clothes

by HANS CHRISTIAN ANDERSEN

Many years ago there was an Emperor who was so excessively fond of new clothes that he spent all his money on them. He cared nothing about his soldiers, nor for the theatre, nor for driving in the woods, except for the sake of showing off his new clothes. He had a costume for every hour in the day, and instead of saying as one does about any other King or Emperor, "He is in his council chamber," here one always said, "The Emperor is in his dressing-room."

Life was very gay in the great town where he lived; hosts of strangers came to visit it every day, and among them one day two swindlers. They gave themselves out as weavers, and said that they knew how to weave the most beautiful stuffs imaginable. Not only were the colours and patterns unusually fine, but the clothes that were made of these stuffs had the peculiar quality of becoming invisible to any person who was not fit for the office he held, or who was impossibly dull.

"Those must be splendid clothes," thought the Emperor. "By wearing them I should be able to discover which men in my kingdom are unfitted for their posts. I shall distinguish the wise men from the fools. Yes, I certainly must order some of that stuff to be woven for me."

He paid the two swindlers a lot of money in advance so that they might begin their work at once. They did put up two looms and pretended to weave, but they had nothing whatever upon their shuttles. At the outset they asked for a quantity of the finest silk and the purest gold thread, all of which they put into their own bags while they worked away at the empty looms far into the night.

"I should like to know how those weavers are getting on with the stuff," thought the Emperor; but he felt a little queer when he reflected that anyone who was stupid or unfit for his post would not be able to see it. He certainly thought that he need have no fears for himself, but still he thought he would send somebody else first to see how it was getting on. Everybody in the town knew what wonderful power the stuff possessed, and everyone was anxious to see how stupid his neighbor was.

"I will send my faithful old minister to the weavers," thought the Emperor. "He will be best able to see how the stuff looks, for he is a clever man and no one fulfils his duties better than he does!"

So the good old minister went into the room where the two swindlers sat working at the empty loom.

"Heaven preserve us!" thought the old minister, opening his eyes very wide. "Why, I can't see a thing!" But he took care not to say so.

Both the swindlers begged him to be good enough to step a little nearer, and asked if he did not think it a good pattern and beautiful colouring. They pointed to the empty loom, and the poor old minister stared as hard as he could but he could not see anything, for of course there was nothing to see.

"Good heavens!" thought he, "is it possible that I am a fool? I have never thought so and nobody must know it. Am I not fit for my post? It will never do to say that I cannot see the stuffs."

"Well, sir, you don't say anything about the stuff," said the one who was pretending to weave.

"Oh, it is beautiful! quite charming!" said the old minister looking through his spectacles; "this pattern and these colours! I will certainly tell the Emperor that the stuff pleases me very much."

"We are delighted to hear you say so," said the swindlers, and then they named all the colours and described the peculiar pattern. The old minister paid great attention to what they said, so as to be able to repeat it when he got home to the Emperor.

Then the swindlers went on to demand more money, more silk, and more gold, to be able to proceed with the weaving; but they put it all into their own pockets—not a single strand was ever put into the loom. They went on weaving at the empty loom.

The Emperor soon sent another faithful official to see how the stuff was getting on, and if it would soon be ready. The same thing happened to him as to the minister; he looked and looked, but as there was only the empty loom, he could see nothing at all.

"Is not this a beautiful piece of stuff?" said both the swindlers, showing and explaining the beautiful pattern and colours which were not there to be seen.

"I know I am not a fool!" thought the man, "so it must be that I am unfit for my good post! It is very strange though! However, one must not let it appear!" So he praised the stuff he did not see, and assured them of his delight in the beautiful colours and the originality of the design. "It is absolutely charming!" he said to the Emperor. Everybody in the town was talking about this splendid stuff.

Now the Emperor thought he would like to see it while it was still on the loom. So, accompanied by a number of selected courtiers, among whom were the two faithful officials who had already seen the imaginary stuff, he went to visit the crafty impostors, who were working away as hard as ever they could at the empty loom.

"It is magnificent!" said both the honest officials. "Only see, Your Majesty, what a design! What colours!" And they pointed to the empty loom, for they thought no doubt the others could see the stuff.

"What!" thought the Emperor; "I see nothing at all! This is terrible! Am I a fool? Am I not fit to be Emperor? Why, nothing worse could happen to me!"

"Oh, it is beautiful!" said the Emperor. "It has my highest approval!" and he nodded his satisfaction as he gazed at the empty

loom. Nothing would induce him to say that he could not see anything.

The whole suite gazed and gazed, but saw nothing more than all the others. However, they all exclaimed with His Majesty, "It is very beautiful!" and they advised him to wear a suit made of this wonderful cloth on the occasion of a great procession which was just about to take place. "It is magnificent! gorgeous! excellent!" went from mouth to mouth; they were all equally delighted with it. The Emperor gave each of the rogues an order of knighthood to be worn in their buttonholes and the title of "Gentlemen Weavers."

The swindlers sat up the whole night, before the day on which the procession was to take place, burning sixteen candles, so that people might see how anxious they were to get the Emperor's new clothes ready. They pretended to take the stuff off the loom. They cut it out in the air with a huge pair of scissors, and they stitched away with needles without any thread in them. At last they said, "Now the Emperor's new clothes are ready!"

The Emperor, with his grandest courtiers, went to them himself, and both the swindlers raised one arm in the air, as if they were holding something, and said, "See, these are the trousers, this is the coat, here is the mantle!" and so on. "It is as light as a spider's web. One might think one had nothing on, but that is the very beauty of it!"

"Yes!" said all the courtiers, but they could not see anything, for there was nothing to see.

"Will Your Imperial Majesty be graciously pleased to take off your clothes," said the impostors, "so that we may put on the new ones, along here before the great mirror."

The Emperor took off all his clothes, and the impostors pretended to give him one article of dress after the other of the new ones which they had pretended to make. They pretended to fasten something round his waist and to tie on something; this was the train, and the Emperor turned round and round in front of the mirror.

"How well His Majesty looks in the new clothes! How becoming they are!" cried all the people round. "What a design, and what colours! They are most gorgeous robes!"

"The canopy is waiting outside which is to be carried over Your Majesty in the procession," announced the master of the ceremonies.

"Well, I am quite ready," said the Emperor. "Don't the clothes fit well?" and then he turned round again in front of the mirror, so that he should seem to be looking at his grand things.

The chamberlains who were to carry the train stooped and pretended to lift it from the ground with both hands, and they walked along with their hands in the air. They dared not let it appear that they could not see anything.

Then the Emperor walked along in the procession under the gorgeous canopy, and everybody in the streets and at the windows exclaimed, "How beautiful the Emperor's new clothes are! What a splendid train! And they fit to perfection!" Nobody would let it appear that he could see nothing, for then he would not be fit for his post, or else he was a fool.

None of the Emperor's clothes had been so successful before.

"But he has got nothing on," said a little child.

"Oh, listen to the innocent," said its father; and one person whispered to the other what the child had said. "He has nothing on; a child says he has nothing on!"

"But he has nothing on!" at last cried all the people.

The Emperor writhed, for he knew it was true, but he thought "the procession must go on now," so he held himself stiffer than ever, and the chamberlains held up the invisible train.

The Sleeping Beauty

by JAKOB *and* WILHELM GRIMM

In times past there lived a king and queen, who said to each other every day of their lives, "Would that we had a child!" and yet they had none. But it happened once that when the queen was bathing, there came a frog out of the water, and he squatted on the ground, and said to her, "Thy wish shall be fulfilled. Before a year has gone by, thou shalt bring a daughter into the world."

And as the frog foretold, so it happened; and the queen bore a daughter so beautiful that the king could not contain himself for joy, and he ordained a great feast. Not only did he bid to it his relations, friends, and acquaintances, but also the wise women, that they might be kind and favorable to the child. There were thirteen of them in his kingdom, but as he had only provided twelve golden plates for them to eat from, one of them had to be left out. However, the feast was celebrated with all splendor; and as it drew to an end, the wise women stood forward to present to the child their wonderful gifts: one bestowed virtue, one beauty, a third riches, and so on, whatever there is in the world to wish for.

And when eleven of them had said their say, in came the uninvited thirteenth, burning to revenge herself, and without greeting or respect, she cried with a loud voice, "In the fifteenth year of her age the princess shall prick herself with a spindle and shall fall down dead."

And without speaking one more word she turned away and left the hall. Every one was terrified at her saying, when the twelfth came forward, for she had not yet bestowed her gift, and though she could not do away with the evil prophecy, yet she could soften it. So she said, "The princess shall not die, but fall into a deep sleep for a hundred years."

Now the king, being desirous of saving his child even from this misfortune, gave commandment that all the spindles in his kingdom should be burnt up.

The maiden grew up, adorned with all the gifts of the wise women; and she was so lovely, modest, sweet, and kind and clever, that no one who saw her could help loving her.

It happened one day, she being already fifteen years old, that the king and queen rode abroad, and the maiden was left behind alone in the castle. She wandered about into all the nooks and corners, and into all the chambers and parlors, as the fancy took her, till at last she came to an old tower. She climbed the narrow winding stair which led to a little door, with a rusty key sticking out of the lock. She turned the key, and the door opened, and there in the little room sat an old woman with a spindle, diligently spinning her flax.

"Good day, mother," said the princess. "What are you doing?"

"I am spinning," answered the old woman, nodding her head.

"What thing is that that twists round so briskly?" asked the maiden, and taking the spindle into her hand she began to spin; but no sooner had she touched it than the evil prophecy was fulfilled, and she pricked her finger with it. In that very moment she fell back upon the bed that stood there, and lay in a deep sleep. And this sleep fell upon the whole castle; the king and queen, who had returned and were in the great hall, fell fast asleep, and with them the whole court. The horses in their stalls, the dogs in the yard, the pigeons on the roof, the flies on the wall, the very fire that flickered on the hearth, became still, and slept like the rest; and the meat on the spit ceased roasting, and the cook, who was going to pull the scullion's hair for some mistake he had made, let him go, and went to sleep. And the wind ceased, and not a leaf fell from the trees about the castle.

Then roundabout that place there grew a hedge of thorns

thicker every year, until at last the whole castle was hidden from view, and nothing of it could be seen but the vane on the roof. And a rumor went abroad in all that country of the beautiful sleeping Rosamond, for so was the princess called; and from time to time many kings' sons came and tried to force their way through the hedge. But it was impossible for them to do so, for the thorns held fast together like strong hands, and the young men were caught by them, and not being able to get free, died a lamentable death.

Many a long year afterwards there came a king's son into that country, and heard an old man tell how there should be a castle standing behind the hedge of thorns, and that there a beautiful enchanted princess named Rosamond had slept for a hundred years, and with her the king and queen, and the whole court. The old man had been told by his grandfather that many kings' sons had sought to pass the thorn-hedge, but had been caught and pierced by the thorns, and had died a miserable death. Then said the young man, "Nevertheless, I do not fear to try; I shall win through and see the lovely Rosamond." The good old man tried to dissuade him, but he would not listen to his words.

For now the hundred years were at an end, and the day had come when Rosamond should be awakened. When the prince drew near the hedge of thorns, it was changed into a hedge of beautiful large flowers, which parted and bent aside to let him pass, and then closed behind him in a thick hedge. When he reached the castle yard, he saw the horses and brindled hunting dogs lying asleep, and on the roof the pigeons were sitting with their heads under their wings. And when he came indoors, the flies on the wall were asleep, the cook in the kitchen had his hand uplifted to strike the scullion, and the kitchen maid had the black fowl on her lap ready to pluck. Then he mounted higher, and saw in the hall the whole court lying asleep, and above them, on their thrones, slept the king and the queen. And still he went farther, and all was so quiet that he could hear his own breathing; and at last he came to the tower, and went up the winding stair, and opened the door of the little room where Rosamond lay. And

when he saw her looking so lovely in her sleep, he could not turn
away his eyes; and presently he stooped and kissed her, and she
awakened, and opened her eyes, and looked very kindly on him.
And she rose, and they went forth together, and the king and the
queen and whole court waked up, and gazed on each other with
great eyes of wonderment. And the horses in the yard got up and
shook themselves, the hounds sprang up and wagged their tails,
the pigeons on the roof drew their heads from under their wings,

looked round, and flew into the field, the flies on the wall crept on a little farther, the kitchen fire leapt up and blazed, and cooked the meat, the joint on the spit began to roast, the cook gave the scullion such a box on the ear that he roared out, and the maid went on plucking the fowl.

Then the wedding of the prince and Rosamond was held with all splendor, and they lived very happily together until the end of their lives.

I Keep Three Wishes Ready

by ANNETTE WYNNE

I keep three wishes ready,
Lest I should chance to meet,
Any day a fairy
Coming down the street.

I'd hate to have to stammer,
Or have to think them out,
For it's very hard to think things up
When a fairy is about.

And I'd hate to lose my wishes,
For fairies fly away,
And perhaps I'd never have a chance
On any other day.

So I keep three wishes ready,
Lest I should chance to meet,
Any day a fairy
Coming down the street.

The Fairy Who Didn't Believe in Children

by MARGARET J. BAKER

"Well, I don't believe in children, so there!" said Tinders and she stamped her foot on the ground. "There could not be such ridiculous creatures. Why, some fairies even say that children's big toes are as long as we are!"

Tinders wasn't a large fairy herself. She was just a little over an inch tall, and she fitted quite easily into the bell of a snapdragon blossom. Her shoes were the smallest possible size, and her stockings often came down to wrinkle round her thin legs. She had yellow, fair hair and a dreadful habit of arguing with everyone, even her mother.

At bedtime all the other fairies listened to stories about some huge wonderful creatures called children, but not Tinders. She lay on her side (because that is the easiest way with wings) and often made up stories for herself, about dragons and witches and hobgoblins. "Of course there aren't any real children. They're just make-believe," she said to her friends at the fairy kindergarten, which was held every morning under a rather gloomy oak tree. "Some silly fairies say children are so clever that they can do sums like Long Division, but everyone knows only our fairy professors possess that secret, and it takes them ages and ages to work it out. Besides, how could children manage to live at all without any wings?"

Tinders flicked her own wings behind her back as she said this, and whisked around the classroom before the fairy teacher came in through the door. Miss Beeswax had filmy, drooping wings and old-fashioned ideas. She wasn't very clever, and she liked to tell long stories about children's adventures instead of teaching arithmetic and other difficult subjects. Tinders was always a great nuisance to Miss Beeswax, asking questions.

"But of course we believe in children, dear," the teacher said one day, as she prepared to tell a story. "All nice little fairies believe in boys and girls."

"But have you ever seen a child?" asked Tinders, fidgeting in her seat. It was the top of an acorn cup, and much too high for her.

"As a matter of fact, I have never seen a child," said Miss Beeswax, "but that is no reason to assume that children are non-existent. Some of our daring fairy explorers have seen boys and girls and have observed their habits, but they have seldom reported the presence of children in these parts."

When talking to Tinders, Miss Beeswax always used the longest words she could think of, hoping that this would keep the obstinate fairy from asking more questions. She went on with her story now, about a park in a big city where children played in charge of larger humans called nursemaids.

Tinders went on fidgeting, but deep in her heart, the little fairy wanted to believe in children. And she suddenly decided to discover a child for herself. And so, when lunchtime came, instead of flying home, she flew straight out of the woods and high in the air, over the trees.

It was a lovely day. Tinders flew on and on. Once she met a swallow who was ten times as large as herself, and she asked him if he had ever seen a child, but the silly bird could not understand a word she said.

Again the fairy flew on, and finally, at dusk, she landed in a large garden. There were flowers everywhere, and best of all, lying on the grass was a creature who must be a child!

Concealing herself behind a birdbath, Tinders looked at the giant-like creature. The child was very long, and yet she did not look grown-up. She had fair hair, just like many of the fairies, and

sandals on her feet. Tinders could see the child's toes. "It's really true," the fairy said to herself. "Those toes are almost as big as I am."

Now Tinders noticed that the child was asleep. Deciding it was safe to go closer, the fairy flew round the birdbath and stared at the little girl's face. It was sunburned and freckled. Tinders thought it was very disagreeable. She flew a little nearer and landed on a button of the child's dress. The button was shiny mother-of-pearl, and it made a pleasant seat. But as Tinders sat there, the little girl sneezed! It was like an earthquake. But the fairy hung onto the button with all her might. "For goodness' sake, don't do that again!" she said as soon as she stopped shaking with fright.

The child sat up and looked at Tinders. "You're not really there," she said. "You must be part of a dream. Nurse always reads those silly fairy stories to me when I go to bed, and I suppose that's why I'm dreaming about such a ridiculous little creature. Fairies are only make-believe. Everyone knows that."

Tinders had never been so angry in her life. "I'm not make-believe," she replied, bouncing up and down on the button. "I'm just as real as you are, so there!"

"You're not," said the child.

"I am," said Tinders, "and I wish I hadn't come. You're not a bit clever like the stories say. You're stupid."

It was a dreadful argument, and in the end, because she was so tired, Tinders burst into tears. She sobbed and sobbed. And she had no pocket handkerchief.

"A daisy petal will do," she said, sniffing, as the child began to comfort her. "I'm hungry, too," the fairy added. "I haven't had anything to eat since breakfast. And I've nowhere to sleep. At home I have a lovely bed with rose-petal sheets."

At that moment she stopped speaking and screamed because she saw an enormous figure hurrying down the path. It was the child's nurse.

"Well now, Janet, you are a naughty child leading me this chase," the nurse declared. "I've been searching all over for you. Please come to supper at once now, and no argument."

There was barely time for Tinders to hop into the girl's pocket before the child rose to go with the nurse. In the house Janet popped the fairy into a flower bowl while Nurse began to set a supper table. "You will be quite safe there," the girl whispered to Tinders. "I'll get you something to eat as soon as I can."

Janet had milk and biscuits for supper, and when the nurse

wasn't watching she gave the fairy a thimbleful of milk and a doll's plate of crumbs.

After their supper, the nurse came back, and while the fairy lay in the flower bowl giggling, Nurse opened up the nursery windows and said good night to Janet. When the huge grown-up creature had gone away, then, the girl fixed a lovely bed for her fairy guest in among some handkerchiefs. Tinders went to sleep at once and dreamed all night long about children.

In the morning, after breakfast, Tinders decided that it was time to say good-bye. Janet gave the fairy a grain of brown sugar and half a raisin wrapped to take home, but before Tinders left, Janet showed her all over the house. Tinders was very much excited about the bathroom, with its shower that was like the rain. She liked Janet's own room, too, with its colored pictures of fairies on the walls.

Janet showed the fairy her schoolbooks then, and Tinders was specially impressed with the arithmetic workbook, with numbers that were nearly as large as the fairy herself, and even some long-division problems which Janet had just begun. Janet's papers were somewhat smudged in places, but Tinders admired all of them very much.

By this time, Tinders felt that she really must start home. So Janet stood at the bedroom window waving good-bye till the fairy looked like a speck of dust gleaming in the morning sun. Then the child raced downstairs to play outdoors.

Back in fairyland, Tinders still argued with Miss Beeswax and with her mother. But she no longer denied the existence of children, and she never again refused to listen to a story about them. And when she grew older, Tinders studied to be a teacher of long division in the fairies' school. After that, she even wrote a schoolbook about children.

And to this day, if any clever young fairy tries to tell Tinders that children are only make-believe, she knows exactly what to say to them in reply.

Toads and Diamonds

by CHARLES PERRAULT

There was once a widow who had two daughters. The elder was so like her mother in temper and face that to have seen the one was to have seen the other. They were both so disagreeable and proud, that it was impossible to live with them. The younger, who was the exact portrait of her father in her kindly and polite ways, was as beautiful a girl as one could see. As we are naturally fond of those who resemble us, the mother doted on her elder daughter, while for the younger she had a most violent aversion and made her take her meals in the kitchen and work hard all day. Among other things that she was obliged to do, this poor child was forced to go twice a day to fetch water from a place a mile or more from the house and carry back a large jug filled to the brim. As she was standing one day by this spring, a poor woman came up to her and asked the girl to give her some water to drink.

"Certainly, my good woman," she replied, and the beautiful girl at once stooped and rinsed out the jug. Then, filling it with water from the clearest part of the spring, she held it up to the woman, continuing to support the jug, that she might drink with great comfort.

Having drunk, the woman said to her, "You are so beautiful, so good and kind, that I cannot refrain from conferring a gift upon you," for she was really a fairy, who had taken the form of a poor village woman, in order to see how far the girl's kind-heartedness would go. "This gift I make you," continued the fairy, "that with

every word you speak, either a flower or a precious stone will fall from your mouth."

The girl had no sooner reached home than her mother began scolding her for being back so late. "I am sorry, mother," said she, "to have been out so long," and as she spoke, there fell from her mouth six roses, two pearls, and two large diamonds.

The mother gazed at her in astonishment.

"What do I see!" she exclaimed. "Pearls and diamonds seem

to be dropping from her mouth! How is this, my daughter?"—It was the first time she had called her daughter. The poor child related in all simplicity what had happened, letting fall quantities of diamonds in the course of her narrative. "I must certainly send my other daughter there," said the mother. "Look, Fanchon, see what falls from your sister's mouth when she speaks! Would you not be glad to receive a similar gift? All you have to do is to go and fetch water from the spring and if an old woman asks you for some to drink, to give it her nicely and politely."

"I should like to see myself going to the spring," answered the rude, cross girl.

"I insist on your going," rejoined the mother, "and that at once."

The elder girl went off, still grumbling; with her she took the handsomest silver bottle she could find in the house.

She had no sooner arrived at the spring, than she saw a lady magnificently dressed walking towards her from the wood, who approached and asked for some water to drink. It was the same fairy who had appeared to the sister, but she had now put on the airs and apparel of a princess, as she wished to see how far this girl's rudeness would go.

"Do you think I came here just to draw water for you?" answered the arrogant and unmannerly girl; "I have, of course, brought this silver bottle on purpose for you to drink from, and all I have to say is—drink from it if you like!"

"You are scarcely polite," said the fairy, without losing her temper; "however, as you are so disobliging, I confer this gift upon you, that with every word you speak a snake or a toad shall fall from your mouth."

Directly her mother caught sight of her, she called out, "Well, my daughter?"

"Well, my mother!" replied the ill-tempered girl, throwing out as she spoke two vipers and a toad.

"Alack!" cried the mother, "what do I see? This is her sister's doing, but I will pay her out for it," and, so saying, she ran towards the younger with intent to beat her. The unhappy girl fled from the house, and went and hid herself in a neighboring forest. The King's son, who was returning from hunting, met her, and seeing how beautiful she was, asked her what she was doing there all alone, and why she was crying.

"Alas! sir, my mother has driven me from home."

The King's son, seeing five or six pearls and as many diamonds falling from her mouth as she spoke, asked her to explain how this was, and she told him all her tale. The King's son fell in love with her; and thinking that such a gift as she possessed was worth more than any ordinary dower brought by another, he carried her off to his father's palace, and there married her.

As for her sister, she made herself so hated that her own mother drove her from the house. The miserable girl, having gone about in vain trying to find someone who would take her in, crept away into the corner of a wood and there died.

Some One

by WALTER DE LA MARE

Some one came knocking
   At my wee, small door;
Some one came knocking,
   I'm sure—sure—sure;
I listened, I opened,
   I looked to left and right,
But nought there was a-stirring
   In the still dark night;
Only the busy beetle
   Tap-tapping in the wall,
Only from the forest
   The screech-owl's call,
Only the cricket whistling
   While the dewdrops fall,
So I know not who came knocking,
   At all, at all, at all.

The Swan Maiden

by HOWARD PYLE

Once there was a king who had a pear tree which bore four and twenty golden pears. Every day he went into the garden and counted them to see that none were missing.

But one morning he found that a pear had been taken during the night, and thereat he was troubled and vexed to the heart, for the pear tree was as dear to him as the apple of his eye. Now, the King had three sons, and so he called the eldest Prince to him.

"See," said he, "if you will watch my pear tree tonight, and will find me the thief who stole the pear, you shall have half of my kingdom now, and the whole of it when I am gone."

You can guess how the Prince was tickled at this: oh, yes, he would watch the tree, and if the thief should come he should not get away again as easily.

Well, that night he sat down beside the tree, with his gun across his knees, to wait for the coming of the thief.

He waited and waited, and still he saw not so much as a thread or a hair. But about the middle of the night there came the very prettiest music that his ears had ever heard, and before he knew what he was about he was asleep and snoring until the little leaves shook upon the tree. When the morning came and he awoke, another pear was gone, and he could tell no more about it than the man in the moon. The next night the second son set out to watch the pear tree. But he fared no better than the first. About midnight came the music, and in a little while he was snoring till the stones rattled. When the morning came another pear was gone, and he had no more to tell about it than his brother.

The third night it was the turn of the youngest son, and he was more clever than the others, for, when the evening came, he stuffed his ears full of wax, so that he was as deaf as a post. About midnight, when the music came, he heard nothing of it, and so he stayed wide awake. After the music had ended he took the wax out of his ears, so that he might listen for the coming of the thief. Presently there was a loud clapping and rattling, and a white swan flew overhead and lit in the pear tree above him. It began picking at one of the pears, and then the Prince raised his gun to shoot at it. But when he looked along the barrel it was not a swan that he saw up in the pear tree, but the prettiest girl that he had ever looked upon.

"Don't shoot me, King's son! Don't shoot me!" cried she.

But the Prince had no thought of shooting her, for he had never seen such a beautiful maiden in all of his days. "Very well," said he, "I will not shoot, but, if I spare your life, will you promise to be my sweetheart and to marry me?"

"That may be as may be," said the Swan Maiden. "For listen! I serve the witch with three eyes. She lives on the glass hill that lies beyond the seven high mountains, the seven deep valleys, and the seven wide rivers; are you man enough to go that far?"

"Oh, yes," said the Prince, "I am man enough for that and more too."

"That is good," said the Swan Maiden, and thereupon she jumped down from the pear tree to the earth. Then she became a swan again, and bade the King's son to mount upon her back at the roots of her wings. When he had done as she had told him, she sprang into the air and flew away, bearing him with her.

On flew the swan, and on and on, until, by and by, she said, "What do you see, King's son?"

"I see the grey sky above me and the dark earth below me, but nothing else," said he.

After that they flew on and on again, until, at last, the Swan Maiden said, "What do you see now, King's son?"

"I see the grey sky above me and the dark earth below me, but nothing else," he said.

So once more they flew on until the Swan Maiden said, for the third time, "And what do you see by now, King's son?"

But this time the Prince said, "I see the grey sky above me and the dark earth below me, and over yonder is a glass hill, and on the hill is a house that shines like fire."

"That is where the witch with three eyes lives," said the Swan

Maiden; "and now listen: when she asks you what it is that you came for, ask her to give you the one who draws the water and builds the fire; for that is myself."

So, when they had come to the top of the hill of glass, the King's son stepped down to the ground, and the swan flew over the roof.

Rap! tap! tap! he knocked at the door, and the old witch herself came and opened it.

"And what do you want here?" said she.

"I want the one who draws the water and builds the fire," said the Prince.

At this the old witch scowled until her eyebrows met.

"Very well," said she, "you shall have what you want if you can clean my stables tomorrow between the rise and the set of the sun. But I tell you plainly, if you fail in the doing, you shall be torn to pieces body and bones."

But the Prince was not to be scared away with empty words. So the next morning the old witch came and took him to the stables where he was to do his task. There stood more than a hundred cattle, and the stable had not been cleaned for at least ten long years.

"There is your work," said the old witch, and then she left him.

Well, the King's son set to work with fork and broom and might and main, but—prut!—he might as well have tried to bale out the great ocean with a bucket.

At noontide who should come to the stable but the pretty Swan Maiden herself.

"When one is tired, one should rest for a while," said she; "come and lay your head in my lap."

The Prince was glad enough to do as she said, for nothing was to be gained by working at that task. So he laid his head in her lap, and she combed his hair with a golden comb till he fell fast asleep. When he awoke the Swan Maiden was gone, the sun was setting, and the stable was as clean as a plate. Presently he heard the old witch coming, so up he jumped and began clearing away a straw here and a speck there, just as though he were finishing the work.

"You never did this by yourself!" said the old witch, and her brows grew as black as a thunderstorm.

"That may be so, and that may not be so," said the King's son, "but you lent no hand to help; so now may I have the one who builds the fire and draws the water?"

At this the old witch shook her head. "No," said she, "there is more to be done yet before you can have what you ask for. If you can thatch the roof of the stable with bird feathers, no two of which shall be of the same color, and can do it between the rise and the set of sun tomorrow, then you shall have your sweetheart and welcome. But if you fail your bones shall be ground as fine as malt in the mill."

Very well; that suited the King's son well enough. So at sunrise he arose and went into the fields with his gun. But if there were birds to be shot, it was few of them that he saw; for at noontide he had but two, and they were both of a color. At that time who should come to him but the Swan Maiden.

"One should not tramp and tramp all day with never a bit of rest," said she; "come hither and lay your head in my lap for a while."

The Prince did as she bade him, and the maiden again combed his hair with a golden comb until he fell asleep. When he awoke the sun was setting, and his work was done. He heard the old witch coming, so up he jumped to the roof of the stable and began laying a feather here and a feather there, for all the world as though he were just finishing his task.

"You never did that work alone," said the old witch.

"That may be so, and that may not be so," said the Prince; "all the same, it was none of your doing. So now may I have the one who draws the water and builds the fire?"

But the witch shook her head. "No," said she, "there is still another task to do before that. Over yonder is a fir tree; on the tree is a crow's nest, and in the nest are three eggs. If you can harry that nest tomorrow between the rising and the setting of the sun, neither breaking nor leaving a single egg, you shall have that for which you ask."

Very well; that suited the Prince. The next morning at the rising of the sun he started off to find the fir tree, and there was no trouble in the finding I can tell you, for it was more than a hundred feet high, and as smooth as glass from root to tip. As for climbing it, he might as well have tried to climb a moonbeam, for in spite of all his trying he did nothing but slip and slip. By and by came the Swan Maiden as she had come before.

"Do you climb the fir tree?" said she.

"None too well," said the King's son.

"Then I may help you in a hard task," said she.

She let down the braids of her golden hair, so that it hung down all about her and upon the ground, and then she began singing to the wind. She sang and sang, and by and by the wind began to blow, and, catching up the maiden's hair, carried it to the top of the fir tree, and there tied it to the branches. Then the Prince climbed the hair and so reached the nest. There were the three eggs; he gathered them, and then he came down as he had gone up. After that the wind came again and loosed the maiden's hair from the branches, and she bound it up as it was before.

"Now, listen," said she to the Prince: "when the old witch asks you for the three crow's eggs which you have gathered, tell her that they belong to the one who found them. She will not be able to take them from you, and they are worth something, I can tell you."

At sunset the old witch came hobbling along, and there sat the Prince at the foot of the fir tree. "Have you gathered the crow's eggs?" said she.

"Yes," said the Prince, "here they are in my handkerchief. And now may I have the one who draws the water and builds the fire?"

"Yes," said the old witch, "you may have her; only give me my crow's eggs."

"No," said the Prince, "the crow's eggs are none of yours, for they belong to him who gathered them."

When the old witch found that she was not to get her crow's eggs in that way, she tried another, and began using words as sweet as honey. "Come, come, there should be no hard feeling between them. The Prince had served her faithfully, and before he went home with what he had come for he should have a good supper, for it is ill to travel on an empty stomach."

So she brought the Prince into the house, and then she left him while she went to put the pot on the fire, and to sharpen the bread knife on the stone doorstep.

While the Prince sat waiting for the witch, there came a tap at the door, and whom should it be but the pretty Swan Maiden.

"Come," said she, "and bring the three eggs with you, for the knife that the old witch is sharpening is for you, and so is the great pot on the fire, for she means to pick your bones in the morning."

She led the Prince down into the kitchen; there they made a figure out of honey and barley meal, so that it was all soft and sticky; then the maiden dressed the figure in her own clothes and set it in the chimney corner by the fire.

After that was done, she became a swan again, and, taking the Prince upon her back, she flew away, over hill and over dale.

As for the old witch, she sat on the stone doorstep, sharpening her knife. By and by she came in, and, look as she might, there was no Prince to be found.

Then if anybody was ever in a rage it was the old witch; off she went, storming and fuming, until she came to the kitchen. There sat the woman of honey and barley meal beside the fire, dressed in the maiden's clothes, and the old woman thought that it was the girl herself. "Where is your sweetheart?" said she; but to this the woman of honey and barley meal answered never a word.

"How now! are you dumb?" cried the old witch; "I will see whether I cannot bring speech to your lips." She raised her hand— *slap!*—she struck, and so hard was the blow that her hand stuck fast to the honey and barley meal. "What!" cried she, "will you hold me?"—*slap!*—she struck with the other hand, and it too stuck fast. So there she was, and, for all that I know, she is sticking to the woman of honey and barley meal to this day.

As for the Swan Maiden and the Prince, they flew over the seven high mountains, the seven deep valleys, and the seven wide rivers, until they came near to the Prince's home again. The Swan Maiden lit in a great wide field, and there she told the Prince to break open one of the crow's eggs. The Prince did as she bade him, and what should he find but the most beautiful little palace, all of pure gold and silver. He set the palace on the ground, and it grew and grew and grew until it covered as much ground as seven large barns. Then the Swan Maiden told him to break another egg, and he did as she said, and what should come out of it but such great herds of cows and sheep that they covered the meadow far and near. The Swan Maiden told him to break the third egg, and out of it came scores and scores of servants all dressed in gold-and-silver livery.

That morning, when the King looked out of his bedroom window, there stood the splendid castle of silver and gold. Then he called all of his people together, and they rode over to see what it meant. On the way they met such herds of fat sheep and cattle that the King had never seen the like in all of his life before; and when he came to the fine castle, there stood the Prince himself. Then there was joy and rejoicing, you may be sure! Only the two elder brothers looked down in the mouth, for since the young Prince had found the thief who stole the golden pears, their father's kingdom was not for them. But the Prince soon set their minds at rest on that score, for he had enough and more than enough of his own.

After that the Prince and the Swan Maiden were married, and a great wedding they had of it, with music of fiddles and kettle-drums, and plenty to eat and to drink. I, too, was there; but all of the good red wine ran down over my tucker, so that not a drop of it passed my lips, and I had to come away empty.

And that is all.

Snow-White and Rose-Red

by JAKOB *and* WILHELM GRIMM

There was once a poor widow who lived in a lonely cottage. In front of the cottage was a garden wherein stood two rose trees, one of which bore white and the other red roses. She had two children who were like the two rose trees, and one was called Snow-White, and the other Rose-Red. They were as good and happy, as busy and cheerful as ever two children in the world were, only Snow-White was more quiet and gentle than Rose-Red. Rose-Red liked better to run about in the meadows and fields seeking flowers and catching butterflies; but Snow-White sat at home with her mother, and helped her with her house-work, or read to her when there was nothing to do.

The two children were so fond of each other that they always held each other by the hand when they went out together, and when Snow-White said, "We will not leave each other," Rose-Red answered, "Never so long as we live," and their mother would add, "What one has she must share with the other."

They often ran about the forest alone and gathered red berries, and no beasts did them any harm, but came close to them trustfully. The little hare would eat a cabbage leaf out of their hands, the roe grazed by their side, the stag leapt merrily by them, and the birds sat still upon the boughs, and sang whatever they knew.

No mishap overtook them; if they had stayed too late in the forest, and night came on, they laid themselves down near one another upon the moss, and slept until morning came, and their mother knew this and had no distress on their account.

Once when they had spent the night in the wood and the dawn had roused them, they saw a beautiful child in a shining white dress sitting near their bed. He got up and looked quite kindly at them, but said nothing and went away into the forest. And when they looked round they found that they had been sleeping quite close to a precipice, and would certainly have fallen into it in the darkness if they had gone only a few paces further. And their mother told them that it must have been the angel who watches over good children.

Snow-White and Rose-Red kept their mother's little cottage so neat that it was a pleasure to look inside it. In the summer Rose-Red took care of the house, and every morning laid a wreath of flowers by her mother's bed before she awoke, in which was a rose from each tree. In the winter Snow-White lit the fire and hung the kettle on the wrekin. The kettle was of copper and shone like gold, so brightly was it polished. In the evening, when the snow-flakes fell, the mother said, "Go, Snow-White, and bolt the door," and then they sat round the hearth, and the mother took her spectacles and read aloud out of a large book, and the two girls listened as they sat and span. And close by them lay a lamb upon the floor, and behind them upon a perch sat a white dove with its head hidden beneath its wings.

One evening, as they were thus sitting comfortably together, some one knocked at the door as if he wished to be let in. The mother said, "Quick, Rose-Red, open the door, it must be a travel-ler who is seeking shelter." Rose-Red went and pushed back the bolt, thinking that it was a poor man, but it was not; it was a bear that stretched his broad, black head within the door.

Rose-Red screamed and sprang back, the lamb bleated, the dove fluttered, and Snow-White hid herself behind her mother's bed. But the bear began to speak and said, "Do not be afraid, I will do you no harm! I am half-frozen, and only want to warm myself a little beside you."

"Poor bear," said the mother, "lie down by the fire, only take care that you do not burn your coat." Then she cried, "Snow-White, Rose-Red, come out, the bear will do you no harm, he means well." So they both came out, and by-and-by the lamb and dove came nearer, and were not afraid of him.

The bear said, "Here, children, knock the snow out of my coat a little." So they brought the broom and swept the bear's hide clean; and he stretched himself by the fire and growled contentedly and comfortably. It was not long before they grew quite at home, and played tricks with their clumsy guest. They tugged his hair with their hands, put their feet upon his back and rolled him about, or they took a hazel-switch and beat him, and when he growled they laughed. But the bear took it all in good part, only when they were too rough he called out, "Leave me alive, children,

"Snowy-White, Rosy-Red,
Will you beat your lover dead?"

When it was bed-time, and the others went to bed, the mother said to the bear, "You can lie there by the hearth, and then you will be safe from the cold and the bad weather." As soon as day dawned the two children let him out, and he trotted across the snow into the forest.

Henceforth the bear came every evening at the same time, laid himself down by the hearth, and let the children amuse themselves with him as much as they liked; and they got so used to him that the doors were never fastened until their black friend had arrived.

When spring had come and all outside was green, the bear said one morning to Snow-White, "Now I must go away, and cannot come back for the whole summer."

"Where are you going, then, dear bear?" asked Snow-White.

"I must go into the forest and guard my treasures from the wicked dwarfs. In the winter, when the earth is frozen hard, they are obliged to stay below and cannot work their way through; but now, when the sun has thawed and warmed the earth, they break through it, and come out to pry and steal. And what once gets

into their hands, and in their caves, does not easily see daylight again."

Snow-White was quite sorry for his going away, and as she unbolted the door for him, and the bear was hurrying out, he caught against the bolt and a piece of his hairy coat was torn off, and it seemed to Snow-White as if she had seen gold shining through it, but she was not sure about it. The bear ran away quickly, and was soon out of sight behind the trees.

A short time afterwards the mother sent her children into the forest to get fire-wood. There they found a big tree which lay felled on the ground, and close by the trunk something was jumping backwards and forwards in the grass, but they could not make out what it was. When they came nearer they saw a dwarf with an old withered face and a snow-white beard a yard long. The end of the beard was caught in a crevice of the tree, and the little fellow was jumping backwards and forwards like a dog tied to a rope, and did not know what to do.

He glared at the girls with his fiery red eyes and cried, "Why do you stand there? Can you not come here and help me?"

"What are you about there, little man?" asked Rose-Red.

"You stupid, prying goose!" answered the dwarf; "I was going to split the tree to get a little wood for cooking. The little bit of food that one of us wants gets burnt up directly with thick logs; we do not swallow so much as you coarse, greedy folk. I had just driven the wedge safely in, and everything was going as I wished; but the wretched wood was too smooth and suddenly sprang asunder, and the tree closed so quickly that I could not pull out my beautiful white beard. So now it is tight in and I cannot get away, and the silly, sleek, milk-faced things laugh! Ugh! how odious you are!"

The children tried very hard, but they could not pull the beard out, it was caught too fast. "I will run and fetch some one," said Rose-Red.

"You senseless goose!" snarled the dwarf; "why should you fetch some one? You are already two too many for me; can you not think of something better?"

"Don't be impatient," said Snow-White, "I will help you," and she pulled her scissors out of her pocket, and cut off the end of the beard.

As soon as the dwarf felt himself free he laid hold of a bag which lay amongst the roots of the tree, and which was full of gold, and lifted it up, grumbling to himself, "Uncouth people, to cut off a piece of my fine beard. Bad luck to you!" and then he swung the bag upon his back, and went off without even once looking at the children.

Some time after that Snow-White and Rose-Red went to catch a dish of fish. As they came near the brook they saw something like a large grasshopper jumping towards the water, as if it were going to leap in. They ran to it and found it was the dwarf. "Where are you going?" said Rose-Red; "you surely don't want to go into the water?"

"I am not such a fool!" cried the dwarf; "don't you see that the accursed fish wants to pull me in?" The little man had been sitting there fishing, and unluckily the wind had twisted his beard with the fishing-line. Just then a big fish bit, and the feeble creature had not strength to pull it out. The fish kept the upper hand and pulled the dwarf towards him. He held on to all the reeds and rushes, but it was of little good, he was forced to follow the movements of the fish, and was in urgent danger of being dragged into the water.

The girls came just in time; they held him fast and tried to free his beard from the line, but all in vain, beard and line were entangled fast together. Nothing was left but to bring out the scissors and cut the beard, whereby a small part of it was lost. When the dwarf saw that he screamed out, "Is that civil, you toad-stool, to disfigure one's face? Was it not enough to clip off the end of my beard? Now you have cut off the best part of it. I cannot let myself be seen by my people. I wish you had been made to run the soles off your shoes!" Then he took out a sack of pearls which lay in the rushes, and without saying a word more he dragged it away and disappeared behind a stone.

It happened that soon afterwards the mother sent the two children to the town to buy needles and thread, and laces and ribbons. The road led them across a heath upon which huge pieces of rock lay strewn here and there. Now they noticed a large bird hovering in the air, flying slowly round and round above them; it sank lower and lower, and at last settled near a rock not far off. Directly afterwards they heard a loud, piteous cry. They ran up and saw with horror that the eagle had seized their old acquaintance the dwarf, and was going to carry him off.

The children, full of pity, at once took tight hold of the little man, and pulled against the eagle so long that at last he let his booty go. As soon as the dwarf had recovered from his first fright he cried with his shrill voice, "Could you not have done it more carefully! You dragged at my brown coat so that it is all torn and full of holes, you helpless clumsy creatures!" Then he took up a sack full of precious stones, and slipped away again under the rock into his hole. The girls, who by this time were used to his thanklessness, went on their way and did their business in the town.

As they crossed the heath again on their way home they surprised the dwarf, who had emptied out his bag of precious stones in a clean spot, and had not thought that any one would come there so late. The evening sun shone upon the brilliant stones; they glittered and sparkled with all colours so beautifully that the children stood still and looked at them. "Why do you stand gaping there?" cried the dwarf, and his ashen-grey face became copper-red with rage. He was going on with his bad words when a loud growling was heard, and a black bear came trotting towards them out of the forest. The dwarf sprang up in a fright, but he could not get to his cave, for the bear was already close. Then in the dread of his heart he cried, "Dear Mr. Bear, spare me, I will give you all my treasures; look, the beautiful jewels lying there! Grant me my life; what do you want with such a slender little fellow as I? You would not feel me between your teeth. Come, take these two wicked girls, they are tender morsels for you, fat as young quails. For mercy's sake eat them!" The bear took no heed of his words, but gave the wicked creature a single blow with his paw, and he did not move again.

The girls had run away, but the bear called to them, "Snow-White and Rose-Red, do not be afraid; wait, I will come with you." Then they knew his voice and waited, and when he came up to them suddenly his bearskin fell off, and he stood there a handsome man, clothed all in gold. "I am a King's son," he said, "and I was bewitched by that wicked dwarf, who had stolen my treasures. I have had to run about the forest as a savage bear until I was freed by his death. Now he has got his well-deserved punishment."

Snow-White was married to him, and Rose-Red to his brother, and they divided between them the great treasure which the dwarf had gathered together in his cave. The old mother lived peacefully and happily with her children for many years. She took the two rose trees with her, and they stood before her window, and every year bore the most beautiful roses, white and red.

Ariel's Song

by WILLIAM SHAKESPEARE

Where the bee sucks, there suck I:
In a cowslip's bell I lie;
There I couch when owls do cry.
On the bat's back I do fly
After summer merrily.
Merrily, merrily, shall I live now
Under the blossom that hangs on the bough.

From *The Tempest*.

The Plain Princess

by PHYLLIS MCGINLEY

Once upon a time, in a distant kingdom, there lived a Princess who was an only child. Her name was Esmeralda and in every way save one she was the most fortunate of young persons.

Her father, the King, was rich and powerful, and the pockets of his waistcoat were always filled with treats. The Queen was an amiable and affectionate mother who dearly loved planning birthday parties and surprises for Esmeralda; and frequently let her dress up in the crown jewels on rainy afternoons.

The Princess's nursery was painted a charming color of her own choosing. In her closet hung dozens of dresses, each more splendid than the other. The court poets composed verses for Esmeralda which were set to enchanting music by the court musicians and sung to her at bedtime.

Did she arrive at the age for roller skates? A skilful workman hurried immediately to his workshop and contrived for her the finest pair to be found in the kingdom. When she outgrew her tricycle and mentioned a two-wheeler, a delegation of bicycle experts was dispatched to fetch her the handsomest bicycle possible, with a silver basket attached to the handlebars.

The castle boasted velvety lawns where she might play croquet; there was a pond with ducks to which she could throw bread at feeding time; and from numberless great trees hung swings for her pleasure. (The King employed a tall gardener whose sole duty it

was to give her run-unders so that she might swing into the top-most branches.)

Two cooks toiled ceaselessly in the kitchen preparing delicious food—puddings and ice cream and enticing salads to tempt her appetite.

She even owned a pony of her own, with a white and crimson saddle made to her measure.

Nevertheless, Esmeralda was *not* the most fortunate Princess in the world and it was on account of her one lack that the whole kingdom mourned.

For Esmeralda was plain.

There weren't two ways about it—the girl had no beauty, and in a royal Princess that is a serious flaw.

"What," the courtiers used to whisper to each other in the corridors, "will happen when Her Highness comes of age? How can she hope to win the affections of Prince Charles Michael who is destined to share her throne?"

And the prettier maids-in-waiting would smooth their hair before the long mirrors, thinking smugly, "We may not be of royal blood but we're luckier than *some* people we could mention, at that."

Aunts and uncles and other relatives spoke frankly.

"Poor child," they'd cluck, shaking their heads, "Heaven knows where she gets her plainness. Not from *our* side of the family, certainly."

Even the King and the Queen, much as they loved their daughter, had to admit that as good looks went, Esmeralda's were nothing to boast about. And as "Esmeralda the Plain" she began to be known throughout the kingdom.

It wasn't her hair. Esmeralda's hair grew golden as the corn and her handmaiden brushed it a hundred times in the morning (so that it shone like silk) and a hundred times at night again, while singing the Princess's favorite lullaby, which went like this:

NIGHT SONG

Now dark comes creeping,
   Now owls awake,
But the swan is sleeping
   Upon the lake,
The thrushes drowse,
   The wood-folk rest
Under the boughs,
   In hole and nest.

> The flower buds furl
>   Their petals fast
> And the busiest girl
>   Must nod at last.
> Sleep, Little princess, sleep.
>
> Over your bed
>   Night's handmaids hover.
> The sky has spread
>   You a royal cover—
> Laid, unwrinkled
>   Between the bars
> A counterpane sprinkled
>   With sapphire stars.
> And the moon (with a curve
>   To its silver handle)
> Waits to serve
>   As your bedside candle.
> Sleep, Esmeralda, sleep.

It wasn't Esmeralda's complexion, either. The court physicians saw to that. She was fed on the most Scientific Diet, containing just the proper number of calories and exactly the right amount of vitamins, and nobody ever forgot her cod-liver oil or her wholesome fruit. So there were always roses in her cheeks.

Governesses attended to her posture, insisting that she walk eleven times daily about the nursery with a book balanced on her head. Dancing masters taught her grace, and the royal dentist fashioned golden braces for her teeth so they would grow straight and even.

No—it wasn't any of these things which marred the loveliness of Esmeralda. It was something odd about her face. Her nose went up where it should have gone down, and her mouth went down where it should have gone up, and her eyes—her otherwise nice blue eyes—had no Glow. And since in that particular kingdom upward-tilting mouths and downward-tilting noses and eyes with a glow and a twinkle to them were generally admired, Esmeralda grew plainer and plainer and the hearts of the King and the Queen grew heavier and heavier.

For a long while the Princess was kept in ignorance of her misfortune. Because she had always been waited on and petted, she had become by the time she was seven years old quite vain and haughty and fancied herself superior to all other young ladies. But on her eighth birthday something rather terrible happened.

The Queen issued invitations to a birthday fête and among those asked was the neighboring Prince, Charles Michael. It was a very elegant party with a cake of seven layers and jeweled gifts for every person present.

Esmeralda sat at the head of the table with her mouth turned down and her nose turned up at an unusually plain angle, and next to her they put the Prince. At least his name was written in gilt letters on the card. But alas! his chair was vacant. He had vanished immediately after pinning the tail on the donkey in the state drawing-room, and when the footmen announced supper he did not come running with the rest. Esmeralda was very cross. She wished Charles Michael to admire the paper crown she had pulled from her snapper; but though the servants scoured the castle, no Prince could they find.

It was only after the feast had been finished that they discovered him down by the duck pond, and with him the daughter of the duck-keeper, who had not been invited to the party at all.

"Your Highness," reproved his tutor after Charles Michael had been fetched in and had made his goodbyes to the King and Queen. "Why ever did you run away from the Princess's fête?"

Charles Michael was a polite boy but he was also honest.

"Because," he answered (and the court could not help but overhear), "I liked the duck-keeper's daughter better. She has a mouth prettily turned up and a nose charmingly tilted down and her eyes have the merriest twinkle in the world."

Well, you can imagine Esmeralda's chagrin! She burst into tears and had to be carried away like a baby by her governess. The King and Queen, casting down their eyes, retired unhappily to their rooms. As for the court, they looked at one another knowingly and murmured, "Just goes to show, doesn't it? It'll be hard, later on, to be ruled over by such a very plain Princess."

All night Esmeralda wept and no one could comfort her. Her father and mother were in despair. They called a consultation of the royal physicians but those sages had little to offer.

"In such cases as this, Your Majesty," said the oldest and wisest of them, "we seldom operate. Tonsils we can take out, but there would be no improvement in cutting off Her Highness's nose. Pills would have no effect upon the shape of her mouth. As for the glow of the royal eye—all the drugs in the kingdom would not bring it there."

"Have you nothing at all to suggest?" asked the King. He looked at the doctors severely, so that they shifted from one foot to the other and fingered their stethoscopes. Finally one of the youngest cleared his throat.

"Your Majesty," he said nervously, "why not try magic?"

"Useless!" snapped the King. "We've been all over that with the Wizard of State."

"Offer a reward," bravely continued the young physician. "In this great country there must be someone who knows the right enchantment."

"We-l-l," meditated the King, "we will take it under our royal consideration." And he dismissed the doctors.

The next day in the newspapers appeared a large advertisement stamped with the King's seal. It went like this:

REWARD

Anyone capable of Transforming a Plain
Young Lady into a Beautiful Young Lady
will be Given a Purse of Gold. Results
must be Guaranteed. Those Failing will
Lose Their Heads.

That wasn't a very tactful advertisement, it must be confessed, for the King had thought it up himself without consulting his Royal Board of Public Relations. And for a week no one came forward to seek the reward, since, naturally, few persons wanted to risk having their heads cut off.

Then on the last day of the week there came knocking at the castle gate a strange visitor. It was neither a wizard in a tall hat nor a great doctor in a black robe. It was a woman and an unfashionable one at that, but she clutched a copy of the newspaper in her hand and smiled quite cheerfully at the King when she was admitted to his presence.

Dropping an agreeable curtsey, she said, "Your Majesty, I have come in answer to your advertisement."

The King looked at her in astonishment.

"Nonsense!" he cried, somewhat rudely. "My good woman, I was expecting a powerful magician."

She did not seem one whit abashed.

"The oddest people make magic nowadays," she answered. "Besides, Your Majesty, I am a widow and on practically no income at all I have fed, clothed and educated five daughters. I claim that in these days, taxes being what they are, that takes a magician of sorts."

And she looked so serenely at the King that he was impressed in spite of himself.

"Certainly, you're the only one brave enough to answer my advertisement," he mused. "Perhaps you have some power I have not heard of."

Remembering to be businesslike, he added, "What references can you show from your former empl—— I mean, have you any proof of your magic?"

The woman fumbled in her purse and drew out a photograph.

"These are my five daughters," she said. "Not a plain one among them."

Truly the King had to admit, as he scanned the picture, that five handsomer girls he had never seen. Every nose tilted daintily down, every mouth turned up, and the photographer had caught the twinkle in every pair of eyes.

"Nice, very nice," murmured the King. "But could you do the same for a young lady who *wasn't* your daughter?"

"Give me thrice three months," said the woman quietly. "I think I could do it in that time. *If* I have a free hand and no interference."

"You realize you'll lose your head if the magic fails?"

"I'm willing to chance it for your sake, Your Majesty, and for the sake of the poor plain little Princ——" She stopped suddenly and clapped her hand over her mouth but the King only said sadly, "Never mind. Everybody knows about Esmeralda. Come, now, Mrs.——er——"

"Goodwit. Dame Goodwit."

"Come, then, Dame Goodwit. I am inclined to trust you. I like your courage and I like your manners. Let us but see the Queen, speak to the Princess, and then you can at once take up your residence in the castle."

"Oh," cried the Dame, "that is one thing I cannot do, Your Majesty. Unless Her Highness go with me and live as one of my daughters, the magic is of no avail."

"What!" roared the King. "Esmeralda leave her home and her comforts to live with you in—no offense meant, madam—what is bound to be a style to which she is unaccustomed?"

The Dame was calm but firm.

"Those are my conditions, Your Majesty," she replied. "Your advisers may examine my home. You may keep watch from afar during the Princess's stay. But come with me she must; and what is more she must take little with her. Not one silken gown or jeweled plaything may she bring if my magic is to be effective."

Well, the King argued and he argued but he got nowhere; and finally he gave in. So did the Queen. For once in their lives, also, they were firm with Esmeralda (who did not take kindly to the idea of going away from home with so common a woman) and insisted she try the power of Dame Goodwit.

The very next day, after the royal emissaries had turned in a report that the Dame lived in respectable though very humble circumstances, off they packed her in a hired coach. (For Dame Goodwit had insisted that the journey begin with no royal fanfare.)

Not one thing, either, was Esmeralda permitted to bring along which might remind her of her exalted state—not her bicycle with the silver basket, nor her roller skates, nor her dolls with their numberless costumes, nor her pony, nor any of her beautiful frocks. The Dame went through her closet and selected two or three of the very plainest dresses and a couple of pinafores and a warm coat and hat. Only in one matter did she relent. She permitted Esmeralda to wear about her neck a little trinket, a pearl locket which had been given her by her Godmother and which, though of slight value, the Princess had worn since babyhood. Esmeralda was still clutching tightly to the locket as she rode weeping away in an ordinary coach to the house of Dame Goodwit and her five daughters.

For three hours they rode—out of the city, through a dim forest, into a meadow, and at last the coachman drew up before a small and shabby cottage. The roof was peaked, the shutters a faded blue, the windows insignificant. Flowers of early spring nodded beside the walk, and near the picket fence flamed beds of crocuses. But Esmeralda saw only the shabbiness and the smallness.

"Oh," she sobbed, "to be shut away here in this horrid spot! How can there be magic in such a place?" And she would have run back to the coach if it had not already galloped away.

Dame Goodwit took no notice of her tears and merely said, "Trot along in, my dear, and take a look around." Then, raising her voice, she called, "Come out, daughters, to greet our guest."

Immediately the little front door popped open and out hurried five handsome girls, all beaming at Esmeralda.

"Esmeralda, these are my daughters," said the Dame. "Their names are Annabelle, Christabelle, Dulcibelle, Floribelle, and Echo. Four belles and an echo, you see. Children, Esmeralda will be living with us for a while. You, Annabelle, take her bag. Christabelle, show her where she will sleep. Fetch her, Dulcibelle, something warm to drink, while you, Flory, put on an egg for her supper. And Echo, my pet, give her the kiss of welcome."

Like five stair steps they were, from a very little girl to a very tall girl, and they all smiled shyly at the Princess and ran to assist her. However, it was as if they were greeting a friend instead of a Princess, for not one of them curtsied or kissed her hand. But Esmeralda found no breath to chide them, so briskly did they bundle her in, every damsel talking at once. Her tears, however, began afresh when she saw the tiny cubicle that held her bed, the rough cup out of which she was supposed to drink, the simple kitchen where supper was prepared. Everything was clean as a scrubbed turnip, but to Esmeralda's eyes, dazzled so long by riches, her surroundings seemed too dreary to bear.

Instead of eating the fresh egg which Floribelle obligingly broke for her, she flung herself on the floor, kicking her heels, and indulged, regrettably, in a temper tantrum. At the castle, ten hand-maids would have bustled about with spirits of ammonia and soothing words. But Dame Goodwit said only, "Let her be, girls. Esmeralda is possibly homesick. She'll feel better in the morning." And the six of them sat down to eat their wholesome supper. Then they cleared away, stepping neatly around Esmeralda, who was still stretched out on the linoleum.

After a while, since no one paid any attention to her, she left off weeping and kicking, arose, and stated, "I'm hungry."

"Christabelle, see if there's any soup left," instructed the Dame.

Christabelle filled a bowl and set it before Esmeralda, who drank it greedily.

"I am also sleepy," the Princess announced. "Ask one of your daughters, Dame, to attend me to bed."

"People," said that lady cheerfully, "attend themselves here. That is part of the magic." So for the first time in her life, Esmeralda took off her own clothes, turned down her own covers and smoothed her own pillow. She did it with bad grace and clumsily, but she managed, and weary as she was, fell asleep quickly even on the hard mattress.

That was the beginning of a strange life for the Princess. Whatever spells Dame Goodwit knew, they were not, at once, evident. She never said "Abracadabra" or "Hocus Pocus," and there wasn't a single wand anywhere about the cottage. And though Esmeralda looked earnestly in the cracked mirror each day, she could see no improvement in her plainness. In fact, she was, if anything, plainer, for her eyes were continually red from weeping over her lot. No one seemed to recall that she was a royal child, entitled to the privileges of her birth. Only the pearl locket, hung around her neck, reminded her; and that she treasured and fingered constantly, to reassure herself that the castle was not a dream.

The Dame treated her kindly but with no more ceremony than she gave to her own daughters. Esmeralda found, to her horror, that she was even expected to assist with the housework.

"We won't ask you to do much at first," said the Dame. "You'd be only a hindrance. But you aren't really stupid; you'll learn."

"Stupid, indeed!" Esmeralda was outraged.

But as time went on, the Princess secretly discovered that the Dame had been no more than right. Compared to Christabelle and Annabelle and the rest, she *was* quite dull. All the things they could do! They could out-run her at races. They could play innumerable games she had never heard of. Even little Echo could climb into the gnarled apple trees more sprly than she. And at housewifely tasks they were incredibly deft. They sewed and patched and darned and embroidered and whipped up delicate puddings out of practically nothing, while she could scarcely pour water without spilling it.

Not that she tried, at first. She demanded to be waited on. But no one ran to do her bidding. If she neglected to make her bed in the morning, she must sleep that night in rumpled sheets. If she refused to help with the table-setting, no place was laid for her. When she forgot to hang up her clothes, they grew creased and wrinkled and nobody pressed them for her.

What amazed her most was how little the Dame's five daughters minded their humble surroundings. When she wasn't sulking she would spin them long tales of how elegantly she had lived at home, or what tempting meals had been served in her royal nursery, or how remarkably well she rode her pony. But Annabelle and Christabelle and Dulcibelle and Floribelle would mumble politely, "How nice for you," or "Wasn't that pleasant?" and go on digging in the garden or ironing a napkin.

Once, after Esmeralda had regaled them with an especially tedious story of her grand life, good-tempered Dulcy said abruptly (for her), "You may have been a Princess but you never learned to jump rope like us or spell so well or sew a decent seam. You hadn't even any sisters or playmates. What good is it, anyhow, being rich and royal?"

Only little Echo listened attentively to her recountings and followed her about like a shadow. And Esmeralda, who had loved nothing except herself, grew excessively fond of the pretty child, taking comfort in her affection.

After the first bitter weeks, she even stopped being scornful of some of the menial tasks she was called upon to perform. She began to envy the clever hands of Floribelle as she beat up a sponge cake. She noticed what satisfaction Christabelle took in embroidering a pocket on her smock. How awkwardly her own fingers held a needle or wielded a spoon on her rare attempts to compete! Into her mind crept the suspicion that perhaps simply being born a Princess did not make her a really superior person. And one day when the first three months were nearly up, she said grudgingly (watching Floribelle taking delicious gingerbread from the oven), "I wish, Flory, that I could be as clever as you."

At that moment a bird sang loudly, a rainbow appeared in the sky though there had been no rain, and Esmeralda felt a strange sensation. Something odd was happening to her. She ran to the mirror and peered into it. And what do you think?

No longer did Esmeralda's nose turn plainly up. It tilted so charmingly down that she cried out with delight. And with what excitement the generous family gathered 'round to compliment her, for it was indeed an improvement.

"The magic is working!" shouted Esmeralda. "Dame Goodwit, you are an enchantress after all!"

But the Dame only smiled. "That is as may be," she said mildly. "Certainly your nose is more attractive, child. But perhaps that is because you have stopped turning it up at the world in general. Perhaps you have found out there are people just as clever and just as fortunate in their own way, as you."

But Esmeralda was sure it was magic and she began to relent in her feeling toward the Dame and the life of the cottage. Its meanness still irked her and at night she still fondled the pearl locket. But her manners improved and she joined the rest of the girls more frequently in their games and at their chores.

She hung up her clothes, nightly, quite by habit. "Let me gather the eggs," she would sometimes ask at evening when it was time to search the hen-house. Almost humbly she followed at the heels of Christabelle or Floribelle while, singing, they swept or dusted or scoured the hearth. Dame Goodwit gave her a tiny plot of ground for her to plant and she grew reasonably adept at coaxing the seeds to climb up into the sunlight. She burned her thumbs trying to make cookies, she scratched her knees blackberrying, she made up stories for Echo which had nothing to do with how important she had been at the castle.

Then, when save for a day and a night another three months had sped, the second magic came to pass.

It happened on an afternoon when a soft rain was falling. The house was quiet, for the Dame and her daughters were resting after a busy morning. Only Esmeralda was awake, standing by the window watching the drops roll down the pane and thinking with a pang of homesickness about her own nursery at tea-time. She remembered how the lamps would have been lighted and it would have been time for muffins to come up on a tray. She was not sad—merely wistful—but she was seized with a sudden desire to taste again those muffins, so hot, so crisp, so buttery. "Why not make some?" she thought daringly. "Goodness knows I've watched the Dame turn out enough hot breads, and I know exactly where she keeps the cook book."

Without more ado, she crept quietly into the little kitchen, found an apron, and set about her task. The Dame and her daughters must have napped well that day, for Esmeralda made more noise than she had counted on, what with beating the eggs and measuring the sugar and dropping things and opening up drawers and testing the oven to see if it was hot enough. But the batter got itself mixed at last and popped into the stove and, just at the moment the family aroused itself and came looking for Esmeralda, that proud young lady was taking out a batch of crusty, golden-brown muffins.

You can imagine what a stir it created in the house. They may not have been the *best* muffins ever baked—perhaps they were just a bit doughy at the center and a trifle lopsided at the edges if you looked closely—but Esmeralda could not have been more pleased had they been perfection. The Dame praised her, the daughters praised her, and Echo kissed her on both cheeks. And Esmeralda just beamed and beamed. Then suddenly a rose beside the door unfolded its petals, a cricket chirped, and Floribelle cried out, "Esmeralda, your mouth! It turns up!"

Sure enough, when the excited Princess flew to the mirror, she saw a wonderful transformation. Beneath her dainty new nose, her mouth—her drooping, sullen little mouth—turned up as sweetly as that of Echo.

"I'm prettier! I'm growing prettier!" cried Esmeralda.

"She's growing prettier!" sang the sisters and they threw their arms about her and hugged her joyously.

"It was the muffins," said Echo.

"It was the magic," bubbled Esmeralda.

But Dame Goodwit merely smiled and said, "That is as may be. Perhaps your mouth turned down because life was dull. Never before, I think, have you known what it was to be proud of the work of your own hands."

After that famous occurrence, Esmeralda forgot to count the days till her exile ended. She grew happier in the cottage than she had been in the castle—except, of course, for missing her father and mother. She forgot about her pony in caring for the brown hens. She forgot about the tall swings, with clambering up the old apple trees for fruit. She left off yearning for her usual luxuries in the pleasure of playing Hop Scotch with Floribelle or of beating Christabelle at races or of doing well at household tasks. She tidied her room; she polished the tin pots until they shone bright as copper; she learned to make gingerbread men with raisins for eyes. The pearl locket lay in a drawer of her rickety dresser and although she looked at it each day, its touch was not now her only consolation. The good Dame was well pleased with Esmeralda and remarked it so frequently that the Princess's turned-up smile got quite dimply with happiness.

Autumn waned. The last three months spent themselves in a haze of soft skies and flaming leaves. Light snow fell. In early December the cottage rocked with whisperings and giggles, for little Echo was to have a birthday.

All the sisters were planning surprises for the child—stitching away, after she had gone to bed, on cloth dolls, embroidering aprons and jolly bonnets. Only Esmeralda looked castdown, for she had been able to contrive no gift for her favorite. She couldn't sew as well as Annabelle or knit like Christabelle, or do fine cross-stitch like Dulcy, or twist yarn into cunning toys like Floribelle. There was no use her baking cookies—Dame Goodwit was already frosting an impressive cake. So for the first time in a long while she felt sad and left out.

"Never mind, Esmeralda," Dulcy soothed her. "Echo knows you love her and would give her something if you could."

Yet on the night before the birthday, Esmeralda let fall a salt tear into her pillow. She thought of her thousand riches at home and of how little they helped her now. Her hands, alone, tomorrow would be empty.

Yet need they be? There was her locket. True, it was what she treasured most of all. Without it she might forget altogether that she was the daughter of the King. But Echo had been her admirer, her comforter, her dear friend.

In the darkness, Esmeralda felt for the locket, fitted her hand about it as if in farewell, then fell peacefully to sleep.

At dawn she awoke, found a piece of paper and tied the pearled bauble gaily with a bit of red string from the grocery bundles. When Echo came to the breakfast table, greeted by the "Happy Birthdays" of the household, there was Esmeralda's present on top of the pile. Echo opened it curiously. Then she cried out, "The locket!" threw herself headlong into Esmeralda's arms, and they both burst into happy tears.

"It was all I had to give you," gulped the Princess. "Wear it for me."

At that moment a gleam of light from the winter morning glittered brightly upon her head, somewhere far off a bell pealed, and Floribelle looked up with amazement.

"Esmeralda," she sang out. "Your eyes! They are glowing like stars."

Once more Esmeralda sped to the cracked mirror and with overwhelming happiness beheld her countenance. What a pair of eyes twinkled back at her, glowing, indeed, like stars!

"The magic," she said softly. "It is complete. I am no longer plain."

Then she turned to Dame Goodwit.

"My father the King will reward you well. You are a powerful enchantress."

"That is as may be," said the Dame placidly. "Perhaps your eyes glow because for the first time in your life you have done an unselfish thing. I am well pleased with you, Esmeralda."

In the midst of the rejoicing there came a rattle of wheels, the sound of horses' hoofs along the frosty road, and someone smote heavily on the door.

It was the King himself, come to fetch his daughter. For thrice three months were gone.

"Come in, Your Majesty, and welcome," spoke the Dame graciously. She dropped a dignified curtsey.

Esmeralda would have run to him but shyness held her and it was only when he called out, "Esmeralda, my child! My lovely child! Is it really you?" that she fled to his embrace.

"Let me look at you," he commanded, holding her at arm's length. "I can scarcely believe it. A mouth like mine, a nose like your mother's, and your eyes, my dear! Such splendid, glowing eyes."

Turning to the Dame, he said, "Well do you deserve the purse of gold which my messengers will shortly bring. I was fearful, very fearful, the magic might not avail. It would have been a sad thing to behead so worthy a widow as yourself."

"The women of my family, Your Majesty," answered the Dame serenely, "seldom lose their heads. As for the purse of gold, I do not want it. Esmeralda herself worked the enchantment."

And try as he would, no reward could he persuade the remarkable woman to accept.

Esmeralda, after bidding a tender goodbye to the Dame and to Annabelle and Christabelle and Dulcibelle and Floribelle and especially to little Echo, stepped into the carriage and was driven away. Strangely enough, as she pressed her face to the coach window, waving her hand as long as the cottage was in sight, her heart seemed almost as heavy as it had been on the journey which had carried her there.

Excitement, however, awaited her at the castle, for the King's messengers had run ahead with the glad news, and now the whole kingdom rejoiced. Flags flew from battlements, cannons fired salutes, and for the occasion the court poets hurried to compose a magnificent ode of fifty verses entitled, simply, "To Esmeralda."

As the Princess walked gracefully between the silken ropes which had been stretched on either side of the castle steps, an audible gasp arose from all the servants and courtiers and guards of honor who were lined up there in their best livery.

"Is it really Esmeralda?" they whispered. "What poise, what charm, what sparkling eyes!"

The aunts and uncles and cousins nodded their heads complacently, observing, "Gets her looks from our side of the family."

The maids-in-waiting glanced furtively into their hand-mirrors and sighed with envy.

And the court physicians murmured, "Miraculous. We must get the case history."

Only Esmeralda herself kept her composure and was so modest and quiet that the Queen thought she must be ill and insisted she take a spoonful of cod-liver oil at once.

But modest she remained, although pleased with her welcome. And the first thing she did, when the flurry died down, was to persuade the King and Queen to remodel one of the gardener's houses into a comfortable dwelling (with telephone and all modern conveniences) and to send for the Dame and her family. They were naturally reluctant to leave their own home, but when the Queen pointed out what advantages the daughters would enjoy in the matter of schools and of acquiring suitable husbands, she consented finally to move into the cozy residence.

Esmeralda spent much of her time there, keeping up her skill at cookie-making, at climbing apple trees, and at excelling in games of Prisoner's Base.

And she lent her bicycle to Christabelle and her pony to Echo and her roller skates to Dulcy whenever they expressed a wish to try them.

Prince Charles Michael at the next castle party did not run down to the duck pond but paid marked attention to the Princess, helping her adjust her paper crown at the table.

As she grew older she became known far and wide not as "Esmeralda the Plain," but as "Esmeralda the Beautiful." And everyone lived happily ever after—or at least as happily as is possible in this mortal world.

Cinderella

by CHARLES PERRAULT

Once there was a gentleman who married, for his second wife, the proudest and most haughty woman that was ever seen. She had, by a former husband, two daughters of her own humor who were, indeed, exactly like her in all things. He had likewise a young daughter but of unparalleled goodness and sweetness of temper, which she took from her mother, who was the best creature in the world.

No sooner were the ceremonies of the wedding over but the mother began to show herself in her true colors. She could not bear the good qualities of this pretty girl, and all the less because they made her own daughters appear the more odious. She employed her in the meanest work of the house: scouring the dishes and tables and scrubbing madam's room, also those of her daughters. The girl slept in a sorry garret, upon a wretched straw bed, while her sisters lay in fine rooms, with floors all inlaid, upon beds of the very newest fashion, and where they had looking glasses so large they might see themselves at full length from head to foot.

The poor girl bore all patiently and dared not tell her father who would have rattled her off, for his wife governed him entirely. When she had done her work, she used to go into the chimney corner and sit down among cinders and ashes, which caused her to be called Cinderwench. But the younger, who was not so rude and uncivil as the elder, called her Cinderella. However, Cinderella, notwithstanding her mean apparel, was a hundred times handsomer than her sisters, though they were always dressed very richly.

It happened that the king's son gave a ball and invited all persons of fashion to it. The two sisters were also invited, for they cut a very grand figure among the quality. They were delighted at this invitation and wonderfully busy in choosing such gowns, petticoats and headdresses as might become them. This was a new trouble to Cinderella, for it was she who ironed her sisters' linen and plaited their ruffles, while they talked all day long of nothing but how they should be dressed.

"For my part," said the elder, "I will wear my red-velvet suit with French trimming."

"And I," said the younger, "shall have my usual petticoat. But then, to make amends for that, I will put on my gold-flowered manteau, and my diamond stomacher, which is far from being the most ordinary one in the world."

They sent for the best wardrobe woman they could get to make up their headdresses and adjust the double wingspreads, and they had their red brushes and patches from Mademoiselle de la Poche. Cinderella was likewise consulted in all these matters, for she had excellent notions, and advised them always for the best and offered her services to dress their hair, which they were very willing she should do. As she was doing this, they said to her:

"Cinderella, would you not like to go to the ball?"

"Alas," she said, "you only jeer at me. It is not for such as I to go thither."

"You are in the right of it," replied they. "It would certainly make people laugh to see a cinderwench at a palace ball."

Anyone but Cinderella would have dressed their heads awry, but she was very good and dressed them perfectly. They were almost two days without eating, so much were they transported with joy. They broke above a dozen of laces in trying to be laced up close, that they might have a fine slender shape, and they were continually at their looking glass. At last the happy day came. They went to court, and Cinderella followed them with her eyes as long as she could, and when she had lost sight of them, she fell a-crying.

Her godmother, who saw her all in tears, asked her what was the matter.

"I wish I could—I wish I could——" She was not able to speak the rest, being interrupted by her tears and sobbing.

This godmother of hers, who was a fairy, said to her, "You wish to go to the ball. Is it not so?"

"Yes," cried Cinderella, with a great sigh.

"Well," said her godmother, "be a good girl, and I will contrive that you shall go." Then she said to her, "Run into the garden and bring me a pumpkin."

Cinderella went immediately to gather the finest one and brought it to her godmother, not being able to imagine how this pumpkin could make her go to the ball. Her godmother scooped out all the inside of it, leaving nothing but the rind; which done, she struck it with her wand, and the pumpkin was instantly turned into a fine coach, gilded all over with gold.

She then went to look into her mousetrap, where she found six mice, all alive. She told Cinderella to lift up the little trap door, when, giving each mouse, as it went out, a little tap with her wand, the mouse was at that moment turned into a fine horse. Altogether they made a very fine set of six horses of a beautiful mouse-colored gray.

Being at a loss for a coachman, Cinderella said, "I will go and see if there is a rat in the rat-trap—we may make a coachman of him."

"You are in the right," replied her godmother. "Go and look."

Cinderella brought the trap to her, and in it there were three huge rats. The fairy made choice of the one which had the largest beard, and having touched him with her wand, he was turned into a fat, jolly coachman, who had the smartest whiskers eyes ever beheld. After that, she said to her:

"Go again into the garden, and you will find six lizards behind the watering pot; bring them to me."

Cinderella had no sooner done so than her godmother turned them into six footmen, who skipped up immediately behind the

coach, with their liveries all covered with gold and silver. They clung as close behind each other as if they had done nothing else their whole lives. The fairy then said to Cinderella:

"Well, you see here an equipage fit to take you to the ball. Are you not pleased with it?"

"Oh, yes," cried Cinderella, "but must I go thither as I am, in these old rags?"

Her godmother just touched her with her wand, and at the same instant her clothes were turned into cloth of gold and silver, all beset with jewels. This done, she gave her a pair of glass slippers, the prettiest in the whole world. Being thus decked out, Cinderella climbed into her coach; but her godmother, above all things, commanded her not to stay till after midnight, telling her, at the same time, that if she stayed one moment longer, the coach would be a pumpkin again, her horses mice, her coachman a rat, her footmen lizards, and her clothes would become just as they had been before.

Cinderella promised her godmother she would not fail to leave the ball before midnight. And then away she drove, scarce able to contain herself for joy. The king's son, who was told that a great princess, whom nobody knew, had come, ran out to receive her. He gave her his hand as she alighted from the coach and led her into the hall, among all the company. There was immediately a profound silence. They left off dancing, and the violins ceased to play, so attentive was everyone to contemplate the singular beauties of the unknown newcomer. Nothing was then heard but the confused noise of:

"Ha! How handsome she is! Ha! How handsome she is!"

The king himself, old as he was, could not help watching her and telling the queen softly that it was a long time since he had seen so beautiful and lovely a creature. All the ladies were busied in considering her clothes and headdress, that they might have some made next day after the same pattern, provided they could meet with such fine materials and find able hands to make them.

The king's son conducted her to the most honorable seat, and afterward took her out to dance with him, and she danced so gracefully that all more and more admired her. A fine collation was served, whereof the young prince ate not a morsel, so intently was he busied in gazing on Cinderella.

She sat down by her sisters, showing them a thousand civilities, giving them part of the oranges and citrons with which the prince had presented her, which very much surprised them, for they did not know her. While Cinderella was thus amusing her sisters, she heard the clock strike eleven and three-quarters, whereupon she immediately made a curtsy to the company and hastened away as fast as she could.

Reaching home, she ran to seek out her godmother and, after having thanked her, said she could not but heartily wish she might go the next day to the ball, because the king's son had asked her. As she was eagerly telling her godmother whatever had passed at the ball, her two sisters knocked at the door, which Cinderella ran and opened.

"How long you have stayed!" cried she, rubbing her eyes and stretching herself as if she had been just waked out of her sleep. She had not, however, had any inclination to sleep since they went from home.

"If you had been at the ball," said one of her sisters, "you would not have been tired with it. There came thither the finest princess, the most beautiful ever seen with mortal eyes; she showed us a thousand civilities and gave us oranges and citrons."

Cinderella seemed very indifferent in the matter but asked them the name of that princess. They told her they did not know it and that the king's son would give all the world to know who she was. At this Cinderella, smiling, replied:

"She must, then, be very beautiful indeed. How happy you have been! Could not I see her? Ah, dear Miss Charlotte, do lend me your yellow clothes which you wear every day."

"Ay, to be sure," cried Miss Charlotte, "lend my clothes to a dirty cinderwench! I should be a fool."

Cinderella, indeed, expected such an answer and was very glad of the refusal, for she would have been sadly put to it if her sister had done what she asked for jestingly.

The next day the two sisters were at the ball, and so was Cinderella, but dressed more magnificently than before. The king's son was always by her and never ceased his compliments and kind speeches to her. All this was so far from being tiresome that she quite forgot what her godmother had commanded; so that she, at last, counted the clock striking twelve when she took it to be no more than eleven. She then rose up and fled, as nimble as a deer. The prince followed but could not overtake her. She left behind one of her glass slippers, which the prince took up most carefully. Cinderella got home, but quite out of breath and in her nasty old clothes, having nothing left her of all her finery but one of the little slippers, fellow to the one she had dropped.

The guards at the palace gate were asked if they had not seen a princess go out. They said they had seen nobody go out but a young girl, very meanly dressed, who had more the air of a poor country wench than a gentlewoman.

When the two sisters returned from the ball Cinderella asked them if they had been well diverted, and if the fine lady had been there.

They told her, yes, but that she hurried away immediately when it struck twelve, and with so much haste that she dropped one of her little glass slippers, the prettiest in the world, which the king's son had taken up. He had done nothing but look at her all the time at the ball, and that most certainly he was very much in love with the beautiful person who owned the glass slipper.

What they said was very true; for a few days after, the king's son caused it to be proclaimed, by sound of trumpet, that he would marry her whose foot this slipper would just fit. They whom he employed began to try it upon the princesses, then the duchesses and all the court, but in vain. It was brought to the two sisters, who did all they possibly could to thrust their foot into the slipper, but they could not effect it. Cinderella, who saw all this and knew her slipper, said to them, laughing:

"Let me see if it will not fit me."

Her sisters burst out a-laughing and began to banter her. The gentleman who was sent to try the slipper looked earnestly at Cinderella, and finding her very handsome, said it was but just that she should try, and that he had orders to let everyone make trial.

He obliged Cinderella to sit down, and, putting the slipper to her foot, he found it went on easily and fitted her as if it had been made of wax. The astonishment of her two sisters was great, but still greater when Cinderella pulled out of her pocket the other slipper and put it on her foot. Thereupon, in came her godmother who, having touched Cinderella's clothes with her wand, made them richer and more magnificent than any she had worn before.

And now her two sisters found her to be that fine, beautiful lady they had seen at the ball. They threw themselves at her feet to beg pardon for all the ill-treatment they had made her undergo. Cinderella raised them up and, as she embraced them, cried that she forgave them with all her heart and desired them always to love her.

She was conducted to the young prince. He thought her more charming than ever and, a few days after, married her. Cinderella, who was no less good than beautiful, gave her two sisters lodgings in the palace, and that very same day matched them with two great lords of the court.

Puck's Song

by WILLIAM SHAKESPEARE

Over hill, over dale,
  Through bush, through brier,
Over park, over pale,
  Through flood, through fire,
  I do wander everywhere,
  Swifter than the moone's sphere,
  And I serve the fairy queen,
  To dew her orbs upon the green.
  The cowslips tall her pensioners be;
  In their gold coats spots you see;
  Those be rubies, fairy favors,
    In those freckles live their savors;
I must go seek some dewdrops here,
And hang a pearl in every cowslip's ear.

From A *Midsummer Night's Dream.*

Aladdin and the Wonderful Lamp

by ANDREW LANG

There once lived a poor tailor, who had a son called Aladdin, a careless, idle boy who would do nothing but play all day long in the streets with little idle boys like himself. This so grieved the father that he died; yet, in spite of his mother's tears and prayers, Aladdin did not mend his ways. One day, when he was playing in the streets as usual, a stranger asked him his age, and if he were not the son of Mustapha the tailor. "I am, sir," replied Aladdin, "but he died a long while ago."

On this the stranger, who was a famous African magician, fell on his neck and kissed him, saying: "I am your uncle, and knew you from your likeness to my brother. Go to your mother and tell her I am coming."

Aladdin ran home, and told his mother of his newly found uncle. "Indeed, child," she said, "your father had a brother, but I always thought he was dead." However, she prepared supper, and bade Aladdin seek his uncle, who came laden with wine and fruit. He presently fell down and kissed the place where Mustapha used to sit, bidding Aladdin's mother not to be surprised at not having seen him before, as he had been forty years out of the country. He then turned to Aladdin, and asked him his trade, at which the boy hung his head, while his mother burst into tears. On learning that Aladdin was idle and would learn no trade, he offered to take a shop for him and stock it with merchandise. Next day he bought Aladdin a fine suit of clothes and took him all over the city, showing him the sights, and brought him home at nightfall to his mother who was overjoyed to see her son so fine.

Next day the magician led Aladdin into some beautiful gardens a long way outside the city gates. They sat down by a fountain and the magician pulled a cake from his girdle, which he divided between them. They then journeyed onwards till they almost reached the mountains. Aladdin was so tired that he begged to go back, but the magician beguiled him with pleasant stories, and led him on in spite of himself. At last they came to two mountains divided by a narrow valley. "We will go no farther," said the false uncle. "I will show you something wonderful; only do you gather up sticks while I kindle a fire."

When it was lit the magician threw on it a powder he had about him, at the same time saying some magical words. The earth trembled a little and opened in front of them, disclosing a square flat stone with a brass ring in the middle to raise it by. Aladdin tried to run away, but the magician caught him and gave him a blow that knocked him down. "What have I done, uncle?" he said piteously; whereupon the magician said more kindly: "Fear nothing, but obey me. Beneath this stone lies a treasure which is to be yours, and no one else may touch it; so you must do exactly as I tell you."

At the word treasure Aladdin forgot his fears, and grasped the ring as he was told, saying the names of his father and grandfather. The stone came up quite easily and some steps appeared. "Go down," said the magician, "at the foot of those steps you will find an open door leading into three large halls. Tuck up your gown and go through them without touching anything, or you will die instantly. These halls lead into a garden of fine fruit trees. Walk on till you come to a niche in a terrace where stands a lighted lamp. Pour out the oil it contains, and bring it to me." He drew a ring from his finger and gave it to Aladdin, bidding him prosper.

Aladdin found everything as the magician had said, gathered some fruit off the trees, and, having got the lamp, arrived at the mouth of the cave. The magician cried out in a great hurry: "Make haste and give me the lamp." This Aladdin refused to do until he was out of the cave. The magician flew into a terrible passion, and throwing some more powder on the fire, he said something, and the stone rolled back into its place.

The magician left China forever, which plainly showed that he was no uncle of Aladdin's, but a cunning magician, who had read in his magic books of a wonderful lamp, which would make him the most powerful man in the world. Though he alone knew where to find it, he could only receive it from the hand of another. He had picked out the foolish Aladdin for this purpose, intending to get the lamp and kill him afterwards.

For two days Aladdin remained in the dark, crying and lamenting. At last he clasped his hands in prayer, and in so doing, rubbed the ring, which the magician had forgotten to take from him. Immediately an enormous and frightful genie rose out of the earth, saying: "What wouldst thou with me? I am the Slave of the Ring, and will obey thee in all things."

Aladdin fearlessly replied: "Deliver me from this place!" whereupon the earth opened, and he found himself outside. As soon as his eyes could bear the light he went home, but fainted on the threshold. When he came to himself, he told his mother what had passed, and showed her the lamp and the fruits he had gathered in the garden, which were in reality precious stones. He then asked for some food.

"Alas! child," she said, "I have nothing in the house, but I have spun a little cotton and will go and sell it."

Aladdin bade her keep her cotton, for he would sell the lamp instead. As it was very dirty, she began to rub it, that it might fetch a higher price. Instantly a hideous genie appeared and asked what she would have. She fainted away, but Aladdin, snatching the lamp, said boldly: "Fetch me something to eat!"

The genie returned with a silver bowl, twelve silver plates containing rich meats, two silver cups, and two bottles of wine. Aladdin's mother, when she came to herself, said: "Whence comes this splendid feast?"

"Ask not, but eat," replied Aladdin. So they sat at breakfast till it was dinner time and Aladdin told his mother about the lamp.

She begged him to sell it, and have nothing to do with devils. "No," said Aladdin, "since chance hath made us aware of its virtues, we will use it and the ring likewise, which I shall always wear on my finger." When they had eaten all the genie had brought, Aladdin sold one of the silver plates, and so on till none were left. He then had recourse to the genie, who gave him another set of plates, and thus they lived for many years.

One day Aladdin heard an order from the Sultan proclaiming that everyone was to stay at home and close his shutters while the Princess, his daughter, went to and from the bath. Aladdin was seized by a desire to see her face, which was very difficult, as she always went veiled. He hid himself behind the door of the bath and peeped through a chink. The Princess lifted her veil as she went in, and looked so beautiful that Aladdin fell in love with her at first sight. He went home so changed that his mother was frightened. He told her he loved the Princess so deeply that he could not live without her, and meant to ask her in marriage of her father. His mother, on hearing this, burst out laughing; but Aladdin at last prevailed upon her to go before the Sultan and carry his request. She fetched a napkin and laid in it the magic fruits from the enchanted garden, which sparkled and shone like the most beautiful jewels. She took these with her to please the Sultan, and set out, trusting in the lamp.

The Grand-Vizier and the lords of council had just gone in as she entered the hall and placed herself in front of the Sultan. He, however, took no notice of her. She went every day for a week, and stood in the same place. When the council broke up on the sixth day the Sultan said to his Vizier: "I see a certain woman in the audience-chamber every day carrying something in a napkin. Call her next time, that I may find out what she wants."

Next day, at a sign from the Vizier, she went up to the foot of the throne and remained kneeling till the Sultan said to her: "Rise, good woman, and tell me what you want." She hesitated, so the Sultan sent away all but the Vizier, and bade her speak freely, promising to forgive her beforehand for anything she might say. She then told him of her son's violent love for the Princess.

"I prayed him to forget her," she said, "but in vain; he threatened to do some desperate deed if I refused to go and ask your Majesty for the hand of the Princess. Now I pray you to forgive not me alone, but my son Aladdin."

The Sultan asked her kindly what she had in the napkin, whereupon she unfolded the jewels and presented them. He was thunderstruck, and turning to the Vizier said: "What sayest thou? Ought I not to bestow the Princess on one who values her at such a price?" The Vizier, who wanted her for his own son, begged the Sultan to withhold her for three months, in the course of which he hoped his son would contrive to make him a richer present. The Sultan granted this, and told Aladdin's mother that, though he consented to the marriage, she must not appear before him again for three months.

Aladdin waited patiently for nearly three months, but after two had elapsed, his mother, going into the city to buy oil, found everyone rejoicing, and asked what was going on. "Do you not know," was the answer, "that the son of the Grand-Vizier is to marry the Sultan's daughter tonight?"

Breathless, she ran and told Aladdin, who was overwhelmed at first, but presently bethought him of the lamp. He rubbed it, and the genie appeared, saying: "What is thy will?"

Aladdin replied: "The Sultan, as thou knowest, has broken his promise to me, and the Vizier's son is to have the Princess. My command is that tonight you bring hither the bride and bridegroom."

"Master, I obey," said the genie. Aladdin then went to his chamber, where, sure enough, at midnight the genie transported the bed containing the Vizier's son and the Princess.

"Take this new-married man," he said, "and put him outside in the cold, and return at daybreak." Whereupon the genie took the Vizier's son out of bed, leaving Aladdin with the Princess. "Fear nothing," Aladdin said to her; "you are my wife, promised to me by your unjust father, and no harm shall come to you." The Princess was too frightened to speak, and passed the most miserable night of her life, while Aladdin lay down beside her and slept soundly. At the appointed hour the genie fetched in the shivering bridegroom, laid him in his place, and transported the bed back to the palace.

Presently the Sultan came to wish his daughter good-morning. The unhappy Vizier's son jumped up and hid himself, while the Princess would not say a word, and was very sorrowful. The Sultan sent her mother to her, who said: "How comes it, child, that you will not speak to your father? What has happened?" The Princess sighed deeply, and at last told her mother how, during the night, the bed had been carried into some strange house, and what had passed there. Her mother did not believe her in the least, but bade her rise and consider it an idle dream.

The following night exactly the same thing happened, and next morning, on the Princess's refusing to speak, the Sultan threatened to cut off her head. She then confessed all, bidding him ask the Vizier's son if it were not so. The Sultan told the Vizier to ask his son, who owned the truth, adding that, dearly as he loved the Princess, he had rather die than go through another such fearful night, and wished to be separated from her. His wish was granted, and there was an end of feasting and rejoicing.

When the three months were over, Aladdin sent his mother to remind the Sultan of his promise. She stood in the same place as before, and the Sultan, who had forgotten Aladdin, at once remembered him and sent for her. On seeing her poverty the Sultan felt less inclined than ever to keep his word, and asked the Vizier's advice, who counseled him to set so high a value on the Princess that no man living could come up to it. The Sultan then turned to Aladdin's mother, saying: "Good woman, a Sultan must remember his promises, and I will remember mine, but your son must first send me forty basins of gold brimful of jewels, carried by forty black slaves, led by as many white ones, splendidly dressed. Tell him that I await his answer."

The mother of Aladdin bowed low and went home, thinking all was lost. She gave Aladdin the message, adding: "He may wait long enough for your answer!"

"Not so long, mother, as you think," her son replied. "I would do a great deal more than that for the Princess." He summoned the genie, and in a few moments the eighty slaves arrived, and filled up the small house and garden. Aladdin made them set out to the palace, two and two, followed by his mother. They were so richly dressed, with such splendid jewels in their girdles, that everyone crowded to see them and the basins of gold they carried on their heads.

They entered the palace and, after kneeling before the Sultan, stood in a half-circle round the throne with their arms crossed, while Aladdin's mother presented them to the Sultan. He hesitated no longer, but said: "Good woman, return and tell your son that I wait for him with open arms." She lost no time in telling Aladdin, bidding him make haste. But Aladdin first called the genie.

"I want a scented bath," he said, "a richly embroidered habit, a horse surpassing the Sultan's, and twenty slaves to attend me. Besides this, six slaves, beautifully dressed, to wait on my mother; and lastly, ten thousand pieces of gold in ten purses." No sooner said than done. Aladdin mounted his horse and passed through the streets, the slaves strewing gold as they went. Those who had played with him in his childhood knew him not, he had grown so handsome. When the Sultan saw him he came down from his throne, embraced him, and led him into a hall where a feast was spread, intending to marry him to the Princess that very day. But Aladdin refused, saying, "I must build a palace fit for her," and took his leave.

Once home, he said to the genie: "Build me a palace of the finest marble, set with jasper, agate, and other precious stones. In the middle you shall build me a large hall with a dome, its four walls of massy gold and silver, each side having six windows, whose lattices, all except one which is to be left unfinished, must be set with diamonds and rubies. There must be stables and horses and grooms and slaves; go and see about it!"

The palace was finished by next day, and the genie carried him there and showed him all his orders faithfully carried out, even to the laying of a velvet carpet from Aladdin's palace to the Sultan's. Aladdin's mother then dressed herself carefully, and walked to the palace with her slaves, while he followed her on horseback. The Sultan sent musicians with trumpets and cymbals to meet them, so that the air resounded with music and cheers. She was taken to the Princess, who saluted her and treated her with great honor. At night the Princess said good-bye to her father, and set out on the carpet for Aladdin's palace, with his mother at her side, and followed by the hundred slaves. She was charmed at the sight of Aladdin, who ran to receive her. "Princess," he said, "blame your beauty for my boldness if I have displeased you." She told him that, having seen him, she willingly obeyed her father in this matter. After the wedding had taken place Aladdin led her into the hall, where a feast was spread, and she supped with him, after which they danced till midnight.

Next day Aladdin invited the Sultan to see the palace. On entering the hall with the four-and-twenty windows, with their rubies, diamonds, and emeralds, he cried: "It is a world's wonder! There is only one thing that surprises me. Was it by accident that one window was left unfinished?"

"No, sir, by design," returned Aladdin. "I wished your Majesty to have the glory of finishing this palace."

The Sultan was pleased, and sent for the best jewelers in the city. He showed them the unfinished window, and bade them fit it up like the others. "Sir," replied their spokesman, "we cannot find jewels enough."

The Sultan had his own fetched, which they soon used, but to no purpose, for in a month's time the work was not half done. Aladdin, knowing that their task was vain, bade them undo their work and carry the jewels back, and the genie finished the window at his command. The Sultan was surprised to receive his jewels again and visited Aladdin, who showed him the window finished. The Sultan embraced him, the envious Vizier meanwhile hinting that it was the work of enchantment. Aladdin had won the hearts of the people by his gentle bearing. He was made captain of the Sultan's armies, and won several battles for him, but remained modest and courteous as before and lived thus in peace and content for several years.

But far away in Africa the magician remembered Aladdin and by his magic arts discovered that Aladdin, instead of perishing miserably in the cave, had escaped and had married a Princess with whom he was living in great honor and wealth. He knew that the poor tailor's son could only have accomplished this by means of the lamp and traveled night and day till he reached the capital of China, bent on Aladdin's ruin. As he passed through the town he heard people talking everywhere about a marvelous palace. "Forgive my ignorance," he said. "What is this palace you speak of?"

"Have you not heard of Prince Aladdin's palace," was the reply, "the greatest wonder of the world? I will direct you if you have a mind to see it."

The magician thanked him who spoke, and having seen the palace knew that it had been raised by the genie of the lamp and became half mad with rage. He determined to get hold of the lamp and again plunge Aladdin into the deepest poverty. Unluckily, Aladdin had gone a-hunting for eight days, which gave the magician plenty of time. He bought a dozen copper lamps, put them into a basket, and went to the palace, crying, "New lamps for old!" followed by a jeering crowd.

The Princess, sitting in the hall of four-and-twenty windows, sent a slave to find out what the noise was about, who came back laughing, so that the Princess scolded her. "Madam," replied the slave, "who can help laughing to see an old fool offering to exchange fine new lamps for old ones?"

Another slave, hearing this, said: "There is an old one on the cornice there which he can have." Now this was the magic lamp, which Aladdin had left there, as he could not take it out hunting with him. The Princess, not knowing its value, laughingly bade the slave take it and make the exchange. She went and said to the magician: "Give me a new lamp for this."

He snatched it and bade the slave take her choice, amid the jeers of the crowd. Little he cared, but left off crying his lamps,

and went out of the city gates to a lonely place, where he remained till nightfall, when he pulled out the lamp and rubbed it. The genie appeared and at the magician's command carried him, together with the palace and the Princess in it, to a lonely place in Africa.

Next morning the Sultan looked out of the window toward Aladdin's palace and rubbed his eyes, for it was gone. He sent for the Vizier and asked what had become of the palace. The Vizier looked out too, and was lost in astonishment. He again put it down to enchantment, and this time the Sultan believed him, and sent thirty men on horseback to fetch Aladdin in chains. They met him riding home, bound him, and forced him to go with them on foot. The people, however, who loved him, followed, armed, to see that he came to no harm. He was carried before the Sultan, who ordered the executioner to cut off his head. The executioner made Aladdin kneel down, bandaged his eyes, and raised his scimitar to strike. At that instant the Vizier, who saw that the crowd had forced their way into the courtyard and were scaling the walls to rescue Aladdin, called to the executioner to stay his hand. The people, indeed, looked so threatening that the Sultan gave way and ordered Aladdin to be unbound, and pardoned him in the sight of the crowd. Aladdin now begged to know what he had done.

"False wretch!" said the Sultan, "come hither," and showed him from the window the place where his palace had stood. Aladdin was so amazed that he could not say a word. "Where is the palace and my daughter?" demanded the Sultan. "For the first I am not so deeply concerned, but my daughter I must have, and you must find her or lose your head."

Aladdin begged for forty days in which to find her, promising if he failed, to return and suffer death at the Sultan's pleasure. His prayer was granted, and he went forth sadly from the Sultan's presence. For three days he wandered about like a madman, asking everyone what had become of his palace, but they only laughed and pitied him. He came to the banks of a river, and knelt down to say his prayers before throwing himself in. In so doing he rubbed the magic ring he still wore. The genie he had seen in the cave appeared, and asked his will. "Save my life, genie," said Aladdin, "and bring my palace back."

"That is not in my power," said the genie; "I am only the Slave of the Ring, you must ask the Slave of the Lamp."

"Even so," said Aladdin, "but thou canst take me to the palace, and set me down under my dear wife's window." He at once found himself in Africa, under the window of the Princess, and fell asleep out of sheer weariness.

He was awakened by the singing of the birds, and his heart was lighter. He saw plainly that all his misfortunes were owing to the loss of the lamp, and vainly wondered who had robbed him of it. That morning the Princess rose earlier than she had done since she had been carried into Africa by the magician, whose company she was forced to endure once a day. She, however, treated him so harshly that he dared not live there altogether. As she was dressing, one of her women looked out and saw Aladdin. The Princess ran and opened the window, and at the noise she made Aladdin looked up. She called to him to come to her, and great was the joy of these lovers at seeing each other again.

After he had kissed her Aladdin said: "I beg of you, Princess, in God's name, before we speak of anything else, for your own sake and mine, tell me what has become of an old lamp I left on the cornice in the hall of windows when I went hunting."

"Alas!" she said, "I am the innocent cause of our sorrows," and told him of the exchange of the lamp.

"Now I know," cried Aladdin, "that we have to thank the African magician for this! Where is the lamp?"

"He carries it about with him," said the Princess. "I know, for he pulled it out of his breast to show me. He wishes me to break my faith with you and marry him, saying that you were beheaded by my father's command. He is forever speaking ill of you, but I only reply by my tears. If I persist, I doubt not that he will use violence."

Aladdin comforted her and left her for a while. He changed clothes with the first person he met in the town, and having bought a certain powder, returned to the Princess, who let him in by a little side door. "Put on your most beautiful dress," he said to her, "and receive the magician with smiles, leading him to believe that you have forgotten me. Invite him to sup with you, and say you wish to taste the wine of his country. He will go for some, and while he is gone, I will tell you what to do."

She listened carefully to Aladdin, and when he left her, arrayed herself gaily for the first time since she left China. She put on a girdle and head-dress of diamonds, and seeing in a glass that she looked more beautiful than ever, received the magician, saying, to his great amazement: "I have made up my mind that Aladdin is dead, and that all my tears will not bring him back to me, so I am resolved to mourn no more, and have therefore invited you to sup with me; but I am tired of the wines of China, and would fain taste those of Africa."

The magician flew to his cellar, and the Princess put the powder Aladdin had given her in her cup. When he returned she asked him to drink her health in the wine of Africa, handing him her cup in exchange for his as a sign she was reconciled to him. Before drinking, the magician made her a speech in praise of her beauty, but the Princess cut him short, saying: "Let me drink first, and you shall say what you will afterwards." She set her cup to her lips and kept it there, while the magician drained his to the dregs and fell back lifeless. The Princess then opened the door to Aladdin, and flung her arms round his neck, but Aladdin put her away, bidding her leave him, as he had more to do. He then went to the dead magician, took the lamp out of his vest, and bade the genie carry the palace and all in it back to China. This was done, and the Princess in her chamber felt only two little shocks, and little thought she was at home again.

The Sultan, who was sitting in his closet, mourning for his lost daughter, happened to look up, and rubbed his eyes, for there stood the palace as before! He hastened thither, and Aladdin received him in the hall of the four-and-twenty windows, with the Princess at his side. Aladdin told him what had happened, and showed him the dead body of the magician, that he might believe. A ten days' feast was proclaimed, and it seemed as if Aladdin might now live the rest of his life in peace; but it was not to be.

The African magician had a younger brother, who was, if possible, more wicked and more cunning than himself. He traveled to China to avenge his brother's death, and went to visit a pious woman called Fatima, thinking she might be of use to him. He entered her cell and clapped a dagger to her breast, telling her to rise and do his bidding on pain of death. He changed clothes with her, colored his face like hers, put on her veil, and murdered her, that she might tell no tales. Then he went towards the palace of Aladdin, and all the people, thinking he was the holy woman, gathered round him, kissing his hands and begging his blessing. When he got to the palace there was such a noise going on round him that the Princess bade her slave look out of the window and ask what was the matter. The slave said it was the holy woman, curing people by her touch of their ailments, whereupon the Princess, who had long desired to see Fatima, sent for her.

On coming to the Princess, the magician offered up a prayer for her health and prosperity. When he had done, the Princess made him sit by her, and begged him to stay with her always. The false Fatima, who wished for nothing better, consented, but kept his veil down for fear of discovery. The Princess showed him the hall, and asked him what he thought of it. "It is truly beautiful," said the false Fatima. "In my mind it wants but one thing."

"And what is that?" said the Princess.

"If only a roc's egg," replied he, "were hung up from the middle of this dome, it would be the wonder of the world."

After this the Princess could think of nothing but a roc's egg, and when Aladdin returned from hunting he found her in a very ill humor. He begged to know what was amiss, and she told him that all her pleasure in the hall was spoilt for the want of a roc's egg hanging from the dome. "If that is all," replied Aladdin, "you shall soon be happy."

He left her and rubbed the lamp, and when the genie appeared commanded him to bring a roc's egg. The genie gave such a loud and terrible shriek that the hall shook. "Wretch!" he cried, "is it not enough that I have done everything for you, but you must command me to bring my master and hang him up in the midst of this dome? You and your wife and your palace deserve to be burnt to ashes; but this request does not come from you, but from the brother of the African magician whom you destroyed. He is now in your palace disguised as the holy woman—whom he murdered. He it was who put that wish into your wife's head. Take care of yourself, for he means to kill you." So saying the genie disappeared.

Aladdin went back to the Princess, saying his head ached, and requesting that the holy Fatima should be fetched to lay her hands on it. But when the magician came near, Aladdin, seizing his dagger, pierced him to the heart.

"What have you done?" cried the Princess. "You have killed the holy woman!"

"Not so," replied Aladdin, "but a wicked magician," and told her of how she had been deceived.

After this Aladdin and his wife lived in peace. He succeeded the Sultan when he died, and reigned for many years, leaving behind him a long line of kings.

The Wild Swans

by HANS CHRISTIAN ANDERSEN

Far away, where the swallows take refuge in winter, lived a king
who had eleven sons and one daughter, Elise. The eleven brothers
—they were all princes—used to go to school with stars on their
breasts and swords at their sides. They wrote upon golden slates
with diamond pencils, and could read just as well without a book
as with one, so there was no mistake about their being real princes.
Their sister Elise sat upon a little footstool of looking-glass, and
she had a picture-book which had cost the half of a kingdom.
Oh, these children were very happy; but it was not to last thus
for ever.

Their father, who was king over all the land, married a wicked
queen who was not at all kind to the poor children; they found
that out on the first day. All was festive at the castle, but when
the children wanted to play at having company, instead of having
as many cakes and baked apples as ever they wanted, she would
only let them have some sand in a teacup, and said they must
make-believe.

In the following week she sent little Elise into the country to
board with some peasants, and it did not take her long to make
the king believe so many bad things about the boys that he cared
no more about them.

"Fly out into the world and look after yourselves," said the
wicked queen, "you shall fly about like birds without voices."

But she could not make things as bad for them as she would

have liked; they turned into eleven beautiful wild swans. They flew out of the palace window with a weird scream, right across the park and the woods.

It was very early in the morning when they came to the place where their sister Elise was sleeping in the peasant's house. They hovered over the roof of the house, turning and twisting their long necks, and flapping their wings; but no one either heard or saw them. They had to fly away again, and they soared up toward the clouds, far out into the wide world, and they settled in a big, dark wood which stretched down to the shore.

Poor little Elise stood in the peasant's room, playing with a green leaf, for she had no other toys. She made a little hole in it, which she looked through at the sun, and it seemed to her as if she saw her brothers' bright eyes. Every time the warm sunbeams shone upon her cheek, it reminded her of their kisses. One day passed just like another. When the wind whistled through the rose hedges outside the house, it whispered to the roses, "Who can be prettier than you are?" But the roses shook their heads and answered, "Elise!" And when the old woman sat in the doorway reading her Psalms, the wind turned over the leaves and said to the book, "Who can be more pious than you?" "Elise!" answered the book. Both the roses and the book of Psalms only spoke the truth.

She was to go home when she was fifteen, but when the queen saw how pretty she was, she got very angry, and her heart was filled with hatred. She would willingly have turned her into a wild swan too, like her brothers, but she did not dare to do it at once, for the king wanted to see his daughter. The queen always went to the bath in the early morning. It was built of marble and adorned with soft cushions and beautiful carpets.

She took three toads, kissed them, and said to the first, "Sit upon Elise's head when she comes to the bath, so that she may become sluggish like yourself. Sit upon her forehead," she said to the second, "that she may become ugly like you, and then her father won't know her! Rest upon her heart," she whispered to the third. "Let an evil spirit come over her, which may be a burden to her." Then she put the toads into the clean water, and a green tinge immediately came over it. She called Elise, undressed her, and made her go into the bath; when she ducked under the water, one of the toads got among her hair, the other got on to her forehead, and the third on to her bosom. But when she stood up three scarlet poppies floated on the water. Had not the creatures been poisonous, and kissed by the sorceress, they would have been changed into crimson roses, but yet they became flowers from merely having rested a moment on her head and her heart. She was far too good and innocent for the sorcery to have any power over her.

When the wicked Queen saw this, she rubbed Elise over with walnut juice, and smeared her face with some evil-smelling salve. She also matted up her beautiful hair; it would have been impossible to recognize pretty Elise. When her father saw her, he was quite horrified and said that she could not be his daughter. Nobody would have anything to say to her, except the yard dog, and the swallows, and they were only poor dumb animals whose opinion went for nothing.

Poor Elise wept, and thought of her eleven brothers who were all lost. She crept sadly out of the palace and wandered about all day, over meadows and marshes, and into a big forest. She did not know in the least where she wanted to go, but she felt very sad, and longed for her brothers, who, no doubt, like herself had been driven out of the palace. She made up her mind to go and look for them, but she had only been in the wood for a short time when night fell. She had quite lost her way, so she lay down upon the soft moss, said her evening prayer, and rested her head on a little hillock. It was very still and the air was mild, hundreds of glowworms shone around her on the grass and in the marsh like green fire. When she gently moved one of the branches over her head, the little shining insects fell over her like a shower of stars.

She dreamt about her brothers all night long. Again they were children playing together: they wrote upon the golden slates with their diamond pencils, and she looked at the picture-book which had cost half a kingdom. But they no longer wrote strokes and noughts upon their slates as they used to do; no, they wrote down all their boldest exploits, and everything that they had seen and experienced. Everything in the picture-book was alive, the birds sang, and the people walked out of the book, and spoke to Elise and her brothers. When she turned over a page, they skipped back into their places again, so that there should be no confusion among the pictures.

When she woke the sun was already high; it is true she could not see it very well through the thick branches of the lofty forest trees, but the sunbeams cast a golden shimmer round beyond the forest. There was a fresh delicious scent of grass and herbs in the air, and the birds were almost ready to perch upon her shoulders. She could hear the splashing of water, for there were many springs around, which all flowed into a pond with a lovely sandy bottom. It was surrounded with thick bushes, but there was one place which the stags had trampled down and Elise passed through the opening to the water side. It was so transparent, that had not the branches been moved by the breeze, she must have thought that they were painted on the bottom, so plainly was every leaf reflected, both those on which the sun played, and those which were in shade.

When she saw her own face she was quite frightened, it was so brown and ugly, but when she wet her little hand and rubbed her eyes and forehead, her white skin shone through again. Then she took off all her clothes and went into the fresh water. A more beautiful royal child than she, could not be found in all the world.

After she had put on her clothes again, and plaited her long hair, she went to a sparkling spring and drank some of the water out of the hollow of her hand. Then she wandered farther into the wood, though where she was going she had not the least idea. She thought of her brothers, and she thought of a merciful God who would not forsake her. He let the wild crab-apples grow to feed the hungry. He showed her a tree, the branches of which were bending beneath their weight of fruit. Here she made her midday meal, and, having put props under the branches, she walked on into the thickest part of the forest. It was so quiet that she heard her own footsteps, she heard every little withered leaf which bent under her feet. Not a bird was to be seen, not a ray of sunlight pierced the leafy branches, and the tall trunks were so close together that when she looked before her it seemed as if a thick fence of heavy beams hemmed her in on every side. The solitude was such as she had never known before.

It was a very dark night, not a single glowworm sparkled in the marsh; sadly she lay down to sleep, and it seemed to her as if the branches above her parted asunder, and the Saviour looked down upon her with His loving eyes, and little angels' heads peeped out above His head and under His arms.

When she woke in the morning she was not sure if she had dreamt this, or whether it was really true.

She walked a little farther, when she met an old woman with a basket full of berries, of which she gave her some. Elise asked if she had seen eleven princes ride through the wood. "No," said the old woman, "but yesterday I saw eleven swans, with golden crowns upon their heads, swimming in the stream close by here."

She led Elise a little farther to a slope, at the foot of which the stream meandered. The trees on either bank stretched out their rich leafy branches toward each other, and where, from their natural growth, they could not reach each other, they had torn their roots out of the ground, and leant over the water so as to interlace their branches.

Elise said good-by to the old woman, and walked along by the river till it flowed out into the great open sea.

The beautiful open sea lay before the maiden, but not a sail was to be seen on it, not a single boat. How was she ever to get any further? She looked at the numberless little pebbles on the beach; they were all worn quite round by the water. Glass, iron, stone, whatever was washed up, had taken their shapes from the water, which yet was much softer than her little hand. "With all its rolling, it is untiring, and everything hard is smoothed down. I will be just as untiring! Thank you for your lesson, you clear rolling waves! Some time, so my heart tells me, you will bear me to my beloved brothers!"

Eleven white swans' feathers were lying on the sea-weed; she picked them up and made a bunch of them. There were still drops of water on them. Whether these were dew or tears no one could tell. It was very lonely there by the shore, but she did not feel it, for the sea was ever-changing. There were more changes on it in the course of a few hours than could be seen on an inland fresh-water lake in a year. If a big black cloud arose, it was just as if the sea wanted to say, "I can look black too," and then the wind blew up and the waves showed their white crests. But if the clouds were red and the wind dropped, the sea looked like a rose leaf, now white, now green. But, however still it was, there was always a little gentle motion just by the shore, the water rose and fell softly like the bosom of a sleeping child.

When the sun was just about to go down, Elise saw eleven wild swans with golden crowns upon their heads flying toward the shore. They flew in a swaying line, one behind the other, like a white ribbon streamer. Elise climbed up on to the bank and hid behind a bush; the swans settled close by her and flapped their great white wings.

As soon as the sun had sunk beneath the water, the swans shed their feathers and became eleven handsome princes; they were Elise's brothers. Although they had altered a good deal, she knew them at once; she felt that they must be her brothers and she sprang into their arms, calling them by name. They were delighted when they recognized their little sister who had grown so big and beautiful. They laughed and cried, and told each other how wickedly their stepmother had treated them all.

"We brothers," said the eldest, "have to fly about in the guise of swans, as long as the sun is above the horizon. When it goes down we regain our human shapes. So we always have to look out for a resting place near sunset, for should we happen to be flying up among the clouds when the sun goes down, we should be hurled to the depths below. We do not live here; there is another land, just as beautiful as this, beyond the sea; but the way to it is very long and we have to cross the mighty ocean to get to it. There is not a single island on the way where we can spend the night,

only one solitary little rock juts up above the water midway. It is only just big enough for us to stand upon close together, and if there is a heavy sea the water splashes over us, yet we thank our God for it.

"We stay there over night in our human forms, and without it we could never revisit our beloved Fatherland, for our flight takes two of the longest days in the year. We are only permitted to visit the home of our fathers once a year, and we dare only stay for eleven days. We hover over this big forest from whence we catch a glimpse of the palace where we were born, and where our father lives; beyond it we can see the high church towers where our mother is buried. We fancy that the trees and bushes here are related to us; and the wild horses gallop over the moors, as we used to see them in our childhood. The charcoal burners still sing the old songs we used to dance to when we were children. This is our Fatherland, we are drawn toward it, and here we have found you again, dear little sister! We may stay here two days longer, and then we must fly away again across the ocean, to a lovely country indeed, but it is not our own dear Fatherland! How shall we ever take you with us, we have neither ship nor boat!"

"How can I deliver you?" said their sister, and they went on talking to each other nearly all night; they only dozed for a few hours.

Elise was awakened in the morning by the rustling of the swan's wings above her; her brothers were again transformed and were wheeling round in great circles, till she lost sight of them in the distance. One of them, the youngest, stayed behind. He laid his head against her bosom, and she caressed it with her fingers. They remained together all day; toward evening the others came back, and as soon as the sun went down they took their natural forms.

"Tomorrow we must fly away, and we dare not come back for a whole year, but we can't leave you like this! Have you courage to go with us? My arm is strong enough to carry you over the forest, so surely our united strength ought to be sufficient to bear you across the ocean."

"Oh yes! take me with you," said Elise.

They spent the whole night in weaving a kind of net of the elastic bark of the willow bound together with tough rushes; they made it both large and strong. Elise lay down upon it, and when the sun rose and the brothers became swans again, they took up the net in their bills and flew high up among the clouds with their precious sister, who was fast asleep. The sunbeams fell straight on to her face, so one of the swans flew over her head so that its broad wings should shade her.

They were far from land when Elise woke; she thought she must still be dreaming, it seemed so strange to be carried through the air so high up above the sea. By her side lay a branch of beautiful ripe berries, and a bundle of savory roots, which her youngest brother had collected for her, and for which she gave him a grateful smile. She knew it was he who flew above her head shading her from the sun. They were so high up that the first ship they saw looked like a gull floating on the water. A great cloud came up behind them like a mountain, and Elise saw the shadow of herself on it, and those of the eleven swans looking like giants. It was a more beautiful picture than any she had ever seen before, but as the sun rose higher, the cloud fell behind, and the shadow picture disappeared.

They flew on and on all day like an arrow whizzing through the air, but they went slower than usual, for now they had their sister to carry. A storm came up, and night was drawing on; Elise saw the sun sinking with terror in her heart, for the solitary rock was nowhere to be seen. The swans seemed to be taking stronger strokes than ever; alas! she was the cause of their not being able to get on faster; as soon as the sun went down they would become men, and they would all be hurled into the sea and drowned. She prayed to God from the bottom of her heart, but still no rock was to be seen! Black clouds gathered, and strong gusts of wind announced a storm; the clouds looked like a great threatening leaden wave, and the flashes of lightning followed each other rapidly.

The sun was now at the edge of the sea. Elise's heart quaked, when suddenly the swans shot downwards so suddenly, that she thought they were falling, then they hovered again. Half of the sun was below the horizon, and there for the first time she saw the little rock below, which did not look bigger than the head of a seal above the water. The sun sank very quickly, it was no bigger than a star, but her foot touched solid earth. The sun went out like the last sparks of a bit of burning paper; she saw her brothers stand arm in arm around her, but there was only just room enough for them. The waves beat upon the rock and washed over them like drenching rain. The heavens shone with continuous fire, and the thunder rolled, peal upon peal. But the sister and brothers held each other's hands and sang a psalm which gave them comfort and courage.

The air was pure and still at dawn. As soon as the sun rose the swans flew off with Elise, away from the islet. The sea still ran high, it looked from where they were as if the white foam on the dark green water were millions of swans floating on the waves.

When the sun rose higher, Elise saw before her half floating in the air great masses of ice, with shining glaciers on the heights. A palace was perched midway a mile in length, with one bold colonnade built above another. Beneath them swayed palm trees and gorgeous blossoms as big as mill wheels. She asked if this was the land to which she was going, but the swans shook their heads, because what she saw was a mirage; the beautiful and ever-changing palace of Fata Morgana. No mortal dared enter it. Elise gazed at it, but as she gazed the palace, gardens and mountains melted away, and in their place stood twenty proud churches with their high towers and pointed windows. She seemed to hear the notes of the organ, but it was the sea she heard. When she got close to the seeming churches, they changed to a great navy sailing beneath her; but it was only a sea mist floating over the waters. Yes, she saw constant changes passing before her eyes, and now she saw the real land she was bound to. Beautiful blue mountains rose before her with their cedar woods and palaces. Long before the sun went down, she sat among the hills in front of a big cave covered with delicate green creepers. It looked like a piece of embroidery.

"Now we shall see what you will dream here tonight," said the youngest brother, as he showed her where she was to sleep.

"If only I might dream how I could deliver you," she said, and this thought filled her mind entirely. She prayed earnestly to God for His help, and even in her sleep she continued her prayer. It seemed to her that she was flying up to Fata Morgana in her castle in the air. The fairy came toward her, she was charming and brilliant, and yet she was very like the old woman who gave her the berries in the wood, and told her about the swans with the golden crowns.

"Your brothers can be delivered," she said, "but have you courage and endurance enough for it? The sea is indeed softer than your hands, and it molds the hardest stones, but it does not feel the pain your fingers will feel. It has no heart, and does not suffer the pain and anguish you must feel. Do you see this stinging nettle I hold in my hand? Many of this kind grow round the cave where you sleep; only these and the ones which grow in the churchyards may be used. Mark that! Those you may pluck although they will burn and blister your hands. Crush the nettles with your feet and you will have flax, and of this you must weave eleven coats of mail with long sleeves. Throw these over the eleven wild swans and the charm is broken! But remember that from the moment you begin this work, till it is finished, even if it takes years, you must not utter a word! The first word you say will fall like a murderer's dagger into the hearts of your brothers. Their lives hang on your tongue. Mark this well!"

She touched her hand at the same moment, it was like burning fire, and woke Elise. It was bright daylight, and close to where she slept lay a nettle like those in her dream. She fell upon her knees with thanks to God and left the cave to begin her work.

She seized the horrid nettles with her delicate hands, and they burnt like fire; great blisters rose on her hands and arms, but she suffered it willingly if only it would deliver her beloved brothers. She crushed every nettle with her bare feet, and twisted it into green flax.

When the sun went down and the brothers came back, they were alarmed at finding her mute; they thought it was some new witchcraft exercised by their wicked stepmother. But when they saw her hands, they understood that it was for their sakes; the youngest brother wept, and wherever his tears fell, she felt no more pain, and the blisters disappeared.

She spent the whole night at her work, for she could not rest till she had delivered her dear brothers. All the following day while her brothers were away she sat solitary, but never had the time flown so fast. One coat of mail was finished and she began the next. Then a hunting-horn sounded among the mountains; she was much frightened, the sound came nearer, and she heard dogs barking. In terror she rushed into the cave and tied the nettles she had collected and woven into a bundle upon which she sat.

At this moment a big dog bounded forward from the thicket, and another and another, they barked loudly and ran backwards and forwards. In a few minutes all the huntsmen were standing outside the cave, and the handsomest of them was the king of the country. He stepped up to Elise: never had he seen so lovely a girl.

"How came you here, beautiful child?" he said.

Elise shook her head; she dared not speak; the salvation and the lives of her brothers depended upon her silence. She hid her hands under her apron, so that the king should not see what she suffered.

"Come with me!" he said; "you cannot stay here. If you are as good as you are beautiful, I will dress you in silks and velvets, put a golden crown upon your head, and you shall live with me and have your home in my richest palace!" Then he lifted her upon his horse, she wept and wrung her hands, but the king said, "I only think of your happiness; you will thank me one day for what I am doing!" Then he darted off across the mountains, holding her before him on his horse, and the huntsmen followed.

When the sun went down, the royal city with churches and cupolas lay before them, and the king led her into the palace, where great fountains played in the marble halls, and where walls and ceilings were adorned with paintings, but she had no eyes for them, she only wept and sorrowed; passively she allowed the women to dress her in royal robes, to twist pearls into her hair, and to draw gloves on to her blistered hands.

She was dazzlingly lovely as she stood there in all her magnificence; the courtiers bent low before her, and the king wooed her as his bride, although the archbishop shook his head, and whispered that he feared the beautiful wood maiden was a witch, who had dazzled their eyes and infatuated the king.

The king refused to listen to him, he ordered the music to play, the richest food to be brought, and the loveliest girls to dance before her. She was led through scented gardens into gorgeous apartments, but nothing brought a smile to her lips, or into her eyes, sorrow sat there like a heritage and a possession for all time. Last of all, the king opened the door of a little chamber close by the room where she was to sleep. It was adorned with costly green carpets, and made to exactly resemble the cave where he found her. On the floor lay the bundle of flax she had spun from the nettles, and from the ceiling hung the shirt of mail which was already finished. One of the huntsmen had brought all these things away as curiosities.

"Here you may dream that you are back in your former home!" said the king. "Here is the work upon which you were engaged; in the midst of your splendor, it may amuse you to think of those times."

When Elise saw all these things so dear to her heart, a smile for the first time played about her lips, and the blood rushed back to her cheeks. She thought of the deliverance of her brothers, and she kissed the king's hand; he pressed her to his heart, and ordered all the church bells to ring marriage peals. The lovely dumb girl from the woods was to be queen of the country.

The archbishop whispered evil words into the ear of the king, but they did not reach his heart. The wedding was to take place, and the archbishop himself had to put the crown upon her head. In his anger he pressed the golden circlet so tightly upon her head as to give her pain. But a heavier circlet pressed upon her heart, her grief for her brothers, so she thought nothing of the bodily pain. Her lips were sealed, a single word from her mouth would cost her brothers their lives, but her eyes were full of love for the good and handsome king, who did everything he could to please her. Every day she grew more and more attached to him, and longed to confide in him, tell him her sufferings; but dumb she must remain, and in silence must bring her labor to completion. Therefore at night she stole away from his side into her secret chamber, which was decorated like a cave, and here she knitted one shirt after another. When she came to the seventh, all her flax was worked up; she knew that these nettles which she was to use grew in the churchyard, but she had to pluck them herself. How was she to get there?

"Oh, what is the pain of my fingers compared with the anguish of my heart," she thought. "I must venture out, the good God will not desert me!" With as much terror in her heart as if she were doing some evil deed, she stole down one night into the moonlit garden, and through the long alleys out into the silent streets to the churchyard. There she saw, sitting on a gravestone, a group of hideous ghouls. Elise had to pass close by them, and they fixed their evil eyes upon her, but she said a prayer as she passed, picked the stinging nettles and hurried back to the palace with them.

Only one person saw her, but that was the archbishop, who watched while others slept. Surely now all his bad opinions of the queen were justified; all was not as it should be with her, she must be a witch, and therefore she had bewitched the king and all the people.

He told the king in the confessional what he had seen and what he feared. When those bad words passed his lips, the pictures of the saints shook their heads as if to say: it is not so, Elise is innocent. The archbishop, however, took it differently, and thought that they were bearing witness against her, and shaking their heads at her sin. Two big tears rolled down the king's cheeks, and he went home with doubt in his heart. He pretended to sleep at night, but no quiet sleep came to his eyes. He perceived how Elise got up and went to her private closet. Day by day his face grew darker, Elise saw it but could not imagine what was the cause of it. It alarmed her, and what was she not already suffering in her heart because of her brothers? Her salt tears ran down upon the royal purple velvet, they lay upon it like sparkling diamonds, and all who saw their splendor wished to be queen.

She had, however, almost reached the end of her labors, only one shirt of mail was wanting, but again she had no more flax and not a single nettle was left. Once more, for the last time, she must go to the churchyard to pluck a few handfuls. She thought with dread of the solitary walk and the horrible ghouls; but her will was as strong as her trust in God.

Elise went, but the king and the archbishop followed her, they saw her disappear within the gateway of the churchyard. When they followed they saw the ghouls sitting on the gravestone as Elise had seen them before; and the king turned away his head because he thought she was among them, she, whose head this very evening had rested on his breast.

"The people must judge her," he groaned, and the people judged. "Let her be consumed in the glowing flames!"

She was led away from her beautiful royal apartments to a dark damp dungeon, where the wind whistled through the grated window. Instead of velvet and silk they gave her the bundle of nettles she had gathered to lay her head upon. The hard burning shirts of mail were to be her covering, but they could have given her nothing more precious.

She set to work again with many prayers to God. Outside her prison the street boys sang derisive songs about her, and not a soul comforted her with a kind word.

Toward evening she heard the rustle of swans' wings close to her window; it was her youngest brother, at last he had found her. He sobbed aloud with joy although he knew that the coming night might be her last, but then her work was almost done and her brothers were there.

The archbishop came to spend her last hours with her as he had promised the king. She shook her head at him, and by looks and gestures begged him to leave her. She had only this night in which to finish her work, or else all would be wasted, all—her pain, tears and sleepless nights. The archbishop went away with bitter words against her, but poor Elise knew that she was innocent, and she went on with her work.

The little mice ran about the floor bringing nettles to her feet, so as to give what help they could, and a thrush sat on the grating of the window where he sang all night as merrily as he could to keep up her courage.

It was still only dawn, and the sun would not rise for an hour when the eleven brothers stood at the gate of the palace, begging to be taken to the king. This could not be done, was the answer, for it was still night; the king was asleep and no one dared wake him. All their entreaties and threats were useless, the watch turned out and even the king himself came to see what was the matter. But just then the sun rose, and no more brothers were to be seen, only eleven wild swans hovering over the palace.

The whole populace streamed out of the town gates, they were all anxious to see the witch burnt. A miserable horse drew the cart in which Elise was seated. They had put upon her a smock of green sacking, and all her beautiful long hair hung loose from the lovely head. Her cheeks were deathly pale, and her lips moved softly, while her fingers unceasingly twisted the green yarn. Even on the way to her death she could not abandon her unfinished work. Ten shirts lay completed at her feet—she labored away at the eleventh, amid the scoffing insults of the populace.

"Look at the witch how she mutters. She has never a book of psalms in her hands, no, there she sits with her loathsome sorcery. Tear it away from her, into a thousand bits!"

The crowd pressed around her to destroy her work, but just then eleven white swans flew down and perched upon the cart flapping their wings. The crowd gave way before them in terror.

"It is a sign from Heaven! She is innocent!" they whispered, but they dared not say it aloud.

The executioner seized her by the hand, but she hastily threw the eleven shirts over the swans, who were immediately transformed to eleven handsome princes; but the youngest had a swan's wing in place of an arm, for one sleeve was wanting to his shirt of mail. She had not been able to finish it.

"Now I may speak! I am innocent."

The populace who saw what had happened bowed down before her as if she had been a saint, but she sank lifeless in her brother's arms; so great had been the strain, the terror and the suffering she had endured.

"Yes, innocent she is indeed," said the eldest brother, and he told them all that had happened.

Whilst he spoke a wonderful fragrance spread around, as of millions of roses. Every faggot in the pile had taken root and shot out branches, and a great high hedge of red roses had arisen. At the very top was one pure white blossom, it shone like a star, and the king broke it off and laid it on Elise's bosom, and she woke with joy and peace in her heart.

All the church bells began to ring of their own accord, and the singing birds flocked around them. Surely such a bridal procession went back to the palace as no king had ever seen before!

Remarkable Animals and Astonishing Things . . .

Fun and
Fantasy

The Story of Doctor Dolittle

THE RAREST ANIMAL OF ALL

by HUGH LOFTING

Doctor Dolittle is a kind and eccentric physician with a great love of pets. He decides to give up his regular practice among people and devote himself entirely to treating animals. With the help of Polynesia, his parrot, he learns the language of the animals and so becomes doubly valuable to them. When we meet the good doctor in this chapter, he has just come to Africa and cured the monkeys of a terrible disease. The character of Doctor Dolittle—kind, patient, sensible, yet full of fantastic humor and ready for any adventure—makes him one of the most delightful personalities in fiction. Most boys and girls who start the first story are eager to read all in the Doctor Dolittle series.

Pushmi-pullyus are now extinct. That means, there aren't any more. But long ago, when Doctor Dolittle was alive, there were some of them still left in the deepest jungles of Africa; and even then they were very, very scarce. They had no tail, but a head at each end, and sharp horns on each head. They were very shy and terribly hard to catch. The black men get most of their animals by sneaking up behind them while they are not looking. But you could not do this with the pushmi-pullyu—because, no matter which way you came towards him, he was always facing you. And besides, only one half of him slept at a time. The other head was always awake—and watching. This was why they were never caught and never seen in Zoos. Though many of the greatest huntsmen and the cleverest menagerie-keepers spent years of their lives searching through the jungles in all weathers for pushmi-pullyus, not a single one had ever been caught. Even then, years ago, he was the only animal in the world with two heads.

Well, the monkeys set out hunting for this animal through the forest. And after they had gone a good many miles, one of them found peculiar footprints near the edge of a river; and they knew that a pushmi-pullyu must be very near that spot.

Then they went along the bank of the river a little way and they saw a place where the grass was high and thick; and they guessed that he was in there.

So they all joined hands and made a great circle round the high grass. The pushmi-pullyu heard them coming; and he tried hard to break through the ring of monkeys. But he couldn't do it. When he saw that it was no use trying to escape, he sat down and waited to see what they wanted.

They asked him if he would go with Doctor Dolittle and be put on show in the Land of the White Men.

But he shook both his heads hard and said, "Certainly not!"

They explained to him that he would not be shut up in a menagerie but would just be looked at. They told him that the Doctor was a very kind man but hadn't any money; and people would pay to see a two-headed animal and the Doctor would get rich and could pay for the boat he had borrowed to come to Africa in.

But he answered, "No. You know how shy I am—I hate being stared at." And he almost began to cry.

Then for three days they tried to persuade him.

And at the end of the third day he said he would come with them and see what kind of a man the Doctor was first.

So the monkeys traveled back with the pushmi-pullyu. And when they came to where the Doctor's little house of grass was, they knocked on the door.

The duck, who was packing the trunk, said, "Come in!"

And Chee-Chee very proudly took the animal inside and showed him to the Doctor.

"What in the world is it?" asked John Dolittle, gazing at the strange creature.

"Lord save us!" cried the duck. "How does it make up its mind?"

"It doesn't look to me as though it had any," said Jip, the dog.

"This, Doctor," said Chee-Chee, "is the pushmi-pullyu—the rarest animal of the African jungles, the only two-headed beast in the world! Take him home with you and your fortune's made. People will pay any money to see him."

"But I don't want any money," said the Doctor.

"Yes, you do," said Dab-Dab, the duck. "Don't you remember how we had to pinch and scrape to pay the butcher's bill in Puddleby? And how are you going to get the sailor the new boat you spoke of—unless we have the money to buy it?"

"I was going to make him one," said the Doctor.

"Oh, do be sensible!" cried Dab-Dab. "Where would you get all the wood and the nails to make one with?—And besides, what are we going to live on? We shall be poorer than ever when we get back. Chee-Chee's perfectly right! Take the funny-looking thing along, do!"

"Well, perhaps there is something in what you say," murmured the Doctor. "It certainly would make a nice new kind of pet. But does the er—what-do-you-call-it really want to go abroad?"

"Yes, I'll go," said the pushmi-pullyu who saw at once, from the Doctor's face, that he was a man to be trusted. "You have been so kind to the animals here—and the monkeys tell me that I am the only one who will do. But you must promise me that if I do not like it in the Land of the White Men you will send me back."

"Why, certainly—of course, of course," said the Doctor. "Excuse me, surely you are related to the Deer Family, are you not?"

"Yes," said the pushmi-pullyu—"to the Abyssinian Gazelles and the Asiatic Chamois—on my mother's side. My father's great-grandfather was the last of the Unicorns."

ILLUSTRATED BY HUGH LOFTING

"Most interesting!" murmured the Doctor; and he took a book out of the trunk which Dab-Dab was packing and began turning the pages. "Let us see if Buffon says anything——"

"I notice," said the duck, "that you only talk with one of your mouths. Can't the other head talk as well?"

"Oh, yes," said the pushmi-pullyu. "But I keep the other mouth for eating—mostly. In that way I can talk while I am eating without being rude. Our people have always been very polite."

When the packing was finished and everything was ready to start, the monkeys gave a grand party for the Doctor, and all the animals of the jungle came. And they had pineapples and mangoes and honey and all sorts of good things to eat and drink.

After they had all finished eating, the Doctor got up and said,

"My friends: I am not clever at speaking long words after dinner, like some men; and I have just eaten many fruits and much honey. But I wish to tell you that I am very sad at leaving your beautiful country. Because I have things to do in the Land of the White Men, I must go. After I have gone, remember never to let the flies settle on your food before you eat it; and do not sleep on the ground when the rains are coming. I—er—er—I hope you will all live happily ever after."

When the Doctor stopped speaking and sat down, all the monkeys clapped their hands a long time and said to one another, "Let it be remembered always among our people that he sat and ate with us, here, under the trees. For surely he is the Greatest of Men!"

And the Grand Gorilla, who had the strength of seven horses in his hairy arms, rolled a great rock up to the head of the table and said,

"This stone for all time shall mark the spot."

And even to this day, in the heart of the jungle, that stone still is there. And monkey-mothers, passing through the forest with their families, still point down at it from the branches and whisper to their children, "Sh! There it is—look—where the Good White Man sat and ate food with us in the Year of the Great Sickness!"

Then, when the party was over, the Doctor and his pets started out to go back to the seashore. And all the monkeys went with him as far as the edge of their country, carrying his trunk and bags, to see him off.

How Doth the Little Crocodile

by LEWIS CARROLL

How doth the little crocodile
    Improve his shining tail,
And pour the waters of the Nile
    On every golden scale!

How cheerfully he seems to grin,
    How neatly spreads his claws,
And welcomes little fishes in,
    With gently smiling jaws!

From *Alice's Adventures in Wonderland.*

Phizzog

by CARL SANDBURG

This face you got,
This here phizzog you carry around,
You never picked it out for yourself, at all, at all
   —did you?
This here phizzog—somebody handed it to you
   —am I right?
Somebody said, "Here's yours, now go see what
   you can do with it."
Somebody slipped it to you and it was like a
   package marked:
"No goods exchanged after being taken away"—
This face you got.

The Elephant

by HILAIRE BELLOC

When people call this beast to mind,
   They marvel more and more
At such a *little* tail behind,
   So LARGE a trunk before.

Rabbit Hill

by ROBERT LAWSON

Georgie is the gay young member of a family of rabbits that lives on Rabbit Hill in Connecticut, along with many other small wild animal friends like Mole and the Gray Squirrel. The story opens with all the little creatures on the Hill boiling with excitement, for Little Georgie has broken the news that "new Folks are coming into the Big House!" It turns out that they are friendly people from whom the rabbits have nothing to fear. But they do have plenty of exciting and funny encounters with Mr. Muldoon, the large house cat and with their regular enemies, the neighborhood dogs. Robert Lawson loves and understands the small animals of the countryside and, though they talk like human beings, each animal retains his own special animal character.

It was barely daylight when Little Georgie started his journey. In spite of her worrying, Mother had managed to put up a small but nourishing lunch. This, along with a letter to Uncle Analdas, was packed in a little knapsack and slung over his shoulder. Father went along as far as the Twin Bridges. As they stepped briskly down the Hill, the whole valley was a lake of mist on which rounded treetops swam like floating islands. From old orchards rose a mounting chorus as the birds greeted the new day. Mothers chirped and chuckled and scolded as they swept and tidied the nests. On the topmost branches their menfolk warbled and shrilled and mocked one another.

ILLUSTRATED BY ROBERT LAWSON

The houses were all asleep, even the dogs of the Fat-Man-at-the-Crossroads were quiet, but the Little Animals were up and about. They met the Gray Fox returning from a night up Weston way. He looked footsore and sleepy and a few chicken feathers still clung to his ruff. The Red Buck trotted daintily across the Black Road to wish them good luck and good morning, but Father, for once, had no time for long social conversation. This was Business, and no rabbit in the county knew his business any better than Father—few as well.

"Now, Son," he said firmly, "your mother is in a very nervous state and you are not to add to her worries by taking unnecessary risks or by carelessness. No dawdling and no foolishness. Keep close to the road but well off it. Watch your bridges and your crossings. What do you do when you come to a bridge?"

"I hide well," answered Georgie, "and wait a good long time. I look all around for dogs. I look up the road for cars and down the road for cars. When everything's clear, I run across—fast. I hide again and look around to be sure I've not been seen. Then I go on. The same thing for crossings."

"Good," said Father. "Now recite your dogs."

Little Georgie closed his eyes and dutifully recited: "Fat-Man-at-the-Crossroads: two Mongrels—Good Hill Road: Dalmatian—House on Long Hill: Collie, noisy, no wind—Norfield Church corner: Police Dog, stupid, no nose—On the High Ridge, red farmhouse: Bulldog and Setter, both fat, don't bother—Farmhouse with the big barns: Old Hound, very dangerous——" and so on he recited every dog on the route clear up to Danbury way. He did it without a mistake and swelled with pride at Father's approving nod.

"Excellent," said Father. "Now do you remember your checks and doublings?" Little Georgie closed his eyes again and rattled off, quite fast, "Sharp right and double left, double left and double right, dead stop and back flip, right jump, left jump, false trip and briar dive."

"Splendid," said Father. "Now attend carefully. Size up your dog; don't waste speed on a plodder, you may need it later. If he's a rusher, check, double, and freeze. Your freeze, by the way, is still rather bad. You have a tendency to flick your left ear, you must watch that. The High Ridge is very open country, so keep in the shadow of the stone walls and mark the earth piles. Porkey has lots of relatives along there and if you are pressed hard, any of them will gladly take you in. Just tell them who you are, and don't forget to thank them. After a chase, hide up and take at least ten minutes' rest. And if you have to *really* run, tighten that knapsack strap, lace back your ears, put your stomach to the ground, and RUN!

"Get along with you now and mind—no foolishness. We shall expect you and Uncle Analdas by tomorrow evening at the latest."

Little Georgie crossed the Twin Bridges in perfect form, returned Father's approving wave, and was off, on his own.

It was gray and misty as he crossed Good Hill Road, and the Dalmatian still slept. So, apparently, did the Collie up the road, for all was quiet as he plodded up Long Hill. People were beginning to stir as he approached Norfield Church corner, little plumes of blue smoke were rising from kitchen chimneys, and the air was pleasant with the smell of frying bacon.

As he expected, the Police Dog rushed him there, but he wasted little time on that affair. Loping along with tantalizing slowness until they were almost on an old fallen apple tree buried in briars, he executed a dead stop, a right jump, and a freeze. The bellowing brute overran him, and plunged headlong into the thorny tangle. His agonized howls were sweet music to Little Georgie as he hopped sedately along toward the High Ridge. He wished Father had been there to see how skillfully he had worked and to note that during the freeze his left ear hadn't flickered once.

The sun was well up when he emerged on the High Ridge. On the porch of the Red Farmhouse the fat Bulldog and the Setter slept soundly, soaking up its warmth. On any other occasion Little Georgie would have been tempted to wake them to enjoy their silly efforts at running, but mindful of Father's instructions he kept dutifully on his way.

The High Ridge was a long and open strip of country, very uninteresting to Little Georgie. The view, over miles and miles of rolling woods and meadows, was very beautiful, but he didn't care especially about views. The brilliant blue sky and the bright little cream-puff clouds were beautiful too. They made him feel good, so did the warm sun, but frankly he was becoming slightly bored. So to ease his boredom he began to make a little song.

The words had been rattling round in his head for some days now and the music was there too, but he couldn't quite get them straight and fitted together. So he hummed and he sang and he whistled. He tried the words this way and that way, he stopped and started and changed the notes around, and finally he got the first line so that it suited him. So Georgie sang that line over and over again to be sure that he wouldn't forget it when he started on the second line.

It must have been this preoccupation with his song that made Little Georgie careless and almost led to his undoing. He scarcely noticed that he had passed the house with the big barns, and he was just starting to sing his first line for the forty-seventh time when there came the roaring rush of the Old Hound right on his heels, so close that he could feel the hot breath.

Instinctively Little Georgie made several wild springs that carried him temporarily out of harm's way. He paused a fraction of a second to tighten the knapsack strap and then set off at a good steady pace. "Don't waste speed on a plodder" was Father's rule.

He tried a few checks and doubles and circlings, although he knew they were pretty useless. The great fields were too bare and the Old Hound knew all the tricks. No matter how he turned and dodged, the Hound was always there, coming along at his heavy gallop. He looked for woodchuck burrows, but there were none in sight. "Well, I guess I'll have to run it out," said Little Georgie.

He pulled the knapsack strap tighter, laced back his ears, put his stomach to the ground, and RAN. And *how* he ran!

The warm sun had loosened his muscles, the air was invigorating, Little Georgie's leaps grew longer and longer. Never had he felt so young and strong. His legs were like coiled springs of steel that released themselves of their own accord. He was hardly conscious of any effort, only of his hind feet pounding the ground, and each time they hit, those wonderful springs released and shot him through the air. He sailed over fences and stone walls as though they were mole runs. Why, this was almost like flying! Now he understood what Zip the Swallow had been driving at when he tried to describe what it was like. He glanced back at the Old Hound, far behind now, but still coming along at his plodding gallop. He was old and must be tiring while he, Little Georgie, felt stronger and more vigorous at every leap. Why didn't the old fool give up and go home?

And then, as he shot over the brow of a slight rise, he suddenly knew. *He had forgotten Deadman's Brook!* There it lay before him, broad and deep, curving out in a great silvery loop. He, the son of Father, gentleman hunter from the Bluegrass, had been driven into a trap, a trap that even Porkey should have been able to avoid! Whether he turned to right or left, the loop of the creek hemmed him in and the Old Hound could easily cut him off. There was nothing for it but to jump!

This sickening realization had not reduced his speed; now he redoubled it. The slope helped and his soaring leaps became prodigious. The wind whistled through his laced-back ears. Still he kept his head, as Father would have wished him to. He picked a spot where the bank was high and firm; he spaced his jumps so they would come out exactly right.

The take-off was perfect. He put every ounce of leg muscle into that final kick and sailed out into space. Below him he could see the cream-puff clouds mirrored in the dark water; he could see the pebbles on the bottom and the silver flash of frightened minnows, dashing away from his flying shadow. Then, with a breath-taking thump, he landed, turned seven somersaults, and came up sitting in a clump of soft lush grass.

He froze, motionless except for heaving sides, and watched the Old Hound come thundering down the slope, slide to a stop and, after eyeing the water disgustedly, take his way slowly homeward, his dripping tongue almost dragging the ground.

Little Georgie did not need to remember Father's rule for a ten-minute rest after a good run. He was blown and he knew it, but he did remember his lunch, so he unstrapped the little knapsack and combined lunch and rest. He had been really scared for a moment, but as his wind came back and his lunch went down, his spirits came up.

Father would be angry, and rightly, for he had made two very stupid mistakes: he had let himself be surprised and he had run right into a dangerous trap. But that leap! Never in the history of the county had any rabbit jumped Deadman's Brook, not even Father. He marked the exact spot and calculated the width of the stream there—at least eighteen feet! And with his rising spirits the words and the notes of his song suddenly tumbled into place.

Little Georgie lay back in the warm grass and sang his song—

> New Folks coming, Oh my!
> New Folks coming, Oh my!
> New Folks coming, Oh my!
> Oh my! Oh my!

There weren't many words and there weren't many notes, and the notes just went up a little and down a little and ended where they began. Lots of people might have thought it monotonous, but it suited Little Georgie completely. He sang it loud and he sang it soft, he sang it as a paean of triumph, a saga of perils met and overcome. He sang it over and over again.

Red-Bellied Robin, flying northward, paused in a sapling and called down, "Hi, Little Georgie, what're you doing way up here?"

"Going to fetch Uncle Analdas. Have you been by the Hill?"

"Just left there," Robin answered. "Everybody's excited. Seems there's new Folks coming."

"Yes, I know," cried Little Georgie eagerly. "I've just made a song about it. Wouldn't you like to hear it? It goes like——"

"No, thanks," called Robin. "Getting along——" and flew on.

Not in the least discouraged, Little Georgie sang his song a few times more while he strapped on his knapsack and took up his journey. It was a good song to walk to, too, so he sang it as he tramped the rest of the High Ridge, as he went down the Windy Hill and circled around Georgetown. He was still singing it in the late afternoon when he got clear up Danbury way.

He had just finished "Oh my!" for the four thousandth time when a sharp voice from the bushes broke in with "Oh my—*what?*"

Little Georgie whirled. "Oh my—*goodness!*" he cried. "Why—why, it's Uncle Analdas."

"Sure is," the voice chuckled. "Uncle Analdas as ever was. Come in, Little Georgie, come in—you're a long way from home. Ef I'd been a dog, I'd got you. Surprised yer Old Man ain't learned you more care—come in, anyhow."

Although Mother had worried about the state of Uncle Analdas's home with no feminine hands around to keep things neat, she could never, in her most pessimistic moments, have pictured anything quite so disorderly as the burrow to which Little Georgie was welcomed.

It was a man's home, there could be no doubt about that, and while Little Georgie rather admired the bachelor freedom of the place, he was forced to admit that it really was extremely dirty and the fleas numerous and active. After his day in the open air, the atmosphere indoors seemed stifling and not at all fragrant. Perhaps it was the sort of tobacco that Uncle Analdas smoked— Little Georgie hoped so. His Uncle's cooking too left something to be desired—their supper consisted of one very ancient and dried-up turnip. After this meager meal, they sat outside, at Little Georgie's suggestion, and Mother's letter was produced.

"S'pose you read it to me, Georgie," said Uncle Analdas. "Seem to've mislaid them dingblasted spectacles." Little Georgie knew that he hadn't mislaid them, in fact that he didn't own any; he'd just never learned to read, but this formality always had to be gone through with, so he dutifully read:

Dear Uncle Analdas:

I hope this finds you well but I know you are lonesome with Mildred married and gone away and all and we are hoping you will spend the summer with us, as we have new Folks coming and we hope they are planting Folks and if they are we will all eat good but they may have dogs or poison or traps and spring-guns and maybe you shouldn't risk your life although you haven't much of it left but we will be looking forward to seeing you anyway.

> Your loving niece,
> Mollie.

There was a postscript which said, "P.S. Please don't let Little Georgie get his feet wet," but Georgie didn't read that out loud. The idea! He, Little Georgie, who had jumped Deadman's Brook, Little Georgie the Leaper, getting his feet wet!

"Well, now," cried Uncle Analdas. "Well, now, that's a real nice letter, real nice. Don't know but what I will. Certainly is dingblasted lonesome 'round here now, with Millie gone and all. And as for food—— Of all the carrot-pinchin', stingy folks I ever see, the folks around here is the stingiest, carrot-pinchin'est. Yes sir, I think I will. 'Course new Folks coming may be good and it may be bad. Either way I don't trust 'em. Don't trust old Folks neither. But with old Folks you kin tell just how much you *can't* trust 'em and with new Folks you can't tell *nothing*. Think I'll do it though, think I will. Does yer Maw still make that peavine and lettuce soup as good as she used to?"

Little Georgie assured him that she still did and wished he had a

bowl of it right then. "I've made up a song about the new Folks,"
he added eagerly. "Would you like to hear it?"

"Don't think I would," answered Uncle Analdas. "Sleep any-
wheres you've a mind to, Georgie. I've got a few knickknacks to
pack up and we'd ought to get an early start. I'll wake you."

Little Georgie decided to sleep outside under the bushes. The
evening was quite warm and the burrow was really pretty strong.
He hummed his song, as a lullaby now, and it was a good lullaby,
for before he'd finished it the third time he was sound asleep.

The Duel

by EUGENE FIELD

The gingham dog and the calico cat
Side by side on the table sat;
'Twas half-past twelve, and (what do you think!)
Nor one nor t'other had slept a wink!
The old Dutch clock and the Chinese plate
Appeared to know as sure as fate
There was going to be a terrible spat.
(*I wasn't there; I simply state*
What was told to me by the Chinese plate!)

The gingham dog went "bow-wow-wow!"
And the calico cat replied "mee-ow!"
The air was littered, an hour or so,
With bits of gingham and calico,
While the old Dutch clock in the chimneyplace
Up with its hands before its face,
For it always dreaded a family row!
(*Now mind: I'm only telling you*
What the old Dutch clock declares is true!)

The Chinese plate looked very blue.
And wailed, "Oh, dear! what shall we do!"
But the gingham dog and the calico cat
Wallowed this way and tumbled that,
Employing every tooth and claw
In the awfullest way you ever saw—
And, oh! how the gingham and calico flew!
(*Don't fancy I exaggerate!*
I got my news from the Chinese plate!)

Next morning, where the two had sat,
They found no trace of dog or cat;
And some folks think unto this day
That burglars stole that pair away!
But the truth about the cat and pup
Is this: they ate each other up!
Now what do you really think of that!
(*The old Dutch clock it told me so,*
And that is how I came to know.)

The Hairy Dog

by HERBERT ASQUITH

My dog's so furry I've not seen
His face for years and years:
His eyes are buried out of sight,
I only guess his ears.

When people ask me for his breed,
I do not know or care:
He has the beauty of them all
Hidden beneath his hair.

Macavity: The Mystery Cat

by T. S. ELIOT

Macavity's a Mystery Cat: he's called the Hidden Paw—
For he's the master criminal who can defy the Law.
He's the bafflement of Scotland Yard, the Flying Squad's despair:
For when they reach the scene of crime—*Macavity's not there!*

Macavity, Macavity, there's no one like Macavity,
He's broken every human law, he breaks the law of gravity.
His powers of levitation would make a fakir stare,
And when you reach the scene of crime—*Macavity's not there!*
You may seek him in the basement, you may look up in the air—
But I tell you once and once again, *Macavity's not there!*

Macavity's a ginger cat, he's very tall and thin;
You would know him if you saw him, for his eyes are sunken in.
His brow is deeply lined with thought, his head is highly domed;
His coat is dusty from neglect, his whiskers are uncombed.
He sways his head from side to side, with movements like a snake;
And when you think he's half asleep, he's always wide awake.

Macavity, Macavity, there's no one like Macavity,
For he's a fiend in feline shape, a monster of depravity.
You may meet him in a by-street, you may see him in the square—
But when a crime's discovered, then *Macavity's not there!*

He's outwardly respectable. (They say he cheats at cards.)
And his footprints are not found in any file of Scotland Yard's.
And when the larder's looted, or the jewel-case is rifled,
Or when the milk is missing, or another Peke's been stifled,
Or the greenhouse glass is broken, and the trellis past repair—
Ay, there's the wonder of the thing! *Macavity's not there!*

And when the Foreign Office find a Treaty's gone astray,
Or the Admiralty lose some plans and drawings by the way,
There may be a scrap of paper in the hall or on the stair—
But it's useless to investigate—*Macavity's not there!*
And when the loss has been disclosed, the Secret Service say:
"It *must* have been Macavity!"—but he's a mile away.
You'll be sure to find him resting, or a-licking of his thumbs,
Or engaged in doing complicated long division sums.

Macavity, Macavity, there's no one like Macavity,
There never was a Cat of such deceitfulness and suavity.
He always has an alibi, and one or two to spare:
At whatever time the deed took place—MACAVITY WASN'T
    THERE!
And they say that all the Cats whose wicked deeds are widely
    known,
(I might mention Mungojerrie, I might mention Griddlebone)
Are nothing more than agents for the Cat who all the time
Just controls their operations: the Napoleon of Crime!

The Adventures of Pinocchio

PINOCCHIO'S FIRST PRANKS

by CARLO COLLODI

Pinocchio, the puppet who comes to life, seems to be irresistibly attracted to every kind of mischief. Maybe that is why he has always been such a great favorite with children. In this chapter, his pranks land his creator, Geppetto, in jail. After Geppetto gets out, Pinocchio runs away from home again, and begins a series of lively and extraordinary adventures. He does some pretty bad things and in return suffers some pretty bad punishments. In the end, however, he truly repents of his reckless behavior and is changed from a puppet into a real (and well-behaved) boy.

The author of Pinocchio is said to have been a rather bad boy himself, one who played pranks at school instead of attending to his studies. But he did succeed in learning enough to be able to create the best puppet story that has ever been written.

Geppetto lived in a small ground floor room that was only lighted from the staircase. The furniture could not have been simpler—a bad chair, a poor bed, and a broken-down table. At the end of the room there was a fireplace with a lighted fire; but the fire was painted, and by the fire was a painted saucepan that was boiling cheerfully, and sending out a cloud of smoke that looked exactly like real smoke.

As soon as he reached home Geppetto took his tools and set to work to cut out and model his puppet.

"What name shall I give him?" he said to himself. "I think I will call him Pinocchio. It is a name that will bring him luck. I once knew a whole family so called. There was Pinocchio the father, Pinocchia the mother, and Pinocchi the children, and all of them did well. The richest of them was a beggar."

Having found a name for his puppet he began to work in good earnest, and he first made his hair, then his forehead, and then his eyes.

The eyes being finished, imagine his astonishment when he perceived that they moved and looked fixedly at him.

Geppetto, seeing himself stared at by those two wooden eyes, took it almost in bad part, and said in an angry voice:

"Wicked wooden eyes, why do you look at me?"

No one answered.

He then proceeded to carve the nose; but no sooner had he made it than it began to grow. And it grew, and grew, and grew, until in a few minutes it had become an immense nose that seemed as if it would never end.

Poor Geppetto tired himself out with cutting it off; but the more he cut and shortened it, the longer did that impertinent nose become!

The mouth was not even completed when it began to laugh and mock at him.

"Stop laughing!" said Geppetto, provoked; but he might as well have spoken to the wall.

"Stop laughing, I say!" he roared in a threatening tone.

The mouth then ceased laughing, but put out its tongue as far as it would go.

Geppetto, not to spoil his handiwork, pretended not to see, and continued his labors. After the mouth he fashioned the chin, then the throat, then the shoulders, the stomach, the arms and the hands.

The hands were scarcely finished when Geppetto felt his wig snatched from his head. He turned round, and what did he see? He saw his yellow wig in the puppet's hand.

"Pinocchio! Give me back my wig instantly!"

But Pinocchio, instead of returning it, put it on his own head, and was in consequence nearly smothered.

Geppetto at this insolent and mocking behavior felt sadder and more melancholy than he had ever been in his life before; and turning to Pinocchio he said to him:

"You young rascal! You are not yet completed, and you are already beginning to show want of respect to your father! That is bad, my boy, very bad!"

And he dried a tear.

The legs and the feet remained to be done.

When Geppetto had finished the feet he received a kick on the point of his nose.

"I deserve it!" he said to himself. "I should have thought of it sooner! Now it is too late!"

He then took the puppet under the arms and placed him on the floor to teach him to walk.

Pinocchio's legs were stiff and he could not move, but Geppetto led him by the hand and showed him how to put one foot before the other.

When his legs became flexible Pinocchio began to walk by himself and to run about the room; until, having gone out of the house door, he jumped into the street and escaped.

Poor Geppetto rushed after him but was not able to overtake him, for that rascal Pinocchio leapt in front of him like a hare, and knocking his wooden feet together against the pavement made as much clatter as twenty pairs of peasants' clogs.

"Stop him! Stop him!" shouted Geppetto; but the people in the street, seeing a wooden puppet running like a race horse, stood still in astonishment to look at it, and laughed, and laughed, and laughed, until it beats description.

At last, as good luck would have it, a policeman arrived who, hearing the uproar, imagined that a colt had escaped from his master. Planting himself courageously with his legs apart in the middle of the road, he waited with the determined purpose of stopping him, and thus preventing the chance of worse disasters.

When Pinocchio, still at some distance, saw the policeman bar-

ricading the whole street, he endeavored to take him by surprise and to pass between his legs. But he failed signally.

The policeman without disturbing himself in the least caught him cleverly by the nose—it was an immense nose of ridiculous proportions that seemed made on purpose to be laid hold of by policemen—and consigned him to Geppetto. Wishing to punish him, Geppetto intended to pull his ears at once. But imagine his feelings when he could not succeed in finding them. And do you know the reason? It was that, in his hurry to model him, he had forgotten to make them.

He then took him by the collar, and as he was leading him away he said to him, shaking his head threateningly:

"We will go home at once, and as soon as we arrive we will regulate our accounts, never doubt it."

At this announcement Pinocchio threw himself on the ground and would not take another step. In the meanwhile a crowd of idlers and inquisitive people began to assemble and to make a ring round them.

Some of them said one thing, some another.

"Poor puppet!" said several. "He is right not to wish to return home! Who knows how Geppetto, that bad old man, will beat him!"

And the others added maliciously:

"Geppetto seems a good man! But with boys he is a regular tyrant! If that poor puppet is left in his hands he is quite capable of tearing him in pieces!"

It ended in so much being said and done that the policeman at last set Pinocchio at liberty and conducted Geppetto to prison. The poor man, not being ready with words to defend himself, cried like a calf, and as he was being led away to prison sobbed out:

"Wretched boy! And to think how I have labored to make him a well-conducted puppet! But it serves me right! I should have thought of it sooner!"

What happened afterwards is a story that really is past all belief, but I will relate it to you in the following chapters.

The Elephant

by HERBERT ASQUITH

Here comes the elephant
Swaying along
With his cargo of children
All singing a song:
To the tinkle of laughter
He goes on his way,
And his cargo of children
Have crowned him with may.
His legs are in leather
And padded his toes:
He can root up an oak
With a whisk of his nose:
With a wave of his trunk
And a turn of his chin
He can pull down a house,
Or pick up a pin.

Beneath his gray forehead
A little eye peers;
Of what is he thinking
Between those wide ears?
Of what does he think?
If he wished to tease,
He could twirl his keeper
Over the trees:
If he were not kind,
He could play cup and ball
With Robert and Helen,
And Uncle Paul:
But that gray forehead,
Those crinkled ears,
Have learned to be kind
In a hundred years.

A Just-So Story

THE ELEPHANT'S CHILD

by RUDYARD KIPLING

Like so many of the other best stories for children, these were written by a father to please his child. Kipling said that he wrote the Just-So Stories *in answer to his own "Best Beloved's one million Hows, two million Wheres, and seven million Whys." Born in Bombay, India, Kipling as a boy spoke the native Hindustani more naturally than he did English, and he grew up steeped in the legends and folk tales of India. "In the high and Far-off times, O Best Beloved" is the way all Indian folk tales traditionally begin, and it's also the opening sentence of the* Just-So Stories. *These are, in fact, a 20th century kind of folk tale, a re-telling with tongue in cheek, of the primitive explanations of such things as how the elephant got its trunk, or the camel its hump. Boys and girls seem to enjoy this elephant story especially, maybe because they enjoy the idea of a child spanking his relatives.*

The Just-So Stories *are the perfect stories for reading aloud. Kipling had such a wonderful way of finding just the right word to create just the rhythm and atmosphere he wanted, and such a magical way of mixing nonsense and reality, that these stories delight everyone. If you are young enough to have them read to you, they will satisfy your "'satiable curtiosity," if you are old enough to read them yourself, you can appreciate their humor and fantasy. Kipling was one of the most original and greatest story*

*tellers of all times. It's nice to know that some of his best work
are his stories for children.*

In the high and Far-Off times the Elephant, O Best Beloved, had
no trunk. He had only a blackish, bulgy nose, as big as a boot,
that he could wriggle about from side to side; but he couldn't
pick up things with it. But there was one Elephant—a new Elephant—an Elephant's Child—who was full of 'satiable curtiosity,
and that means he asked ever so many questions. *And* he lived in
Africa, and he filled all Africa with his 'satiable curtiosities. He
asked his tall aunt, the Ostrich, why her tail-feathers grew just so,
and his tall aunt the Ostrich spanked him with her hard, hard
claw. He asked his tall uncle, the Giraffe, what made his skin
spotty, and his tall uncle, the Giraffe, spanked him with his hard,
hard hoof. And still he was full of 'satiable curtiosity! He asked
his broad aunt, the Hippopotamus, why her eyes were red, and his
broad aunt, the Hippopotamus, spanked him with her broad,
broad hoof; and he asked his hairy uncle, the Baboon, why melons
tasted just so, and his hairy uncle, the Baboon, spanked him with
his hairy, hairy paw. And *still* he was full of 'satiable curtiosity! He
asked questions about everything that he saw, or heard, or felt, or
smelt, or touched, and all his uncles and his aunts spanked him.
And still he was full of 'satiable curtiosity!

One fine morning in the middle of the Precession of the
Equinoxes this 'satiable Elephant's Child asked a new fine question that he had never asked before. He asked, "What does the
Crocodile have for dinner?" Then everybody said, "Hush!" in a
loud and dretful tone, and they spanked him immediately and
directly, without stopping for a long time.

By and by, when that was finished, he came upon Kolokolo
Bird sitting in the middle of a wait-a-bit thorn-bush, and he said,
"My father has spanked me, and my mother has spanked me; all
my aunts and uncles have spanked me for my 'satiable curtiosity;
and *still* I want to know what the Crocodile has for dinner!"

Then Kolokolo Bird said, with a mournful cry, "Go to the

banks of the great grey-green, greasy Limpopo River, all set about with fever-trees, and find out."

That very next morning, when there was nothing left of the Equinoxes, because the Precession had preceded according to precedent this 'satiable Elephant's Child took a hundred pounds of bananas (the little short red kind), and a hundred pounds of sugarcane (the long purple kind), and seventeen melons (the greeny-crackly kind), and said to all his dear families, "Good-bye. I am going to the great grey-green, greasy Limpopo River, all set about with fever-trees, to find out what the Crocodile has for dinner." And they all spanked him once more for luck, though he asked them most politely to stop.

Then he went away, a little warm, but not at all astonished, eating melons, and throwing the rind about, because he could not pick it up.

He went from Graham's Town to Kimberley, and from Kimberley to Khama's Country, and from Khama's Country he went east and north, eating melons all the time, till he at last came to the banks of the great grey-green, greasy Limpopo River, all set about with fever-trees, precisely as Kolokolo Bird had said.

Now you must know and understand, O Best Beloved, that till that very week, and day, and hour, and minute, this 'satiable Elephant's Child had never seen a Crocodile, and did not know what one was like. It was all his 'satiable curtiosity.

The first thing that he found was a Bi-Coloured-Python-Rock-Snake curled round a rock.

" 'Scuse me," said the Elephant's Child most politely, "but have you seen such a thing as a Crocodile in these promiscuous parts?"

"*Have* I seen a Crocodile?" said the Bi-Coloured-Python-Rock-Snake, in a voice of dretful scorn. "What will you ask me next?"

" 'Scuse me," said the Elephant's Child, "but could you kindly tell me what he has for dinner?"

Then the Bi-Coloured-Python-Rock-Snake uncoiled himself very quickly from the rock, and spanked the Elephant's Child with his scalesome, flailsome tail.

"That is odd," said the Elephant's Child, "because my father and my mother, and my uncle and my aunt, not to mention my other aunt, the Hippopotamus, and my other uncle, the Baboon, have all spanked me for my 'satiable curtiosity—and I suppose this is the same thing."

So he said good-bye very politely to the Bi-Coloured-Python-Rock-Snake, and helped to coil him up on the rock again, and went on, a little warm, but not at all astonished, eating melons, and throwing the rind about because he could not pick it up, till he trod on what he thought was a log of wood at the very edge of the great grey-green, greasy Limpopo River, all set about with fever-trees.

But it was really the Crocodile, O Best Beloved, and the Crocodile winked one eye—like this!

" 'Scuse me," said the Elephant's Child most politely, "but do you happen to have seen a Crocodile in these promiscuous parts?"

Then the Crocodile winked the other eye, and lifted half his tail out of the mud; and the Elephant's Child stepped back most politely, because he did not wish to be spanked again.

"Come hither, Little One," said the Crocodile. "Why do you ask such things?"

" 'Scuse me," said the Elephant's Child most politely, "but my father has spanked me, my mother has spanked me, not to mention my tall aunt, the Ostrich, and my tall uncle, the Giraffe, who can kick ever so hard, as well as my broad aunt, the Hippopotamus, and my hairy uncle, the Baboon, *and* including the Bi-Coloured-Python-Rock-Snake, with the scalesome, flailsome tail, just up the bank, who spanks harder than any of them; and *so*, if it's quite all the same to you, I don't want to be spanked any more."

"Come hither, Little One," said the Crocodile, "for I am the Crocodile," and he wept crocodile-tears to show it was quite true.

Then the Elephant's Child grew all breathless, and panted, and kneeled down on the bank and said, "You are the very person I have been looking for all these long days. Will you please tell me what you have for dinner?"

"Come hither, Little One," said the Crocodile, "and I'll whisper."

Then the Elephant's Child put his head down close to the Crocodile's musky, tusky mouth, and the Crocodile caught him by his little nose, which up to that very week, day, hour, and minute, had been no bigger than a boot, though much more useful.

"I think," said the Crocodile—and he said it between his teeth, like this—"I think today I will begin with Elephant's Child!"

At this, O Best Beloved, the Elephant's Child was much annoyed, and he said, speaking through his nose, like this, "Led go! You are hurtig be!"

Then the Bi-Coloured-Python-Rock-Snake scuffled down from the bank and said, "My young friend, if you do not now, immediately and instantly, pull as hard as ever you can, it is my opinion that your acquaintance in the large-pattern leather ulster" (and by this he meant the Crocodile) "will jerk you into yonder limpid stream before you can say Jack Robinson."

This is the way Bi-Coloured-Python-Rock-Snakes always talk.

Then the Elephant's Child sat back on his little haunches, and pulled, and pulled, and pulled, and his nose began to stretch. And the Crocodile floundered into the water, making it all creamy with great sweeps of his tail, and *he* pulled, and pulled, and pulled.

And the Elephant's Child's nose kept on stretching; and the Elephant's Child spread all his little four legs and pulled, and pulled, and pulled, and his nose kept on stretching; and the Crocodile threshed his tail like an oar, and *he* pulled, and pulled, and pulled, and at each pull the Elephant's Child's nose grew longer and longer—and it hurt him hijjus!

Then the Elephant's Child felt his legs slipping, and he said through his nose, which was now nearly five feet long, "This is too butch for be!"

Then the Bi-Coloured-Python-Rock-Snake came down from the bank, and knotted himself in a double-clove-hitch round the Elephant's Child's hind legs, and said, "Rash and inexperienced traveller, we will now seriously devote ourselves to a little high tension, because if we do not, it is my impression that yonder self-propelling man-of-war with the armour-plated upper deck" (and by this, O Best Beloved, he meant the Crocodile), "will permanently vitiate your future career."

That is the way all Bi-Coloured-Python-Rock-Snakes always talk.

So he pulled, and the Elephant's Child pulled, and the Crocodile pulled; but the Elephant's Child and the Bi-Coloured-Python-Rock-Snake pulled hardest; and at last the Crocodile let go of the Elephant's Child's nose with a plop that you could hear all up and down the Limpopo.

Then the Elephant's Child sat down most hard and sudden; but first he was careful to say "Thank you" to the Bi-Coloured-

Python-Rock-Snake; and next he was kind to his poor pulled nose, and wrapped it all up in cool banana leaves, and hung it in the great grey-green, greasy Limpopo to cool.

"What are you doing that for?" said the Bi-Coloured-Python-Rock-Snake.

"'Scuse me," said the Elephant's Child, "but my nose is badly out of shape, and I am waiting for it to shrink."

"Then you will have to wait a long time," said the Bi-Coloured-Python-Rock-Snake. "Some people do not know what is good for them."

The Elephant's Child sat there for three days waiting for his nose to shrink. But it never grew any shorter, and besides, it made him squint. For, O Best Beloved, you will see and understand that the Crocodile had pulled it out into a really truly trunk same as all Elephants have to-day.

At the end of the third day a fly came and stung him on the shoulder, and before he knew what he was doing he lifted up his trunk and hit that fly dead with the end of it.

"'Vantage number one!" said the Bi-Coloured-Python-Rock-Snake. "You couldn't have done that with a mere-smear nose. Try and eat a little now."

Before he thought what he was doing the Elephant's Child put out his trunk and plucked a large bundle of grass, dusted it clean against his forelegs, and stuffed it into his own mouth.

"'Vantage number two!" said the Bi-Coloured-Python-Rock-Snake. "You couldn't have done that with a mere-smear nose. Don't you think the sun is very hot here?"

"It is," said the Elephant's Child, and before he thought what he was doing he schlooped up a schloop of mud from the banks of the great grey-green, greasy Limpopo, and slapped it on his head, where it made a cool schloopy-sloshy mud-cap all trickly behind his ears.

"'Vantage number three!" said the Bi-Coloured-Python-Rock-Snake. "You couldn't have done that with a mere-smear nose. Now how do you feel about being spanked again?"

"'Scuse me," said the Elephant's Child, "but I should not like it at all."

"How would you like to spank somebody?" said the Bi-Coloured-Python-Rock-Snake.

"I should like it very much indeed," said the Elephant's Child.

"Well," said the Bi-Coloured-Python-Rock-Snake, "you will find that new nose of yours very useful to spank people with."

"Thank you," said the Elephant's Child, "I'll remember that; and now I think I'll go home to all my dear families and try."

So the Elephant's Child went home across Africa frisking and whisking his trunk. When he wanted fruit to eat he pulled fruit down from a tree, instead of waiting for it to fall as he used to do. When he wanted grass he plucked grass up from the ground, instead of going on his knees as he used to do. When the flies bit him he broke off the branch of a tree and used it as a fly-whisk; and he made himself a new, cool, slushy-squshy mud-cap whenever the sun was hot. When he felt lonely walking through Africa he sang to himself down his trunk, and the noise was louder than several brass bands. He went especially out of his way to find a broad Hippopotamus (she was no relation of his), and he spanked her very hard, to make sure that the Bi-Coloured-Python-Rock-Snake had spoken the truth about his new trunk. The rest of the time he picked up the melon rinds that he had dropped on his way to the Limpopo—for he was a Tidy Pachyderm.

One dark evening he came back to all his dear families, and he coiled up his trunk and said, "How do you do?" They were very glad to see him, and immediately said, "Come here and be spanked for your 'satiable curtiosity."

"Pooh," said the Elephant's Child. "I don't think you peoples know anything about spanking; but I do, and I'll show you."

Then he uncurled his trunk and knocked two of his dear brothers head over heels.

"O Bananas!" said they, "where did you learn that trick, and what have you done to your nose?"

"I got a new one from the Crocodile on the banks of the great grey-green, greasy Limpopo River," said the Elephant's Child. "I asked him what he had for dinner, and he gave me this to keep."

"It looks very ugly," said his hairy uncle, the Baboon.

"It does," said the Elephant's Child. "But it's very useful," and he picked up his hairy uncle, the Baboon, by one hairy leg, and hove him into a hornet's nest.

Then that bad Elephant's Child spanked all his dear families for a long time, till they were very warm and greatly astonished. He pulled out his tall Ostrich aunt's tail-feathers; and he caught his tall uncle, the Giraffe, by the hindleg, and dragged him through a thorn-bush; and he shouted at his broad aunt, the Hippopotamus, and blew bubbles into her ear when she was sleeping in the water after meals; but he never let any one touch Kolokolo Bird.

At last things grew so exciting that his dear families went off one by one in a hurry to the banks of the great grey-green, greasy Limpopo River, all set about with fever-trees, to borrow new noses from the Crocodile. When they came back nobody spanked anybody any more; and ever since that day, O Best Beloved, all the Elephants you will ever see, besides all those that you won't, have trunks precisely like the trunk of the 'satiable Elephant's Child.

Eletelephony

by LAURA E. RICHARDS

Once there was an elephant,
Who tried to use the telephant—
No! no! I mean an elephone
Who tried to use the telephone—
(Dear me! I am not certain quite
That even now I've got it right.)

Howe'er it was, he got his trunk
Entangled in the telephunk;
The more he tried to get it free,
The louder buzzed the telephee—
(I fear I'd better drop the song
Of elephop and telephong!)

Elmer and the Dragon

THE SECRET

by RUTH STILES GANNETT

Before Elmer Elevator, aged nine, arrives on the mysterious Feather Island, he has just rescued the baby dragon who has been held captive by ferocious animals. The island is inhabited solely by canaries escaped from cages, and one of them, Flute, turns out to be Elmer's own canary. After finding the treasure, he has a few more adventures on Feather Island before the dragon brings him safely home and then flies off to his dragon family. This completely original story, which combines the most absurd situations with a matter-of-fact style, is one of the most delightful of modern fantasies.

"Wake up! Wake up! It's time to see the King!" chirped Flute as the red sun settled over the meadow. Elmer opened his eyes and forgot for a moment where he was. Then he jumped up and put on his knapsack.

"I want to come, too," yawned the dragon.

"You weren't invited," said Flute.

"Neither were you, Flute, come to think of it," said Elmer.

"Let's all go and see what happens," suggested the dragon. So off they went to see the King. He was waiting for them at the foot of the very tall tree, nervously hopping from one foot to the other, pecking at imaginary mosquitoes.

"What's that?" he asked, pointing to the dragon

"That's my good friend the baby dragon. I rescued him two days ago and now he's taking me home."

"I don't like him," said the King, feeling small and helpless.

"Oh, yes you do!" said Flute.

"Quiet, Flute! I guess I know what I like and what I don't!" The dragon drooped his head and began to back away.

"Oh well," said the King, "come on back. If I'm going to tell the secret to anyone it'll never be a secret any more, and I suppose you might as well know, too. I do wish it weren't such an old secret."

Flute, the dragon and Elmer waited quietly while the King looked at the ground, then up at the tree, and then down at the ground.

"Treasure!" he whispered so suddenly that they all jumped into the air. "At least I think it's treasure, but I can't find out without your help."

"Where?" asked Elmer.

"It's—it's—it's not very far from here," said the King. Elmer, Flute and the dragon looked every-which-way to see where the treasure could be.

"Oh gosh, I guess I'll have to tell you where, too," said poor old King Can XI. "It's buried—it's buried right under this tree— in a big iron chest."

"What sort of treasure?" asked Elmer.

"That's what I'm dying of curiosity to know," said the King.

"So that's it!" sighed Flute.

"And you're sure this is the right tree?" asked Elmer.

"Absolutely! You see, it's much bigger than the others, and that's because it was the only one here when the settlers came. They planted the other pines and the apple orchard so they'd have wood and food when they returned. But they never came back, and their chest is still buried right here."

Everybody waited for the King to continue, but he didn't, so Elmer said, "Let's dig it up!"

"Yes, let's!" echoed Flute.

"All right," said the King. "My secret's all spoiled now, anyway. You'll find the shovel—under that rock."

"What shovel?" asked Elmer.

"The settlers left a shovel over there. It's rusty by now, but it's probably better than nothing."

Elmer went to get the shovel while the King danced around on the pine needles chirping, "I'm feeling better already." The Queen kept tittering and muttering to herself, "I never thought I'd live to see this day."

"Now, where should I begin digging?" asked Elmer.

"It's a rhyme," said the King. "It goes like this:

Four shovel lengths from the trunk of the pine,
Making the rock the guide for the line."

Elmer carefully measured the distance and began to dig. The dragon did his best to help while Flute and the King and Queen sat watching the hole growing deeper. By now it was dark in the pine forest, but enough moonlight filtered through the branches of the tall trees so that they could just see what they were doing. They dug for six hours, without ever hitting a root or a rock or anything like an iron chest.

"Are you certain this is the right place?" asked Elmer, tired and discouraged.

"I'm positive!" said the King. Just then the moon went under the clouds and Elmer's shovel hit something with a loud clang.

"The chest!" they all shouted, but it was too dark to see. And they waited so long for the moon to come out that they all went to sleep still waiting.

TREASURE

Flute woke up and trilled so loudly that he startled the King and the Queen and Elmer and the dragon wide awake. The other canaries had been up for an hour and were crowding around to see what was happening under the tree. Everybody peered into the big hole and gasped, "A real treasure chest, with a ring in the top! But how will we ever get it out?"

The King looked at Elmer, and Elmer looked at the dragon. "Dragon, do you think you could put your tail through the ring and pull up the chest?"

"I'll try," said the dragon, puffing up with importance as the swarms of canaries moved aside for him. He backed up to the hole, stuck his tail down and through the ring, and pulled.

Nothing happened.

"Couldn't you pull harder?" suggested the King.

"That's exactly what I was going to try. Just let me catch my breath," said the dragon somewhat crossly. "After all, I'm not used to lifting heavy chests with my tail." He took a deep, deep breath and pulled very, very hard, and suddenly the chest moved. He grunted and strained and struggled and panted and slowly, slowly hoisted the chest up out of the hole.

"Far enough!" yelled Elmer. "Now walk forward and set it down."

Crash! The chest fell down on the pine needles and the dragon staggered off to sit down while the canaries shouted "Bravo!"

"Quiet! Quiet!" yelled King Can XI. "I am now about to tell you the last part of the secret. The key to this chest—the key to this chest—well, anyway, this is the last part of the secret. My illustrious ancestor, King Can I, stole the key from the settlers, and the key to this chest is in my nest. Go get it, Flute. No, never mind. I'll go get it myself."

The King flew up to his nest and down again with a big brass key in his beak. Elmer pried out the dirt in the keyhole with his jackknife and put in the key.

Click! The lock turned. Elmer threw back the lid, and picked up a note lying on top of a piece of heavy canvas. "Can you read what it says?" asked the King.

"Yes," said Elmer, feeling sick with excitement as he read the note aloud:

This chest was left here by Oliver Hinckle, for the purpose of

*helping him and his friends to settle on this island when he re-
turns. In the event that he does not return to find the chest himself, the chest becomes the property of whosoever discovers it.*

The following is a list of the items herein buried:

12 *pewter plates*
 6 *pewter cups*
12 *table settings—sterling silver*
 1 *iron skillet*
 2 *iron pots, with lids*
 1 *coffee mill*

"Rubbish!" interrupted the King. "Isn't there anything but
cooking utensils?"

"Let me finish the list," said Elmer. He continued reading:

can each of salt and sugar
1 *axe*
1 *tinder box*
5 *bags seed, including squash, corn, cabbage, wheat and millet*
1 *gold watch and chain, belonging to my wife Sarah*
1 *sterling silver harmonica*
6 *bags of gold pieces*

"Gold! I knew it! Just think of it, Queen. Six bags of gold!"
trilled the King.

"What will you do with them, King dear?" asked the Queen.

"I won't do anything with them. I'll just have them and be
rich."

"Shall I unpack now?" asked Elmer, who was anxious to see the
sterling silver harmonica.

"By all means," ordered King Can XI, strutting back and forth
in front of the twittering canaries.

Elmer unpacked everything, and at last came to the sterling
silver harmonica. He blew on it gently, and the sound was so
sweet that all the canaries stopped chattering and listened. The
King listened, too, with tears in his eyes. When Elmer had finished playing "The Bear Went Over the Mountain" the King

flew up to a branch of the pine and said solemnly, "Elmer, on
behalf of the Queen and myself, and all the other Feather Is-
landers, I want to thank you and your dragon friend for digging
up this treasure and thereby ridding us of the plague of curiosity.
I now present you with that silver harmonica, which you play so

beautifully, and three of the six bags of gold. And to this brave dragon I present the gold watch and chain. Elmer, fasten it around his neck."

Elmer hooked the chain around the dragon's neck, arranging the watch at his throat. "How's that?" asked Elmer.

"I can't see it, but it feels just fine," said the proud baby dragon.

The birds all clapped their wings and then the dragon, who really didn't care for speeches, remarked, "Looking at those pots and plates makes me hungry. Let's celebrate and eat something!"

"Goodness!" said the Queen. "I don't believe we've ever had a celebration before. What shall we eat?"

"Tangerines!" said Elmer. "I bet you've never tasted one."

Elmer peeled twelve of the thirty-one tangerines he had left in his knapsack, and put one on each of the twelve pewter plates. Then he hurried off to pick a good mess of skunk cabbages and ostrich ferns for the dragon. When he came back everyone crowded around to feast. Elmer sat beside the dragon and ate nine tangerines all by himself. Then he played "Turkey in the Straw" on the sterling silver harmonica while the King did a jig on a pewter plate. Soon everybody joined in the dancing, and they danced themselves to sleep, all over the pine needles under the great tall tree.

Grizzly Bear

by MARY AUSTIN

If you ever, ever, ever meet a grizzly bear,
You must never, never, never ask him *where*
He is going,
Or *what* he is doing;
For if you ever, ever, dare
To stop a grizzly bear,
You will never meet *another* grizzly bear.

The Rhinoceros

by OGDEN NASH

The rhino is a homely beast,
For human eyes he's not a feast.
Farewell, farewell, you old rhinoceros,
I'll stare at something less prepoceros!

The Skunk

by ROBERT P. TRISTRAM COFFIN

When the sun has slipped away
And the dew is on the day,
Then the creature comes to call
Men malign the most of all.

The little skunk is very neat,
With his sensitive, plush feet
And a dainty, slim head set
With diamonds on bands of jet.

He walks upon his evening's duty
Of declaring how that beauty
With her patterns is not done
At the setting of the sun.

He undulates across the lawn,
He asks nobody to fawn
On his graces. All that he
Asks is that men let him be.

A Rootabaga Story

THE HUCKABUCK FAMILY AND HOW THEY RAISED
POPCORN IN NEBRASKA AND QUIT AND CAME BACK

by CARL SANDBURG

*The author had complained to his two little daughters,
whom he called Spink and Skabootch, that he was tired of telling
them stories of kings and queens and castles in foreign lands. So he
made up the gay and fantastic stories collected in his* Rootabaga
Stories *and* Rootabaga Pigeons, *and told them in the language of
the common people. These are hard to describe because they are
fairy tales that blend simple everyday things, nonsense plus poetry,
and a strong feeling for American folklore. Certainly they are like
no other stories ever written. Carl Sandburg is one of our finest
poets and this is reflected in his prose too. Reading these stories
aloud helps to bring out their distinctive rhythm and humor.*

Jonas Jonas Huckabuck was a farmer in Nebraska with a wife
Mama Mama Huckabuck, and a daughter, Pony Pony Huckabuck.

"Your father gave you two names the same in front," people
had said to him.

And he answered, "Yes, two names are easier to remember. If
you call me by my first name Jonas and I don't hear you then
when you call me by my second name Jonas maybe I will.

"And," he went on, "I call my pony-face girl Pony Pony because if she doesn't hear me the first time she always does the
second."

And so they lived on a farm where they raised popcorn, these

three, Jonas Jonas Huckabuck, his wife, Mama Mama Huckabuck, and their pony-face daughter, Pony Pony Huckabuck.

After they harvested the crop one year they had the barns, the
cribs, the sheds, the shacks, and all the cracks and corners of the
farm, all filled with popcorn.

"We came out to Nebraska to raise popcorn," said Jonas Jonas.
"And I guess we got nearly enough popcorn this year for the popcorn poppers and all the friends and relations of all the popcorn
poppers in these United States."

And this was the year Pony Pony was going to bake her first
squash pie all by herself. In one corner of the corn crib, all covered
over with popcorn, she had a secret, a big round squash, a fat
yellow squash, a rich squash all spotted with spots of gold.

She carried the squash into the kitchen, took a long, sharp,
shining knife, and then she cut the squash in the middle till she
had two big half squashes. And inside just like outside it was rich
yellow spotted with spots of gold.

And there was a shine of silver. And Pony Pony wondered why
silver should be in a squash. She picked and plunged with her
fingers till she pulled it out.

"It's a buckle," she said. "A silver buckle, a Chinese silver slipper buckle."

She ran with it to her father and said, "Look what I found
when I cut open the golden yellow squash spotted with gold spots
—it is a Chinese silver slipper buckle."

"It means our luck is going to change, and we don't know
whether it will be good luck or bad luck," said Jonas Jonas to his
daughter Pony Pony Huckabuck.

Then she ran with it to her mother and said, "Look what I
found when I cut open the yellow squash spotted with spots of
gold—it is a Chinese silver slipper buckle."

"It means our luck is going to change, and we don't know
whether it will be good luck or bad luck," said Mama Mama
Huckabuck.

And that night a fire started in the barns, cribs, sheds, shacks,
cracks, and corners where the popcorn harvest was kept. All night

long the popcorn popped. In the morning the ground, all the farm-house and the barn were covered with white popcorn, so it looked like a heavy fall of snow.

All the next day the fire kept on and the popcorn popped till it was up to the shoulders of Pony Pony when she tried to walk from the house to the barn. And that night in all the barns, cribs, sheds, shacks, cracks, and corners of the farm, the popcorn went on popping.

In the morning when Jonas Jonas Huckabuck looked out of the upstairs window he saw the popcorn popping and coming higher and higher. It was nearly up to the window. Before evening and dark of that day, Jonas Jonas Huckabuck, and his wife Mama Mama Huckabuck, and their daughter Pony Pony Huckabuck, all went away from the farm saying, "We came to Nebraska to raise popcorn but this is too much. We will not come back till the wind blows away the popcorn. We will not come back till we get a sign and a signal."

They went to Oskaloosa, Iowa. And the next year Pony Pony Huckabuck was very proud because when she stood on the sidewalks in the street she could see her father sitting high on the seat of a coal wagon, driving two big spanking horses hitched with shining brass harness in front of the coal wagon. And though Pony Pony and Jonas Jonas were proud, very proud all that year, there never came a sign, a signal.

The next year again was a proud year, exactly as proud a year as they spent in Oskaloosa. They went to Paducah, Kentucky, to Defiance, Ohio; Peoria, Illinois; Indianapolis, Indiana; Walla Walla, Washington. And in all these places Pony Pony Huckabuck saw her father, Jonas Jonas Huckabuck standing in rubber boots deep down in a ditch with a shining steel shovel shoveling yellow clay and black mud from down in the ditch high and high over his shoulders. And though it was a proud year they got no sign, no signal.

The next year came. It was the proudest of all. This was the year Jonas Jonas Huckabuck and his family lived in Elgin, Illinois, and Jonas Jonas was watchman in a watch factory watching the watches.

"I know where you have been," Mama Mama Huckabuck would say of an evening to Pony Pony Huckabuck. "You have been down to the watch factory watching your father watch the watches."

"Yes," said Pony Pony, "yes, and this evening when I was watching father watch the watches in the watch factory, I looked over my left shoulder and I saw a policeman with a star and brass buttons, and he was watching me to see if I was watching father watch the watches in the watch factory."

It was a proud year. Pony Pony saved her money. Thanksgiving came. Pony Pony said, "I am going to get a squash to make a squash pie." She hunted from one grocery to another; she kept her eyes on the farm wagons coming into Elgin with squashes.

She found what she wanted, the yellow squash spotted with gold spots. She took it home, cut it open, and saw the inside was like the outside, all rich yellow spotted with gold spots.

There was a shine like silver. She picked and plunged with her fingers and pulled and pulled till at last she pulled out the shine of silver.

"It's a sign; it is a signal," she said. "It is a buckle, a slipper buckle, a Chinese silver slipper buckle. It is the mate to the other buckle. Our luck is going to change. Yoo hoo! Yoo hoo!"

She told her father and mother about the buckle. They went back to the farm in Nebraska. The wind had been blowing and blowing for three years, and all the popcorn was blown away.

"Now we are going to be farmers again," said Jonas Jonas Huckabuck to Mama Mama Huckabuck and to Pony Pony Huck-abuck. "And we are going to raise cabbages, beets, and turnips, we are going to raise squash, rutabuga, pumpkins, and peppers for pickling. We are going to raise wheat, oats, barley, rye. We are going to raise corn such as Indian corn and kaffir corn—but we are *not* going to raise any popcorn for the popcorn poppers to be popping."

And the pony-face daughter was proud because she had on new black slippers, and around her ankles holding the slippers on the left foot and the right foot, she had two buckles, silver buckles, Chinese silver slipper buckles. They were mates.

Sometimes on Thanksgiving Day and Christmas and New Year's, she tells her friends to be careful when they open a squash.

"Squashes make your luck change good to bad and bad to good," says Pony Pony.

A Bird Came Down the Walk

by EMILY DICKINSON

A bird came down the walk:
He did not know I saw;
He bit an angle-worm in halves
And ate the fellow, raw.

And then he drank a dew
From a convenient grass,
And then hopped sidewise
   to the wall
To let a beetle pass.

Bingo Has an Enemy

by ROSE FYLEMAN

Bingo is kind and friendly,
  A gentleman right to the core,
But he can't bear rats
And he hates all cats
  And the fuzzy brown dog next door.

There's a nice little girl who lives there,
  But they glare at us more and more;
So we never can call,
And the cause of it all
  Is the fuzzy brown dog next door.

Bingo is limping a little
  And one of his ears is sore,
He's rather a fright,
But, oh, what a sight
  Is the fuzzy brown dog next door!

Bambi

HOW BAMBI FOUND THE MEADOW

by FELIX SALTEN

After Bambi has been introduced to the meadow world by his mother, he passes through many other experiences—some of them sad and frightening, but all intensely interesting to him— until he becomes a grown deer able to take care of himself. This story of a forest deer is unequalled in its tender and sympathetic understanding of wild animals. Of course Bambi does think and reason rather like a human being, but he acts like a deer, and somehow the author makes you feel what it would be like to be a deer. The book was first written for grownups, but it has since proved to be a great favorite with children.

In early summer the trees stood still under the blue sky, held their limbs outstretched and received the direct rays of the sun. On the shrubs and bushes in the undergrowth, the flowers unfolded their red, white, and yellow stars. On some the seed pods had begun to appear again. They perched innumerable on the fine tips of the branches, tender and firm and resolute, and seemed like small, clenched fists. Out of the earth came whole troops of flowers, like motley stars, so that the soil of the twilit forest floor shone with a silent, ardent, colorful gladness. Everything smelled of fresh leaves, of blossoms, of moist clods and green wood. When morning broke, or when the sun went down, the whole woods resounded with a thousand voices, and from morning till night, the bees hummed, the wasps droned, and filled the fragrant stillness with their murmur.

These were the earliest days of Bambi's life. He walked behind his mother on a narrow track that ran through the midst of the bushes. How pleasant it was to walk there! The thick foliage stroked his flanks softly and bent supplely aside. The track appeared to be barred and obstructed in a dozen places and yet they advanced with the greatest ease. There were tracks like this everywhere, running criss-cross through the whole woods. His mother knew them all, and if Bambi sometimes stopped before a bush as if it were an impenetrable green wall, she always found where the path went through, without hesitation or searching.

Bambi questioned her. He loved to ask his mother questions. It was the pleasantest thing for him to ask a question and then to hear what answer his mother would give. Bambi was never surprised that question after question should come into his mind continually and without effort. He found it perfectly natural, and it delighted him very much. It was very delightful, too, to wait expectantly till the answer came. If it turned out the way he wanted, he was satisfied. Sometimes, of course, he did not understand, but that was pleasant also because he was kept busy picturing what he had not understood, in his own way. Sometimes he felt very sure that his mother was not giving him a complete answer, was intentionally not telling him all she knew. And, at first, that was very pleasant, too. For then there would remain in him such a lively curiosity, such suspicion, mysteriously and joyously flashing through him, such anticipation, that he would become anxious and happy at the same time, and grow silent.

Once he asked, "Whom does this trail belong to, Mother?"

His mother answered, "To us."

Bambi asked again, "To you and me?"

"Yes."

"Only to us two?"

"No," said his mother, "to us deer."

"What are deer?" Bambi asked, and laughed.

His mother looked at him from head to foot and laughed too.

"You are a deer and I am a deer. We're both deer," she said. "Do you understand?"

Bambi sprang into the air for joy. "Yes, I understand," he said. "I'm a little deer and you're a big deer, aren't you?"

His mother nodded and said, "Now you see."

But Bambi grew serious again. "Are there other deer besides you and me?" he asked.

"Certainly," his mother said. "Many of them."

"Where are they?" cried Bambi.

"Here, everywhere."

"But I don't see them."

"You will soon," she said.

"When?" Bambi stood still, wild with curiosity.

"Soon." The mother walked on quietly. Bambi followed her. He kept silent for he was wondering what "soon" might mean. He came to the conclusion that "soon" was certainly not "now." But he wasn't sure at what time "soon" stopped being "soon" and began to be a "long while." Suddenly he asked, "Who made this trail?"

"We," his mother answered.

Bambi was astonished. "We? You and I?"

The mother said, "We, we . . . we deer."

Bambi asked, "Which deer?"

"All of us," his mother said sharply.

They walked on. Bambi was in high spirits and felt like leaping off the path, but he stayed close to his mother. Something rustled in front of them, close to the ground. The fern fronds and wood-lettuce concealed something that advanced in violent motion. A threadlike, little cry shrilled out piteously; then all was still. Only the leaves and the blades of grass shivered back into place. A ferret had caught a mouse. He came slinking by, slid sideways, and prepared to enjoy his meal.

"What was that?" asked Bambi excitedly.

"Nothing," his mother soothed him.

"But," Bambi trembled, "but I saw it."

"Yes, yes," said his mother. "Don't be frightened. The ferret has killed a mouse." But Bambi was dreadfully frightened. A vast, unknown horror clutched at his heart. It was long before he could speak again. Then he asked, "Why did he kill the mouse?"

"Because," his mother hesitated. "Let us walk faster," she said as though something had just occurred to her and as though she had forgotten the question. She began to hurry. Bambi sprang after her.

A long pause ensued. They walked on quietly again. Finally Bambi asked anxiously, "Shall we kill a mouse, too, sometime?"

"No," replied his mother.

"Never?" asked Bambi.

"Never," came the answer.

"Why not?" asked Bambi, relieved.

"Because we never kill anything," said his mother simply.

Bambi grew happy again.

Loud cries were coming from a young ash tree which stood near their path. The mother went along without noticing them, but Bambi stopped inquisitively. Overhead two jays were quarreling about a nest they had plundered.

"Get away, you murderer!" cried one.

"Keep cool, you fool," the other answered, "I'm not afraid of you."

"Look for your own nests," the first one shouted, "or I'll break your head for you." He was beside himself with rage. "What vulgarity!" he chattered, "what vulgarity!"

The other jay had spied Bambi and fluttered down a few branches to shout at him. "What are you gawking at, you freak?" he screamed.

Bambi sprang away terrified. He reached his mother and walked behind her again, frightened and obedient, thinking she had not noticed his absence.

After a pause he asked, "Mother, what is vulgarity?"

"I don't know," said his mother.

Bambi thought a while; then he began again. "Why were they both so angry with each other, Mother?" he asked.

"They were fighting over food," his mother answered.

"Will we fight over food, too, sometime?" Bambi asked.

"No," said his mother.

Bambi asked, "Why not?"

"Because there is enough for all of us," his mother replied.

Bambi wanted to know something else. "Mother," he began.

"What is it?"

"Will we be angry with each other sometime?" he asked.

"No, child," said his mother, "we don't do such things."

They walked along again. Presently it grew light ahead of them. It grew very bright. The trail ended with the tangle of vines and bushes. A few steps more and they would be in the bright open space that spread out before them. Bambi wanted to bound forward, but his mother had stopped.

"What is it?" he asked impatiently, already delighted.

"It's the meadow," his mother answered.

"What is a meadow?" asked Bambi insistently.

His mother cut him short. "You'll soon find out for yourself," she said. She had become very serious and watchful. She stood motionless, holding her head high and listening intently. She sucked in deep breathfuls of air and looked very severe.

"It's all right," she said at last, "we can go out."

Bambi leaped forward, but his mother barred the way.

"Wait till I call you," she said. Bambi obeyed at once and stood still. "That's right," said his mother, to encourage him, "and now listen to what I am saying to you." Bambi heard how seriously his mother spoke and felt terribly excited.

"Walking on the meadow is not so simple," his mother went on. "It's a difficult and dangerous business. Don't ask me why. You'll find that out later on. Now do exactly as I tell you to. Will you?"

"Yes," Bambi promised.

"Good," said his mother, "I'm going out alone first. Stay here and wait. And don't take your eyes off me for a minute. If you see me run back here, then turn round and run as fast as you can. I'll catch up with you soon." She grew silent and seemed to be thinking. Then she went on earnestly, "Run anyway as fast as your legs will carry you. Run even if something should happen . . . even if you should see me fall to the ground. . . . Don't think of me, do you understand? No matter what you see or hear, start running right away and just as fast as you possibly can. Do you promise me to do that?"

"Yes," said Bambi softly. His mother spoke so seriously.

She went on speaking. "Out there if I should call you," she said, "there must be no looking around and no questions, but you must get behind me instantly. Understand that. Run without pausing or stopping to think. If I begin to run, that means for you to run too, and no stopping until we are back here again. You won't forget, will you?"

"No," said Bambi in a troubled voice.

"Now I'm going ahead," said his mother, and seemed to become calmer.

She walked out. Bambi, who never took his eyes off her, saw how she moved forward with slow, cautious steps. He stood there full of expectancy, full of fear and curiosity. He saw how his mother listened in all directions, saw her shrink together, and shrank together himself, ready to leap back into the thickets. Then his mother grew calm again. She stretched herself. Then she looked around satisfied and called, "Come!"

Bambi bounded out. Joy seized him with such tremendous force that he forgot his worries in a flash. Through the thicket he could see only the green tree-tops overhead. Once in a while he caught a glimpse of the blue sky.

Now he saw the whole heaven stretching far and wide and he rejoiced without knowing why. In the forest he had seen only a stray sunbeam now and then, or the tender, dappled light that played through the branches. Suddenly he was standing in the blinding hot sunlight whose boundless power was beaming upon him. He stood in the splendid warmth that made him shut his eyes but which opened his heart.

Bambi was as though bewitched. He was completely beside himself with pleasure. He was simply wild. He leaped into the air three, four, five times. He had to do it. He felt a terrible desire to leap and jump. He stretched his young limbs joyfully. His breath came deeply and easily. He drank in the air. The sweet smell of the meadow made him so wildly happy that he had to leap into the air.

Bambi was a child. If he had been a human child he would have shouted. But he was a young deer, and deer cannot shout, at least not the way human children do. So he rejoiced with his legs and with his whole body as he flung himself into the air. His mother stood by and was glad. She was happy that Bambi was wild. She watched how he bounded into the air and fell again awkwardly, in one spot. She saw how he stared around him, dazed and bewildered, only to leap up over and over again. She understood that Bambi knew only the narrow deer tracks in the forest and how his brief life was used to the limits of the thicket. He did not move from one place because he did not understand how to run freely around the open meadow.

So she stretched out her forefeet and bent laughingly towards Bambi for a moment. Then she was off with one bound, racing around in a circle so that the tall grass stems swished.

Bambi was frightened and stood motionless. Was that a sign for him to run back to the thicket? His mother had said to him, "Don't worry about me no matter what you see or hear. Just run as fast as you can." He was going to turn around and run as she had commanded him to, but his mother came galloping up suddenly. She came up with a wonderful swishing sound and stopped two steps from him. She bent towards him, laughing as she had at first and cried, "Catch me." And in a flash she was gone.

Bambi was puzzled. What did she mean? Then she came back again running so fast that it made him giddy. She pushed his flank with her nose and said quickly, "Try to catch me," and fled away.

Bambi started after her. He took a few steps. Then his steps became short bounds. He felt as if he were flying without any effort on his part. There was a space under his hoofs, space under his bounding feet, space and still more space. Bambi was beside himself with joy.

The swishing grass sounded wonderful to his ears. It was marvelously soft and as fine as silk where it brushed against him. He ran round in a circle. He turned and flew off in a new circle, turned around again and kept running.

His mother was standing still, getting her breath again. She kept following Bambi with her eyes. He was wild.

Suddenly the race was over. He stopped and came up to his mother, lifting his hoofs elegantly. He looked joyfully at her. Then they strolled contentedly side by side.

Since he had been in the open, Bambi had felt the sky and the sun and the green meadow with his whole body. He took one blinding, giddy glance at the sun, and he felt its rays as they lay warmly on his back.

Presently he began to enjoy the meadow with his eyes also. Its wonders amazed him at every step he took. You could not see the tiniest speck of earth the way you could in the forest. Blade after blade of grass covered every inch of the ground. It tossed and waved luxuriantly. It bent softly aside under every footstep, only to rise up unharmed again. The broad green meadow was starred with white daisies, with the thick, round red and purple clover blossoms and bright, golden dandelion heads.

"Look, look, Mother!" Bambi exclaimed. "There's a flower flying."

"That's not a flower," said his mother, "that's a butterfly."

Bambi stared at the butterfly, entranced. It had darted lightly from a blade of grass and was fluttering about in its giddy way. Then Bambi saw that there were many butterflies flying in the air above the meadow. They seemed to be in a hurry and yet moved slowly, fluttering up and down in a sort of game that delighted him. They really did look like gay flying flowers that would not stay on their stems but had unfastened themselves in order to dance a little. They looked, too, like flowers that come to rest at sundown but have no fixed places and have to hunt for them, dropping down and vanishing as if they really had settled somewhere, yet always flying up again, a little way at first, then higher and higher, and always searching farther and farther because all the good places have already been taken.

Bambi gazed at them all. He would have loved to see one close by. He wanted to see one face to face but he was not able to. They sailed in and out continually. The air was aflutter with them.

When he looked down at the ground again he was delighted with the thousands of living things he saw stirring under his hoofs. They ran and jumped in all directions. He would see a wild swarm of them, and the next moment they had disappeared in the grass again.

"Who are they, Mother?" he asked.

"Those are ants," his mother answered.

"Look," cried Bambi, "see that piece of grass jumping. Look how high it can jump!"

"That's not grass," his mother explained, "that's a nice grass-hopper."

"Why does he jump that way?" asked Bambi.

"Because we're walking here," his mother answered; "he's afraid we'll step on him."

"O," said Bambi, turning to the grasshopper who was sitting on a daisy; "O," he said again politely, "you don't have to be afraid; we won't hurt you."

"I'm not afraid," the grasshopper replied in a quavering voice; "I was only frightened for a moment when I was talking to my wife."

"Excuse us for disturbing you," said Bambi shyly.

"Not at all," the grasshopper quavered. "Since it's you it's perfectly all right. But you never know who's coming and you have to be careful."

"This is the first time in my life that I've ever been on the meadow," Bambi explained; "my mother brought me. . . ."

The grasshopper was sitting with his head lowered as though he were going to butt. He put on a serious face and murmured, "That doesn't interest me at all. I haven't time to stand here gossiping with you. I have to be looking for my wife. Hopp!" And he gave a jump.

"Hopp!" said Bambi in surprise at the high jump with which the grasshopper vanished.

Bambi ran to his mother. "Mother, I spoke to him," he cried.

"To whom?" his mother asked.

"To the grasshopper," Bambi said, "I spoke to him. He was very nice to me. And I like him so much. He's so wonderful and green and you can see through his sides. They look like leaves, but you can't see through a leaf."

"Those are his wings," said his mother.

"O," Bambi went on, "and his face is so serious and wise. But he was very nice to me anyhow. And how he can jump! 'Hopp!' he said, and he jumped so high I couldn't see him any more."

They walked on. The conversation with the grasshopper had excited Bambi and tired him a little, for it was the first time he had ever spoken to a stranger. He felt hungry and pressed close to his mother to be nursed.

Then he stood quietly and gazed dreamily into space for a little while with a sort of joyous ecstasy that came over him every time he was nursed by his mother. He noticed a bright flower moving in the tangled grasses. Bambi looked more closely at it. No, it wasn't a flower, but a butterfly. Bambi crept closer.

The butterfly hung heavily to a grass stem and fanned its wings slowly.

"Please sit still," Bambi said.

"Why should I sit still? I'm a butterfly," the insect answered in astonishment.

"O, please sit still, just for a minute," Bambi pleaded. "I've wanted so much to see you close to. Please."

"Well," said the butterfly, "for your sake I will, but not for long."

Bambi stood in front of him. "How beautiful you are!" he cried fascinated; "how wonderfully beautiful, like a flower!"

"What?" cried the butterfly, fanning his wings, "did you say like a flower? In my circle it's generally supposed that we're handsomer than flowers."

Bambi was embarrassed. "O, yes," he stammered, "much handsomer, excuse me, I only meant. . . ."

"Whatever you meant is all one to me," the butterfly replied.

He arched his thin body affectedly and played with his delicate feelers.

Bambi looked at him enchanted. "How elegant you are!" he said. "How elegant and fine! And how splendid and white your wings are!"

The butterfly spread his wings wide apart, then raised them till they folded together like an upright sail.

"O," cried Bambi, "I know that you are handsomer than the flowers. Besides, you can fly and the flowers can't because they grow on stems, that's why."

The butterfly spread his wings. "It's enough," he said, "that I can fly." He soared so lightly that Bambi could hardly see him or follow his flight. His wings moved gently and gracefully. Then he fluttered into the sunny air.

"I only sat still that long on your account," he said, balancing in the air in front of Bambi. "Now I'm going."

That was how Bambi found the meadow.

The Purple Cow

by GELETT BURGESS

I never saw a Purple Cow,
    I never hope to see one;
But I can tell you, anyhow,
    I'd rather see than be one.

You Are Old, Father William

by LEWIS CARROLL

"You are old, Father William," the young man said,
  "And your hair has become very white;
And yet you incessantly stand on your head—
  Do you think, at your age, it is right?"

"In my youth," Father William replied to his son,
  "I feared it might injure the brain;
But, now that I'm perfectly sure I have none,
  Why, I do it again and again."

"You are old," said the youth, "as I mentioned before.
  And have grown most uncommonly fat;
Yet you turned a back-somersault in at the door—
  Pray, what is the reason of that?"

"In my youth," said the sage, as he shook his grey locks,
  "I kept all my limbs very supple
By the use of this ointment—one shilling the box—
  Allow me to sell you a couple?"

"You are old," said the youth, "and your jaws are too weak
  For anything tougher than suet;
Yet you finished the goose, with the bones and the beak—
  Pray, how did you manage to do it?"

"In my youth," said his father, "I took to the law,
  And argued each case with my wife;
And the muscular strength, which it gave to my jaw
  Has lasted the rest of my life."

ILLUSTRATED BY JOHN TENNIEL

"You are old," said the youth, "one would hardly suppose
    That your eye was as steady as ever;
Yet you balanced an eel on the end of your nose—
    What made you so awfully clever?"

"I have answered three questions, and that is enough,"
    Said his father. "Don't give yourself airs!
Do you think I can listen all day to such stuff?
    Be off, or I'll kick you down-stairs!"

From *Alice's Adventures in Wonderland*.

The Wind in the Willows

THE OPEN ROAD

by KENNETH GRAHAME

Like many other of the most famous books for children, The
Wind in the Willows *was not originally planned as a book but
started out as bedtime stories told by the author to his small son.
When the boy went away to the seashore, he insisted on his father
writing him the continuation of the little stories about Mole, Rat,
Badger, and intelligent Mr. Toad. These letters were luckily
saved and became the basis for the book. There are probably no
more delightful animals to be found anywhere in fiction than
these friendly and philosophical creatures that Kenneth Grahame
created. Because of the book's unique wit, charm and beautiful
style, it has become one of the best loved classics for children.*

"Ratty," said the Mole suddenly, one bright summer morning, "if
you please, I want to ask you a favour."

The Rat was sitting on the river bank, singing a little song. He
had just composed it himself, so he was very taken up with it, and
would not pay proper attention to Mole or anything else. Since
early morning he had been swimming in the river in company
with his friends the ducks. And when the ducks stood on their
heads suddenly, as ducks will, he would dive down and tickle their
necks just under where their chins would be if ducks had chins, till
they were forced to come to the surface again in a hurry, splutter-
ing and angry and shaking their feathers at him, for it is impossible
to say quite *all* you feel when your head is under water. At last

they implored him to go away and attend to his own affairs and leave them to mind theirs. So the Rat went away, and sat on the river bank in the sun, and made up a song about them, which he called

DUCKS' DITTY

All along the backwater,
Through the rushes tall,
Ducks are a-dabbling,
Up tails all!

Ducks' tails, drakes' tails,
Yellow feet a-quiver,
Yellow bills all out of sight
Busy in the river!

Slushy green undergrowth
Where the roach swim—
Here we keep our larder,
Cool and full and dim.

Every one for what he likes!
We like to be
Heads down, tails up,
Dabbling free!

High in the blue above
Swifts whirl and call—
We are down a-dabbling
Up tails all!

"I don't know that I think so *very* much of that little song, Rat," observed the Mole cautiously. He was no poet himself and didn't care who knew it; and he had a candid nature.

"Nor don't the ducks neither," replied the Rat cheerfully. "They say, '*Why* can't fellows be allowed to do what they like *when* they like and *as* they like, instead of other fellows sitting on banks and watching them all the time and making remarks, and

poetry and things about them? What *nonsense* it all is!' That's
what the ducks say."

"So it is, so it is," said the Mole, with great heartiness.

"No, it isn't!" cried the Rat indignantly.

"Well then, it isn't, it isn't," replied the Mole soothingly. "But
what I wanted to ask you was, won't you take me to call on Mr.
Toad? I've heard so much about him, and I do so want to make
his acquaintance."

"Why, certainly," said the good-natured Rat, jumping to his
feet and dismissing poetry from his mind for the day. "Get the
boat out, and we'll paddle up there at once. It's never the wrong
time to call on Toad. Early or late he's always the same fellow.
Always good-tempered, always glad to see you, always sorry when
you go!"

"He must be a very nice animal," observed the Mole, as he got
into the boat and took the sculls, while the Rat settled himself
comfortably in the stern.

"He is indeed the best of animals," replied Rat. "So simple, so
good-natured, and so affectionate. Perhaps he's not very clever—
we can't all be geniuses; and it may be that he is both boastful
and conceited. But he has got some great qualities, has Toady."
Rounding a bend in the river, they came in sight of a handsome,
dignified old house of mellowed red brick, with well-kept lawns
reaching down to the water's edge.

"There's Toad Hall," said the Rat; "and that creek on the left,
where the notice-board says, 'Private. No landing allowed,' leads
to his boat-house, where we'll leave the boat. The stables are over
there to the right. That's the banqueting-hall you're looking at
now—very old, that is. Toad is rather rich, you know, and this is
really one of the nicest houses in these parts, though we never admit as much to Toad."

They glided up the creek, and the Mole shipped his sculls as
they passed into the shadow of a large boat-house. Here they saw
many handsome boats, slung from the cross-beams or hauled up
on a slip, but none in the water; and the place had an unused and
deserted air.

The Rat looked around him. "I understand," said he. "Boating is played out. He's tired of it, and done with it. I wonder what new fad he has taken up now? Come along and let's look him up. We shall hear all about it quite soon enough."

They disembarked, and strolled across the gay flower-decked lawns in search of Toad, whom they presently happened upon resting in a wicker garden-chair, with a preoccupied expression of face, and a large map spread out on his knees.

"Hooray!" he cried, jumping up on seeing them, "this is splendid!" He shook the paws of both of them warmly, never waiting for an introduction to the Mole. "How *kind* of you!" he went on, dancing round them. "I was just going to send a boat down the river for you, Ratty, with strict orders that you were to be fetched up here at once, whatever you were doing. I want you badly—both of you. Now what will you take? Come inside and have something! You don't know how lucky it is, your turning up just now!"

"Let's sit quiet a bit, Toady!" said the Rat, throwing himself into an easy chair, while the Mole took another by the side of him and made some civil remark about Toad's "delightful residence."

"Finest house on the whole river," cried Toad boisterously. "Or anywhere else, for that matter," he could not help adding.

Here the Rat nudged the Mole. Unfortunately the Toad saw him do it, and turned very red. There was a moment's painful silence. Then Toad burst out laughing. "All right, Ratty," he said. "It's only my way, you know. And it's not such a very bad house, is it? You know you rather like it yourself. Now, look here. Let's be sensible. You are the very animals I wanted. You've got to help me. It's most important!"

"It's about your rowing, I suppose," said the Rat, with an innocent air. "You're getting on fairly well, though you splash a good bit still. With a great deal of patience, and any quantity of coaching, you may—"

"O, pooh! boating!" interrupted the Toad, in great disgust. "Silly boyish amusement. I've given that up *long* ago. Sheer waste of time, that's what it is. It makes me downright sorry to see you fellows, who ought to know better, spending all your energies in that aimless manner. No, I've discovered the real thing, the only genuine occupation for a lifetime. I propose to devote the remainder of mine to it, and can only regret the wasted years that lie behind me, squandered in trivialities. Come with me, dear Ratty, and your amiable friend also, if he will be so very good, just as far as the stable-yard, and you shall see what you shall see!"

He led the way to the stable-yard accordingly, the Rat following with a most mistrustful expression; and there, drawn out of the coach-house into the open, they saw a gipsy caravan, shining with newness, painted a canary-yellow picked out with green, and red wheels.

"There you are!" cried the Toad, straddling and expanding himself. "There's real life for you, embodied in that little cart. The open road, the dusty highway, the heath, the common, the hedgerows, the rolling downs! Camps, villages, towns, cities! Here today, up and off to somewhere else to-morrow! Travel, change, interest, excitement! The whole world before you, and a horizon that's always changing! And mind, this is the very finest cart of its sort that was ever built, without any exception. Come inside and look at the arrangements. Planned 'em all myself, I did!"

The Mole was tremendously interested and excited, and followed him eagerly up the steps and into the interior of the caravan. The Rat only snorted and thrust his hands deep into his pockets, remaining where he was.

It was indeed very compact and comfortable. Little sleeping-bunks—a little table that folded up against the wall—a cooking-stove, lockers, bookshelves, a bird-cage with a bird in it; and pots, pans, jugs and kettles of every size and variety.

"All complete!" said the Toad triumphantly, pulling open a locker. "You see—biscuits, potted lobster, sardines—everything you can possibly want. Soda-water here—baccy there—letter-paper, bacon, jam, cards and dominoes—you'll find," he continued, as they descended the steps again, "you'll find that nothing whatever has been forgotten, when we make our start this afternoon."

"I beg your pardon," said the Rat slowly, as he chewed a straw,

"but did I overhear you say something about '*we*' and '*start*' and 'this *afternoon*'?"

"Now, you dear good old Ratty," said Toad imploringly, "don't begin talking in that stiff and sniffy sort of way, because you know you've *got* to come. I can't possibly manage without you, so please consider it settled, and don't argue—it's the one thing I can't stand. You surely don't mean to stick to your dull fusty old river all your life, and just live in a hole in a bank, and *boat*? I want to show you the world! I'm going to make an *animal* of you, my boy!"

"I don't care," said the Rat doggedly. "I'm not coming, and that's flat. And I *am* going to stick to my old river, *and* live in a hole, *and* boat, as I've always done. And what's more, Mole's going to stick to me and do as I do, aren't you, Mole?"

"Of course I am," said the Mole loyally. "I'll always stick to you, Rat, and what you say is to be—has got to be. All the same, it sounds as if it might have been—well, rather fun, you know!" he added wistfully. Poor Mole! The Life Adventurous was so new a thing to him, and so thrilling; and this fresh aspect of it was so tempting; and he had fallen in love at first sight with the canary-coloured cart and all its little fitments.

The Rat saw what was passing in his mind, and wavered. He hated disappointing people, and he was fond of the Mole, and would do almost anything to oblige him. Toad was watching both of them closely.

"Come along in and have some lunch," he said diplomatically, "and we'll talk it over. We needn't decide anything in a hurry. Of course, I don't really care. I only want to give pleasure to you fellows. 'Live for others!' That's my motto in life."

During luncheon—which was excellent, of course, as everything at Toad Hall always was—the Toad simply let himself go. Disregarding the Rat, he proceeded to play upon the inexperienced Mole as on a harp. Naturally a voluble animal, and always mastered by his imagination, he painted the prospects of the trip and the joys of the open life and the roadside in such glowing colours that the Mole could hardly sit in his chair for excitement. Somehow it soon seemed taken for granted by all three that the trip was a settled thing; and the Rat, though still unconvinced in his mind, allowed his good-nature to override his personal objections. He could not bear to disappoint his two friends, who were already deep in schemes and anticipations, planning out each day's separate occupation for several weeks ahead.

When they were quite ready, the now triumphant Toad led his companions to the paddock and set them to capture the old grey horse, who, without having been consulted, and to his own extreme annoyance, had been told off by Toad for the dustiest job in this dusty expedition. He frankly preferred the paddock, and took a deal of catching. Meantime Toad packed the lockers still tighter with necessaries, and hung nose-bags, nets of onions, bundles of hay, and baskets from the bottom of the cart. At last the horse was caught and harnessed, and they set off, all talking at once, each animal either trudging by the side of the cart or sitting on the shaft, as the humour took him. It was a golden afternoon. The smell of the dust they kicked up was rich and satisfying; out of thick orchards on either side the road, birds called and whistled to them cheerily; good-natured wayfarers, passing them, gave them "Good day," or stopped to say nice things about their beautiful cart; and rabbits, sitting at their front doors in the hedgerows, held up their fore paws, and said, "O my! O my! O my!"

Late in the evening, tired and happy and miles from home, they drew up on a remote common far from habitations, turned the horse loose to graze, and ate their simple supper sitting on the grass by the side of the cart. Toad talked big about all he was going to do in the days to come, while stars grew fuller and larger all around them, and a yellow moon, appearing suddenly and silently from nowhere in particular, came to keep them company and listen to their talk. At last they turned into their little bunks in the cart; and Toad, kicking out his legs, sleepily said, "Well, good night, you fellows! This is the real life for a gentleman! Talk about your old river!"

"I *don't* talk about my river," replied the patient Rat. "You *know* I don't, Toad. But I *think* about it," he added pathetically, in a lower tone: "I think about it—all the time!"

The Mole reached out from under his blanket, felt for the Rat's paw in the darkness, and gave it a squeeze. "I'll do whatever you like, Ratty," he whispered. "Shall we run away to-morrow morning, quite early—*very* early—and go back to our dear old hole on the river?"

"No, no, we'll see it out," whispered back the Rat. "Thanks awfully, but I ought to stick by Toad till this trip is ended. It wouldn't be safe for him to be left to himself. It won't take very long. His fads never do. Good night!"

The end was indeed nearer than even the Rat suspected.

After so much open air and excitement the Toad slept very soundly, and no amount of shaking could rouse him out of bed next morning. So the Mole and Rat turned to, quietly and manfully, and while the Rat saw to the horse, and lit a fire, and cleaned last night's cups and platters and got things ready for breakfast, the Mole trudged off to the nearest village, a long way off, for milk and eggs and various necessaries the Toad had, of course, forgotten to provide. The hard work had all been done, and the two animals were resting, thoroughly exhausted, by the time Toad appeared on the scene, fresh and gay, remarking what a pleasant easy life it was they were all leading now, after the cares and worries and fatigues of housekeeping at home.

They had a pleasant ramble that day over grassy downs and along narrow by-lanes, and camped, as before, on a common, only this time the two guests took care that Toad should do his fair share of work. In consequence, when the time came for starting next morning, Toad was by no means so rapturous about the simplicity of the primitive life, and indeed attempted to resume his place in his bunk, whence he was hauled by force. Their way lay, as before, across country by narrow lanes, and it was not till the afternoon that they came out on the high road, their first high road; and there disaster, fleet and unforeseen, sprang out on them —disaster momentous indeed to their expedition, but simply overwhelming in its effect on the after-career of Toad.

They were strolling along the high road easily, the Mole by the horse's head, talking to him, since the horse had complained that he was being frightfully left out of it, and nobody considered him in the least; the Toad and the Water Rat walking behind the cart talking together—at least Toad was talking, and Rat was saying at intervals, "Yes, precisely; and what did *you* say to *him?*"—and thinking all the time of something very different, when far behind them they heard a faint warning hum, like the drone of a distant bee. Glancing back, they saw a small cloud of dust, with a dark centre of energy, advancing on them at incredible speed, while from out the dust a faint "Poop-poop!" wailed like an uneasy animal in pain. Hardly regarding it, they turned to resume their conversation, when in an instant (as it seemed) the peaceful scene was changed, and with a blast of wind and a whirl of sound that made them jump for the nearest ditch, it was on them! The "Poop-poop" rang with a brazen shout in their ears, they had a moment's glimpse of an interior of glittering plate-glass and rich morocco, and the magnificent motor-car, immense, breath-snatching, passionate, with its pilot tense and hugging his wheel, possessed all earth and air for the fraction of a second, flung an enveloping cloud of dust that blinded and enwrapped them utterly, and then dwindled to a speck in the far distance, changed back into a droning bee once more.

The old grey horse, dreaming, as he plodded along, of his quiet paddock, in a new raw situation such as this simply abandoned himself to his natural emotions. Rearing, plunging, backing steadily, in spite of all the Mole's efforts at his head, and all the Mole's lively language directed at his better feelings, he drove the cart backwards towards the deep ditch at the side of the road. It wavered an instant—then there was a heart-rending crash—and the canary-coloured cart, their pride and their joy, lay on its side in the ditch, an irredeemable wreck.

The Rat danced up and down in the road, simply transported with passion. "You villains!" he shouted, shaking both fists. "You scoundrels, you highwaymen, you—you—road-hogs! ——I'll have the law of you! I'll report you! I'll take you through all the Courts!" His home-sickness had quite slipped away from him, and for the moment he was the skipper of the canary-coloured vessel driven on a shoal by the reckless jockeying of rival mariners, and he was trying to recollect all the fine and biting things he used to say to masters of steam-launches when their wash, as they drove too near the bank, used to flood his parlour carpet at home.

Toad sat straight down in the middle of the dusty road, his legs stretched out before him, and stared fixedly in the direction of the disappearing motor-car. He breathed short, his face wore a placid, satisfied expression, and at intervals he faintly murmured "Poop-poop!"

The Mole was busy trying to quiet the horse, which he succeeded in doing after a time. Then he went to look at the cart, on its side in the ditch. It was indeed a sorry sight. Panels and windows smashed, axles hopelessly bent, one wheel off, sardine-tins scattered over the wide world, and the bird in the bird-cage sobbing pitifully and calling to be let out.

The Rat came to help him, but their united efforts were not sufficient to right the cart. "Hi! Toad!" they cried. "Come and bear a hand, can't you!"

The Toad never answered a word, or budged from his seat in the road; so they went to see what was the matter with him. They found him in a sort of trance, a happy smile on his face, his eyes still fixed on the dusty wake of their destroyer. At intervals he was still heard to murmur "Poop-poop!"

The Rat shook him by the shoulder. "Are you coming to help us, Toad?" he demanded sternly.

"Glorious, stirring sight!" murmured Toad, never offering to move. "The poetry of motion! The *real* way to travel! The *only* way to travel! Here to-day—in next week to-morrow! Villages skipped, towns and cities jumped—always somebody else's horizon! O bliss! O poop-poop! O my! O my!"

"O *stop* being an ass, Toad!" cried the Mole despairingly.

"And to think I never *knew!*" went on the Toad in a dreamy monotone. "All those wasted years that lie behind me, I never knew, never even *dreamt!* But *now*—but now that I know, now that I fully realize! O what a flowery track lies spread before me, henceforth! What dust-clouds shall spring up behind me as I speed on my reckless way! What carts I shall fling carelessly into the ditch in the wake of my magnificent onset! Horrid little carts —common carts—canary-coloured carts!"

"What are we to do with him?" asked the Mole of the Water Rat.

"Nothing at all," replied the Rat firmly. "Because there is really nothing to be done. You see, I know him from of old. He is now possessed. He has got a new craze, and it always takes him that way, in its first stage. He'll continue like that for days now, like an animal walking in a happy dream, quite useless for all practical purposes. Never mind him. Let's go and see what there is to be done about the cart."

A careful inspection showed them that, even if they succeeded in righting it by themselves, the cart would travel no longer. The axles were in a hopeless state, and the missing wheel was shattered into pieces.

The Rat knotted the horse's reins over his back and took him by the head, carrying the bird-cage and its hysterical occupant in the other hand. "Come on!" he said grimly to the Mole. "It's five or six miles to the nearest town, and we shall just have to walk it The sooner we make a start the better."

"But what about Toad?" asked the Mole anxiously, as they set off together. "We can't leave him here, sitting in the middle of the road by himself, in the distracted state he's in! It's not safe Supposing another Thing were to come along?"

"O, *bother* Toad," said the Rat savagely; "I've done with him!"

They had not proceeded very far on their way, however, when there was a pattering of feet behind them, and Toad caught them up and thrust a paw inside the elbow of each of them; still breathing short and staring into vacancy.

"Now, look here, Toad!" said the Rat sharply; "as soon as we get to the town, you'll have to go straight to the police-station, and see if they know anything about that motor-car and who it belongs to, and lodge a complaint against it. And then you'll have to go to a blacksmith's or wheelwright's and arrange for the cart to be fetched and mended and put to rights. It'll take time, but it's not quite a hopeless smash. Meanwhile, the Mole and I will go to an Inn and find comfortable rooms where we can stay till the cart's ready, and till your nerves have recovered from their shock "

"Police-station! Complaint!" murmured Toad dreamily "Me *complain* of that beautiful, that heavenly vision that has been vouchsafed me! *Mend* the *cart!* I've done with carts forever I never want to see the cart, or to hear of it, again. O, Ratty! You can't think how obliged I am to you for consenting to come on this trip! I wouldn't have gone without you, and then I might never have seen that—that swan, that sunbeam, that thunderbolt! I might never have heard that entrancing sound, or smelt that bewitching smell! I owe it all to you, my best of friends!"

The Rat turned from him in despair. "You see what it is?" he said to the Mole, addressing him across Toad's head: "He's quite hopeless. I give it up—when we get to the town we'll go to the railway-station, and with luck we may pick up a train there that'll get us back to River Bank to-night. And if ever you catch me going a-pleasuring with this provoking animal again!" ——He snorted, and during the rest of that weary trudge addressed his remarks exclusively to Mole.

On reaching the town they went straight to the station and deposited Toad in the second-class waiting-room, giving a porter twopence to keep a strict eye on him. They then left the horse at an inn stable, and gave what directions they could about the cart and its contents. Eventually, a slow train having landed them at a station not very far from Toad Hall, they escorted the spellbound, sleep-walking Toad to his door, put him inside it, and instructed his housekeeper to feed him, undress him, and put him to bed. Then they got out their boat from the boat-house, sculled down the river home, and at a very late hour sat down to supper in their own cosy riverside parlour, to the Rat's great joy and contentment.

The following evening the Mole, who had risen late and taken things very easy all day, was sitting on the bank fishing, when the Rat, who had been looking up his friends and gossiping, came strolling along to find him. "Heard the news?" he said. "There's nothing else being talked about, all along the river bank. Toad went up to Town by an early train this morning. And he has ordered a large and very expensive motor-car."

The Octopus

by OGDEN NASH

Tell me, O Octopus, I begs,
Is those things arms, or is they legs?
I marvel at thee, Octopus;
If I were thou, I'd call me Us.

Eight Limericks

by EDWARD LEAR

ILLUSTRATED BY EDWARD LEAR

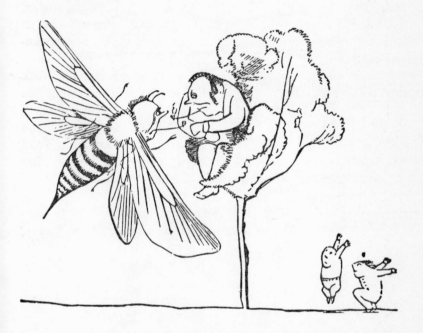

There was an Old Man in a tree,
Who was horribly bored by a Bee;
When they said, "Does it buzz?" he replied, "Yes, it does!
It's a regular brute of a Bee."

There was an Old Person of Ware,
Who rode on the back of a bear:
When they ask'd, "Does it trot?" he said, "Certainly not!
He's a Moppsikon Floppsikon bear!"

There was an Old Man with a beard,
Who said, "It is just as I feared!—
Two Owls and a Hen, four Larks and a Wren,
Have all built their nests in my beard."

There was an Old Man who said, "Hush!
I perceive a young bird in this bush!"
When they said, "Is it small?" he replied, "Not at all;
It is four times as big as the bush!"

There was a Young Lady whose chin
Resembled the point of a pin;
So she had it made sharp, and purchased a harp,
And played several tunes with her chin.

There was a Young Lady of Norway,
Who casually sat in a doorway;
When the door squeezed her flat, she exclaimed, "What of that?"
This courageous Young Lady of Norway.

There was an Old Man on the Border,
Who lived in the utmost disorder;
He danced with the cat, and made tea in his hat,
Which vexed all the folks on the Border.

There was an Old Man on whose nose
Most birds of the air could repose;
But they all flew away at the closing of day,
Which relieved that Old Man and his nose.

Alice's Adventures in Wonderland

DOWN THE RABBIT-HOLE

by LEWIS CARROLL

Lewis Carroll was a shy man who loved children and spent his life as a lecturer in mathematics at Oxford University. It was to please the three little daughters of one of his friends that he made up the odd adventures of a girl named Alice. This tale of an up-side down world, of sense and nonsense, is generally thought of as the greatest masterpiece of children's literature in English. Yet many youngsters are disappointed when they first read this famous story. Probably because they try it too early, when they can appreciate only the action, but not the wonderful humor and play on words. You can be too young, but never too old to enjoy Alice. In fact, many grownups read it over and over again regularly and never tire of the subtle charm of its absurd yet logical nonsense. No book ever written for children enjoys such a wide and enthusiastic audience among adults, or is so frequently quoted. If you can't see its genius now, just try it again in a year or two, and it will probably be revealed to you.

Alice was beginning to get very tired of sitting by her sister on the bank, and of having nothing to do; once or twice she had peeped into the book her sister was reading, but it had no pictures or conversations in it, "and what is the use of a book," thought Alice, "without pictures or conversations?"

So she was considering in her own mind (as well as she could, for the hot day made her feel very sleepy and stupid), whether the pleasure of making a daisy-chain would be worth the trouble of getting up and picking the daisies, when suddenly a white rabbit with pink eyes ran close by her.

There was nothing so *very* remarkable in that; nor did Alice think it so *very* much out of the way to hear the Rabbit say to itself, "Oh dear! Oh dear! I shall be too late!" (when she thought it over afterward, it occurred to her that she ought to have wondered at this, but at the time it all seemed quite natural); but when the Rabbit actually *took a watch out of its waistcoat-pocket*, and looked at it, and then hurried on, Alice started to her feet, for it flashed across her mind that she had never before seen a rabbit with either a waistcoat-pocket or a watch to take out of it, and, burning with curiosity, she ran across the field after it, and was just in time to see it pop down a large rabbit-hole under the hedge.

In another moment down went Alice after it, never once considering how in the world she was to get out again.

The rabbit-hole went straight on like a tunnel for some way, and then dipped suddenly down, so suddenly that Alice had not a moment to think about stopping herself before she found herself falling down what seemed to be a very deep well.

Either the well was very deep, or she fell very slowly, for she had plenty of time as she went down to look about her, and to wonder what was going to happen next. First, she tried to look down and make out what she was coming to, but it was too dark to see anything: then she looked at the sides of the well, and noticed that they were filled with cupboards and bookshelves: here and there she saw maps and pictures hung upon pegs. She took down a jar from one of the shelves as she passed; it was labeled "Orange Marmalade," but to her great disappointment it was empty; she did not like to drop the jar for fear of killing somebody underneath, so managed to put it into one of the cupboards as she fell past it.

"Well!" thought Alice to herself, "after such a fall as this, I shall think nothing of tumbling down stairs! How brave they'll all think me at home! Why I wouldn't say anything about it, even if I fell off the top of the house!" (Which was very likely true.)

Down, down, down. Would the fall *never* come to an end? "I wonder how many miles I've fallen by this time?" she said aloud. "I must be getting somewhere near the center of the earth. Let me see: that would be four thousand miles down, I think (for, you see, Alice had learnt several things of this sort in her lessons in the schoolroom, and though this was not a *very* good opportunity for showing off her knowledge, as there was no one to listen to her, still it was good practice to say it over) "yes, that's about the right distance—but then I wonder what latitude or longitude I've got to?" (Alice had not the slightest idea what latitude was, or longitude either, but she thought they were nice grand words to say.)

Presently she began again: "I wonder if I shall fall right *through* the earth! How funny it'll seem to come out among the people that walk with their heads downwards! The Antipathies, I think" (she was rather glad there *was* no one listening, this time, as it didn't sound at all the right word) "but I shall have to ask them what the name of the country is, you know. Please, ma'am, is this New Zealand or Australia?" (And she tried to curtsey as she spoke —fancy *curtseying* as you're falling through the air! Do you think you could manage it?) "And what an ignorant little girl she'll think me for asking! No, it'll never do to ask: perhaps I shall see it written up somewhere."

Down, down, down. There was nothing else to do, so Alice soon began talking again. "Dinah'll miss me very much tonight, I should think!" (Dinah was the cat.) "I hope they'll remember her saucer of milk at tea-time. Dinah, my dear! I wish you were down here with me! There are no mice in the air, I'm afraid, but you might catch a bat, and that's very like a mouse, you know. But do cats eat bats, I wonder?" And here Alice began to get rather sleepy, and went on saying to herself, in a dreamy sort of way, "Do cats eat bats? Do cats eat bats?" and sometimes, "Do bats eat cats?" for, you see, as she couldn't answer either question, it didn't much matter which way she put it. She felt that she was dozing off, and had just begun to dream that she was walking hand in hand with Dinah, and was saying to her very earnestly, "Now, Dinah, tell me the truth: did you ever eat a bat?" when suddenly, thump! thump! down she came upon a heap of sticks and dry leaves, and the fall was over.

Alice was not a bit hurt, and she jumped up on to her feet in a moment: she looked up, but it was all dark overhead; before her was another long passage, and the White Rabbit was still in sight, hurrying down it. There was not a moment to be lost: away went Alice like the wind, and was just in time to hear it say, as it turned a corner, "Oh, my ears and whiskers, how late it's getting!" She was close behind it when she turned the corner, but the Rabbit was no longer to be seen: she found herself in a long, low hall, which was lit up by a row of lamps hanging from the roof.

There were doors all round the hall, but they were all locked, and when Alice had been all the way down one side and up the other, trying every door, she walked sadly down the middle, wondering how she was ever to get out again.

Suddenly she came upon a little three-legged table, all made of solid glass; there was nothing on it but a tiny golden key, and Alice's first idea was that this might belong to one of the doors of the hall; but, alas! either the locks were too large, or the key was too small, but at any rate it would not open any of them. However, on the second time round, she came upon a low curtain she had not noticed before, and behind it was a little door about fifteen inches high: she tried the little golden key in the lock, and to her great delight it fitted!

Alice opened the door and found it led into a small passage, not much larger than a rathole: she knelt down and looked along the passage into the loveliest garden you ever saw. How she longed to get out of that dark hall, and wander about among those beds of bright flowers and those cool fountains, but she could not even get her head through the doorway; "and even if my head would go through," thought poor Alice, "it would be of very little use without my shoulders. Oh, how I wish I could shut up like a telescope! I think I could, if I only knew how to begin." For, you see, so many out-of-the-way things had happened lately that Alice had begun to think that very few things indeed were really impossible.

There seemed to be no use in waiting by the little door, so she went back to the table, half hoping she might find another key on it, or at any rate a book of rules for shutting people up like telescopes: this time she found a little bottle on it ("which certainly was not here before," said Alice) and tied round the neck of the bottle was a paper label with the words "DRINK ME" beautifully printed on it in large letters.

ILLUSTRATED BY JOHN TENNIEL

It was all very well to say "Drink me," but the wise little Alice was not going to do *that* in a hurry: "no, I'll look first," she said, "and see whether it's marked '*poison*' or not": for she had read several nice little stories about children who had got burnt, and eaten up by wild beasts, and other unpleasant things, all because they *would* not remember the simple rules their friends had taught them, such as, that a red-hot poker will burn you if you hold it too long; and that if you cut your finger *very* deeply with a knife, it usually bleeds; and she had never forgotten that, if you drink much from a bottle marked "poison," it is almost certain to disagree with you, sooner or later.

However, this bottle was *not* marked "poison," so Alice ventured to taste it, and finding it very nice (it had, in fact, a sort of mixed flavour of cherry-tart, custard, pineapple, roast turkey, toffy, and buttered toast) she very soon finished it off.

* * * *
* * *
* * * *

"What a curious feeling!" said Alice, "I must be shutting up like a telescope."

And so it was indeed: she was now only ten inches high, and her face brightened up at the thought that she was now the right size for going through the little door into that lovely garden. First, however, she waited for a few minutes to see if she was going to shrink further: she felt a little nervous about this, "for it might end, you know," said Alice to herself, "in my going out altogether, like a candle. I wonder what I should be like then?" And she tried to fancy what the flame of a candle looks like after the candle is blown out, for she could not remember ever having seen such a thing.

After a while, finding that nothing more happened, she decided on going into the garden at once, but, alas for poor Alice! when she got to the door, she found she had forgotten the little golden key and when she went back to the table for it, she found she could not possibly reach it: for she could see it quite plainly through the glass, and she tried her best to climb up one of the legs of the table, but it was too slippery, and when she had tired herself out with trying, the poor little thing sat down and cried.

"Come, there's no use in crying like that!" said Alice to herself, rather sharply, "I advise you to leave off this minute!" She generally gave herself very good advice (though she very seldom followed it) and sometimes she scolded herself so severely as to bring tears into her eyes, and once she remembered trying to box her own ears for having cheated herself in a game of croquet she was playing against herself, for this curious child was very fond of pretending to be two people. "But it's no use now," thought poor Alice, "to pretend to be two people! Why, there's hardly enough of me left to make *one* respectable person!"

Soon her eye fell on a little glass box that was lying under the table: she opened it, and found in it a very small cake, on which the words "EAT ME" were beautifully marked in currants. "Well, I'll eat it," said Alice, "and if it makes me grow larger, I can reach the key; and if it makes me grow smaller, I can creep under the door; so either way I'll get into the garden, and I don't care which happens!"

She ate a little bit, and said anxiously to herself, "Which way? Which way?" holding her hand on the top of her head to feel which way it was growing, and she was quite surprised to find that she remained the same size: to be sure, this is what generally happens when one eats cake, but Alice had got so much into the way of expecting nothing but out-of-the-way things to happen, that it seemed quite dull and stupid for life to go on in the common way.

So she set to work, and very soon finished off the cake.

A MAD TEA-PARTY

After we leave Alice at the bottom of the rabbit hole, she has some of the most remarkable adventures. She keeps on growing larger and smaller, but when we see her now at the tea-party, she is back to her normal size again.

There was a table set out under a tree in front of the house, and the March Hare and the Hatter were having tea at it: a Dormouse was sitting between them, fast asleep, and the other two were using it as a cushion, resting their elbows on it, and talking over its head. "Very uncomfortable for the Dormouse," thought Alice; "only, as it's asleep, I suppose it doesn't mind."

The table was a large one, but the three were all crowded together at one corner of it: "No room! No room!" they cried out when they saw Alice coming. "There's *plenty* of room!" said Alice

ILLUSTRATED BY JOHN TENNIEL

indignantly, and she sat down in a large arm-chair at one end of the table.

"Have some wine," the March Hare said in an encouraging tone.

Alice looked all round the table, but there was nothing on it but tea. "I don't see any wine," she remarked.

"There isn't any," said the March Hare.

"Then it wasn't very civil of you to offer it," said Alice angrily.

"It wasn't very civil of you to sit down without being invited," said the March Hare.

"I didn't know it was *your* table," said Alice; "it's laid for a great many more than three."

"Your hair wants cutting," said the Hatter. He had been looking at Alice for some time with great curiosity, and this was his first speech.

"You should learn not to make personal remarks," Alice said with some severity: "It's very rude."

The Hatter opened his eyes very wide on hearing this; but all he *said* was, "Why is a raven like a writing-desk?"

"Come, we shall have some fun now!" thought Alice. "I'm glad they've begun asking riddles—I believe I can guess that," she added aloud.

"Do you mean that you think you can find out the answer to it?" said the March Hare.

"Exactly so," said Alice.

"Then you should say what you mean," the March Hare went on.

"I do," Alice hastily replied; "at least—at least I mean what I say—that's the same thing, you know."

"Not the same thing a bit!" said the Hatter. "Why, you might just as well say that 'I see what I eat' is the same thing as 'I eat what I see'!"

"You might just as well say," added the March Hare, "that 'I like what I get' is the same thing as 'I get what I like'!"

"You might just as well say," added the Dormouse, who seemed to be talking in his sleep, "that 'I breathe when I sleep' is the same thing as 'I sleep when I breathe'!"

"It *is* the same thing with you," said the Hatter, and here the conversation dropped, and the party sat silent for a minute, while Alice thought over all she could remember about ravens and writing-desks, which wasn't much.

The Hatter was the first to break the silence. "What day of the month is it?" he said, turning to Alice: he had taken his watch out of his pocket, and was looking at it uneasily, shaking it every now and then, and holding it to his ear.

Alice considered a little, and said, "The fourth."

"Two days wrong!" sighed the Hatter. "I told you butter wouldn't suit the works!" he added, looking angrily at the March Hare.

"It was the *best* butter," the March Hare meekly replied.

"Yes, but some crumbs must have got in as well," the Hatter grumbled: "you shouldn't have put it in with the bread-knife."

The March Hare took the watch and looked at it gloomily: then he dipped it into his cup of tea, and looked at it again: but he could think of nothing better to say than his first remark, "It was the *best* butter, you know."

Alice had been looking over his shoulder with some curiosity. "What a funny watch!" she remarked. "It tells the day of the month, and doesn't tell what o'clock it is!"

"Why should it?" muttered the Hatter. "Does *your* watch tell you what year it is?"

"Of course not," Alice replied very readily: "but that's because it stays the same year for such a long time together."

"Which is just the case with *mine*," said the Hatter.

Alice felt dreadfully puzzled. The Hatter's remark seemed to her to have no sort of meaning in it, and yet it was certainly English. "I don't quite understand you," she said, as politely as she could.

"The Dormouse is asleep again," said the Hatter, and he poured a little hot tea on to its nose.

The Dormouse shook its head impatiently, and said, without opening its eyes, "Of course, of course: just what I was going to remark myself."

"Have you guessed the riddle yet?" the Hatter said, turning to Alice again.

"No, I give it up," Alice replied: "what's the answer?"

"I haven't the slightest idea," said the Hatter.

"Nor I," said the March Hare.

Alice sighed wearily. "I think you might do something better with the time," she said, "than wasting it in asking riddles that have no answers."

"If you knew Time as well as I do," said the Hatter, "you wouldn't talk about wasting *it*! It's *him*."

"I don't know what you mean," said Alice.

"Of course you don't!" the Hatter said, tossing his head contemptuously. "I dare say you never even spoke to Time!"

"Perhaps not," Alice cautiously replied: "but I know I have to beat time when I learn music."

"Ah! That accounts for it," said the Hatter. "He won't stand beating. Now, if you only kept on good terms with him, he'd do almost anything you liked with the clock.

"For instance, suppose it were nine o'clock in the morning, just time to begin lessons: you'd only have to whisper a hint to Time, and round goes the clock in a twinkling! Half-past one, time for dinner!"

("I only wish it was," the March Hare said to itself in a whisper.)

"That would be grand, certainly," said Alice thoughtfully; "but then—I shouldn't be hungry for it, you know."

"Not at first, perhaps," said the Hatter; "but you could keep it to half-past one as long as you liked."

"Is that the way *you* manage?" Alice asked.

The Hatter shook his head mournfully. "Not I!" he replied. "We quarreled last March—just before *he* went mad, you know—" (pointing with his teaspoon at the March Hare,) "—it was at the great concert given by the Queen of Hearts, and I had to sing

'Twinkle, twinkle, little bat!
How I wonder what you're at!'

You know the song, perhaps?"

"I've heard something like it," said Alice.

"It goes on, you know," the Hatter continued, "in this way:—

'Up above the world you fly,
Like a teatray in the sky.
      Twinkle, twinkle—'"

Here the Dormouse shook itself, and began singing in its sleep *"Twinkle, twinkle, twinkle, twinkle—"* and went on so long that they had to pinch it to make it stop.

"Well, I'd hardly finished the first verse," said the Hatter, "when the Queen bawled out 'He's murdering the time! Off with his head!'"

"How dreadfully savage!" exclaimed Alice.

"And ever since that," the Hatter went on in a mournful tone, "he won't do a thing I ask! It's always six o'clock now."

A bright idea came into Alice's head. "Is that the reason so many tea-things are put out here?" she asked.

"Yes, that's it," said the Hatter with a sigh: "it's always tea-time, and we've no time to wash the things between whiles."

"Then you keep moving round, I suppose?" said Alice.

"Exactly so," said the Hatter: "as the things get used up."

"But when you come to the beginning again?" Alice ventured to ask.

"Suppose we change the subject," the March Hare interrupted, yawning. "I'm getting tired of this. I vote the young lady tells us a story."

"I'm afraid I don't know one," said Alice, rather alarmed at the proposal.

"Then the Dormouse shall!" they both cried. "Wake up, Dormouse!" And they pinched it on both sides at once.

The Dormouse slowly opened his eyes. "I wasn't asleep," he said in a hoarse, feeble voice: "I heard every word you fellows were saying."

"Tell us a story!" said the March Hare.

"Yes, please do!" pleaded Alice.

"And be quick about it," added the Hatter, "or you'll be asleep again before it's done."

"Once upon a time there were three little sisters," the Dormouse began in a great hurry; "and their names were Elsie, Lacie, and Tillie; and they lived at the bottom of a well—"

"What did they live on?" said Alice, who always took a great interest in questions of eating and drinking.

"They lived on treacle," said the Dormouse, after thinking a minute or two.

"They couldn't have done that, you know," Alice gently remarked. "They'd have been ill."

"So they were," said the Dormouse; "*very* ill."

Alice tried a little to fancy to herself what such an extraordinary way of living would be like, but it puzzled her too much, so she went on: "But why did they live at the bottom of a well?"

"Take some more tea," the March Hare said to Alice, very earnestly.

"I've had nothing yet," Alice replied in an offended tone, "so I can't take more."

"You mean you can't take *less*," said the Hatter: "it's very easy to take *more* than nothing."

"Nobody asked *your* opinion," said Alice.

"Who's making personal remarks now?" the Hatter asked triumphantly.

Alice did not quite know what to say to this: so she helped herself to some tea and bread-and-butter, and then turned to the Dormouse, and repeated her question. "Why did they live at the bottom of a well?"

The Dormouse again took a minute or two to think about it, and then said, "It was a treacle-well."

"There's no such thing!" Alice was beginning very angrily, but the Hatter and the March Hare went "Sh! Sh!" and the Dormouse sulkily remarked, "If you can't be civil, you'd better finish the story for yourself."

"No, please go on!" Alice said very humbly. "I won't interrupt you again. I dare say there may be *one*."

"One, indeed!" said the Dormouse indignantly. However, he consented to go on. "And so these three little sisters—they were learning to draw, you know—"

"What did they draw?" said Alice, quite forgetting her promise.

"Treacle," said the Dormouse, without considering at all this time.

"I want a clean cup," interrupted the Hatter: "let's all move one place on."

He moved on as he spoke, and the Dormouse followed him: the March Hare moved into the Dormouse's place, and Alice rather unwillingly took the place of the March Hare. The Hatter was the only one who got any advantage from the change: and Alice was a good deal worse off than before, as the March Hare had just upset the milk-jug into his plate.

Alice did not wish to offend the Dormouse again, so she began very cautiously: "But I don't understand. Where did they draw the treacle from?"

"You can draw water out of a water-well," said the Hatter; "so I should think you could draw treacle out of a treacle-well—eh, stupid?"

"But they were *in* the well," Alice said to the Dormouse, not choosing to notice this last remark.

"Of course they were," said the Dormouse,—"well in."

This answer so confused poor Alice, that she let the Dormouse go on for some time without interrupting it.

"They were learning to draw," the Dormouse went on, yawning and rubbing his eyes, for it was getting very sleepy; "and they drew all manner of things—everything that begins with an M—"

"Why with an M?" said Alice.

"Why not?" said the March Hare.

Alice was silent.

The Dormouse had closed its eyes by this time, and was going off into a doze, but, on being pinched by the Hatter, it woke up again with a little shriek, and went on: "—that begins with an M, such as mousetraps, and the moon, and memory, and muchness —you know you say things are 'much of a muchness'—did you ever see such a thing as a drawing of a muchness?"

"Really, now you ask me," said Alice, very much confused, "I don't think——"

"Then you shouldn't talk," said the Hatter.

This piece of rudeness was more than Alice could bear: she got up in great disgust, and walked off: the Dormouse fell asleep instantly, and neither of the others took the least notice of her going, though she looked back once or twice, half hoping that they would call after her: the last time she saw them, they were trying to put the Dormouse into the teapot.

"At any rate I'll never go *there* again!" said Alice as she picked her way through the wood. "It's the stupidest tea-party I ever was at in all my life!"

Just as she said this, she noticed that one of the trees had a door leading right into it. "That's very curious!" she thought. "But everything's curious today. I think I may as well go in at once." And in she went.

Once more she found herself in the long hall, and close to the little glass table. "Now, I'll manage better this time," she said to herself, and began by taking the little golden key, and unlocking the door that led into the garden. Then she set to work nibbling at the mushroom (she had kept a piece of it in her pocket) till she was about a foot high: then she walked down the little passage: and *then*—she found herself at last in the beautiful garden, among the bright flowerbeds and the cool fountains.

Jonathan Bing

by BEATRICE CURTIS BROWN

Poor old Jonathan Bing
Went out in his carriage to visit the King,
But everyone pointed and said, "Look at that!
Jonathan Bing has forgotten his hat!"
(He'd forgotten his hat!)

Poor old Jonathan Bing
Went home and put on a new hat for the King,
But up by the palace a soldier said, "Hi!
You can't see the King; you've forgotten your tie!"
(He'd forgotten his tie!)

Poor old Jonathan Bing,
He put on a *beautiful* tie for the King,
But when he arrived an Archbishop said, "Ho!
You can't come to court in pyjamas, you know!"

Poor old Jonathan Bing
Went home and addressed a short note to the King:

       If you please will excuse me
       I won't come to tea;
       For home's the best place for
       All people like me!

Stories Told Long Ago . . .

Fables
and
Folk Tales

Aesop's Fables

Although these little stories are always called Aesop's Fables, *nobody knows exactly who Aesop was—though he is generally believed to have been a Greek slave who lived in the 7th or 6th century* B.C.—*or whether he actually did write, or rather, tell them. For like all folk tales, they were told by one person to another. These fables were used to teach morals to people (grownups as well as children) by making ideas of good, bad, wise, and foolish behavior easier to remember through concrete examples, usually animal characters. They certainly proved more popular than straight lectures, for they've lasted more than two thousand years. Today they still furnish the background for understanding many expressions in our speech such as, "he's a dog in the manger," "don't count your chickens," or "that's just sour grapes." Even if you don't bother with the moral, these fables present a dramatic story in a remarkably short space.*

THE TOWN MOUSE AND THE COUNTRY MOUSE

A Town Mouse once went on a visit to his cousin the Country Mouse whose home was in the fields. His country cousin made him heartily welcome and offered him all the best food he could find—beans, peas, and crusts of bread. The Town Mouse picked a little here and there, but it was clear that he did not enjoy the simple country fare.

"Cousin," he finally said, "I don't understand how you put up with such dull food. But of course you can't expect anything better in the country. Come home with me, and when you have lived in town for a week, you will never want to come back here."

The two set out for the city that very evening and arrived late at night. "You must be tired and hungry after your long journey," said the Town Mouse, and took his guest at once into a grand dining room where they found the remains of a fine feast—all kinds of meats, cheeses, cakes, jellies and other dainties. The dazzled Country Mouse was just trying to decide which tempting morsel to eat first, when the door opened, and in came a servant with a light. Both mice scampered off and hid until he left the room. When all was quiet again, they went back to their supper. But hardly had the Country Mouse swallowed his first mouthful, than he heard a terrific growling and barking and two huge dogs bounded into the room. Half frightened to death, he ran down from the table and into a hole where he saw the Town Mouse disappearing.

"Good-bye, Cousin," said the Country Mouse.

"What, going so soon?" said the other.

"Yes," he replied, "I seem to have lost my appetite."

A crust of bread in peace is better than a feast in fear.

THE CROW AND THE PITCHER

A thirsty Crow flew around looking in vain for some water until she finally found a pitcher which had some in it. The water was so far down at the bottom, however, that she could not reach it with her beak. Again and again she tried, but was not able to catch a drop. The poor bird thought she would surely die of thirst, right there within sight of the water.

Suddenly she hit upon a plan. Gathering up some pebbles, she began to drop them into the water, one by one. With each pebble, the water rose higher and higher, until at last it reached the brim of the pitcher. Then the clever Crow was able to quench her thirst.

Necessity is the mother of invention.

THE FOX AND THE GRAPES

One hot summer day a Fox was strolling through an orchard when
he spied a tempting bunch of grapes hanging over a high branch.
"Just the thing to quench my thirst," said he. Drawing back a few
steps, he took a run and a jump, but he just missed the grapes.
He went back, took a running start once more, and jumped, but
with no greater success this time. He looked up at the grapes, his
mouth watering. Again and again, he tried to jump high enough
to reach them, until at last, exhausted, he had to give up.

Then he walked away with his nose in the air, saying, "I didn't
really want them, I'm sure they are sour."

It is easy to scorn what you can't get.

THE MILKMAID AND HER PAIL

A farmer's daughter was walking to market one day, carefully carrying her pail of milk upon her head. As she walked along the road, she fell to dreaming about what she would do with the money she would get for the milk.

"With the money I earn," she said to herself, "I shall buy some eggs; and when these are hatched, they will produce chickens. And these will lay eggs and produce more chickens, and by and by, I shall have dozens and dozens of chickens. Then I shall sell them all, and with the money they bring in, I shall be able to buy myself a new gown which I shall wear when I go to the fair. And I shall look so fine that all the young men will admire me and want to walk with me. But do you think I shall let them? Oh no, I shall just toss my head at them as if to say . . ."

Suiting her action to her words, and forgetting all about the pail, she did toss her head. Down went the pail, all the milk spilled out, and all her fine dreams vanished into the air.

Don't count your chickens before they are hatched.

BELLING THE CAT

One day the mice held a general council to consider what they might do to protect themselves against their common enemy, the Cat. Some said one thing and some said another, but at last a Young Mouse stood up and announced that he had a plan which he thought would solve the problem.

"You will all agree," said he, "that our chief danger lies in the unexpected and sly manner in which our enemy comes upon us. Now, if we could receive some warning of her approach, we could easily hide from her. I propose, therefore, that a small bell be obtained and attached by a ribbon to the neck of the Cat. In this way we could always know when she was coming and be able to make our escape."

This proposal was met with great applause, until an Old Mouse arose and said, "This is all very fine, but who among us is so brave? Who will bell the Cat?" The mice looked at one another in silence and nobody volunteered.

It is easier to suggest a plan than to carry it out.

THE HARE AND THE TORTOISE

The Hare was always boasting to the other animals about how fast he could run. "No one can beat me," he said, "when I really run at full speed. I challenge anyone here to race me."

To his surprise, it was the Tortoise who answered quietly, "I accept your challenge."

The Hare could not keep from laughing out loud. "A slow fellow like you—race me? Why, I could run back and forth ten times while you crept along."

"Don't boast until you've beaten me. Shall we start?"

So a course was arranged and they started out at once. The Hare ran along for a few minutes until he saw that he had left the Tortoise so far behind that he was out of sight. Then, to show how little he feared his slow moving rival, he lay down by the side of the road to have a little nap. "I can certainly overtake that fellow whenever I wake up," he said to himself.

Meanwhile, the Tortoise plodded on steadily without stopping. When the Hare awoke, he ran as fast as he could to overtake him. But he did not get there in time because the Tortoise had already crossed the goal line.

Slow and steady sometimes wins the race.

THE WOLF IN SHEEP'S CLOTHING

A hungry Wolf found it very difficult to get at any of the sheep in a flock because they were so well guarded by the shepherd. But one day he found the skin of a sheep, and putting it on his own back, he joined the flock. For a long time he succeeded in fooling the sheep and the shepherd; and he went on making a meal of one of the sheep whenever he felt like it. One day, however, when the shepherd had planned to use one of the sheep for food, he picked up the Wolf by mistake. This time he killed him on the spot.

Appearances may be deceptive.

THE WIND AND THE SUN

The Wind and the Sun once fell into an argument about who was the stronger, and so they decided to put the matter to the test. They saw a traveller coming down the road, and the Sun said, "The one who can make that man take off his cloak faster will be judged the stronger. Suppose you try first."

So the Wind began to blow as hard as he could upon the traveller, making his cloak whirl wildly about him. But the harder the Wind blew, the more closely did the man wrap his cloak around him. The Wind finally had to give up in defeat.

Now it was the Sun's turn. The Sun came out, began to smile on the traveller, and to shine brilliantly. At first the man loosened his cloak, and then as the air grew warmer and warmer, he finally flung off his cloak.

Persuasion is better than force.

THE SHEPHERD BOY AND THE WOLF

There was once a young shepherd boy who took care of his sheep in a field near a dark forest. It was rather lonely and dull tending the sheep all day, so he hit on a plan for making things more lively. Running towards the village, he cried, "Wolf! Wolf!" And all the village people came rushing out with clubs and pitchforks to help him. The boy was very pleased with all this excitement and a few days later he tried the same trick, and again the villagers came rushing to help him.

Then one day a Wolf really did come out of the forest and began to attack the sheep. The frightened boy cried, "Wolf! Wolf!" over and over again as loudly as he could. But the villagers thought he was deceiving them once more and nobody came to his rescue. So the Wolf killed the boy's entire flock.

Nobody believes a liar even when he tells the truth.

THE FOX AND THE CROW

A Fox was eagerly watching a Crow as she settled in the branch of a tree because in her beak he spied a large piece of cheese. "That's for me, as sure as I am a Fox," he said to himself as he walked up to the tree.

"Good morning, Mistress Crow," he began, "how lovely you look today! How black and glossy are your feathers, how bright your eyes! I am sure that your voice, like your beauty, surpasses all the other birds. Just let me hear you sing a little song, so that I may know that you are really the Queen of Birds."

The Crow was so pleased with all these compliments that she lifted up her head and began to caw. Naturally the moment she opened her mouth the piece of cheese dropped to the ground and was snapped up by the Fox. "That will do," said he. "This is all I wanted."

Never trust a flatterer.

THE DOG IN THE MANGER

A Dog jumped into the manger of an Ox and lay down for his afternoon nap. Soon the tired Ox, returning from his work in the fields, came up to the manger and tried to eat some of his hay. But the Dog rose up and snarled and snapped at him whenever he came near the hay and would not let him touch a single mouthful.

"Mean creature," said the Ox as he walked away. "You can't eat the hay yourself, and yet you won't let me have any."

Don't begrudge others what you can't use yourself.

THE LION AND THE MOUSE

While a Lion was lying asleep one day, a little Mouse ran across his paws and awakened him. The Lion pounced on the Mouse with one of his huge paws and was about to make an end of the tiny creature when the Mouse cried out, "Forgive me, O King! Please let me go this time. I shall be grateful forever, and perhaps I shall be able to do you a good turn one of these days."

The King of the Beasts roared with laughter, and was so tickled at the idea of the tiny Mouse being able to help him that he lifted his paw and let him escape.

A short time later, the Lion found himself trapped in a big net that had been set by some hunters. The Little Mouse, who happened to be passing by, heard the Lion roaring in pain, and came closer to see what the trouble was. Seeing the Lion entangled thus, he quickly began to gnaw away at the ropes, and soon he succeeded in setting the huge animal free. "Now wasn't I right?" asked the Mouse.

Even the humblest friend may be of great help.

The Mountain and the Squirrel

by RALPH WALDO EMERSON

The mountain and the squirrel
Had a quarrel,
And the former called the latter "Little Prig."
Bun replied,
"You are doubtless very big;
But all sorts of things and weather
Must be taken in together
To make up a year
And a sphere.
And I think it no disgrace
To occupy my place.
If I'm not so large as you,
You are not so small as I,
And not half so spry.
I'll not deny you make
A very pretty squirrel track;
Talents differ; all is well and wisely put;
If I cannot carry forests on my back,
Neither can you crack a nut."

Fables of La Fontaine

Jean de la Fontaine, in the 17th century, drew many of the subjects for his fables from Aesop, though he also made up original ones that poked sly fun at the manners of the times. These fables, composed in verse, had unusually clever rhymes; but unfortunately, much of the wit and charm of his rhymed fables are lost in translation. In France they are so popular that all the children learn them by heart, in much the same way as children here learn to recite Mother Goose.

THE GRASSHOPPER AND THE ANT

All summer long the grasshopper had been singing gayly. When the cold winter winds began to blow, he found himself without the tiniest morsel of food. So he went to his neighbor, the ant, who had been busily storing away grain during the summer.

"Kind friend, I am starving!" cried the grasshopper. "Please lend me some grain," he begged, "so that I may live until the spring comes. I will pay you back before August. I promise on my solemn oath as a grasshopper, that I will pay you back double the amount you lend me."

But the ant isn't a lending creature—that's one of her little faults. "What were you doing when it was warm?" she asked the pleading grasshopper.

"Night and day, for everyone who came around, I sang, if you please."

"You sang? Well, then I'm not a bit troubled about you. Now you may dance."

THE GOOSE WITH THE GOLDEN EGGS

Once upon a time there was a man who had a goose—a special kind of goose that laid a golden egg every day. With this gold, he was day by day gradually putting by a good store of money. But the man was greedy and impatient to be rich. "Suppose I kill the goose," he said to himself. "Surely she must be filled with gold. Then I shall be able to get at all the treasure inside her at once."

So he killed the goose and cut her open. But what did he find? She was the same inside as any of his other geese whose eggs brought him only a few pennies. Thus he himself had wasted his most precious possession. Too late he learned, like many other greedy people, that one can become poor in trying to grow rich too quickly.

Translated from *Fables Choisies Pour les Enfants* by Jean de la Fontaine.

The Blind Men and the Elephant

by JOHN G. SAXE

It was six men of Indostan
   To learning much inclined,
Who went to see the Elephant
   (Though all of them were blind),
That each by observation
   Might satisfy his mind.

The First approached the Elephant,
   And happening to fall
Against his broad and sturdy side,
   At once began to bawl:
"God bless me! but the Elephant
   Is very like a wall!"

The Second, feeling of the tusk,
   Cried, "Ho! what have we here
So very round and smooth and sharp?
   To me 'tis mighty clear
This wonder of an Elephant
   Is very like a spear!"

The Third approached the animal,
  And happening to take
The squirming trunk within his hands,
  Thus boldly up and spake:
"I see," quoth he, "the Elephant
  Is very like a snake!"

The Fourth reached out his eager hand,
  And felt about the knee.
"What most this wondrous beast is like
  Is mighty plain," quoth he;
" 'Tis clear enough the Elephant
  Is very like a tree!"

The Fifth, who chanced to touch the ear
  Said, "E'en the blindest man
Can tell what this resembles most;
  Deny the fact who can,
This marvel of an Elephant
  Is very like a fan!"

The Sixth no sooner had begun
  About the beast to grope,
Than, seizing on the swinging tail
  That fell within his scope,
"I see," quoth he, "the Elephant
  Is very like a rope!"

And so these men of Indostan
  Disputed loud and long,
Each in his own opinion
  Exceeding stiff and strong,
Though each was partly in the right,
  And all were in the wrong!

The Thief of Cathay

by ADELE M. FIELDE

This little folk tale was told in China many hundreds, per-
haps thousands of years ago. Yet it has a remarkable resemblance
to the incident in Victor Hugo's famous novel Les Miserables
where the convict Jean Valjean is shielded from the police by the
Bishop whose silver he has tried to steal. As in this story, the unex-
pected act of kindness changes the thief's whole life.

It was the birthday of an honored man, and his sons and servants
were busy receiving messengers who came with gifts and con-
gratulations. A thief, who knew that among the presents there
were articles of value, slipped in and secreted himself by lying
face downward on a tie-beam in the roof of the great hall where
a banquet was to be served in the evening. From this vantage corner he overlooked the opening of parcels of silk, crepe, jade and
jewels, and took note where they were deposited, intending to
take them away after the guests had departed and the family gone
to sleep.

The master of the house arranged his birthday gifts for the inspection of his relatives, and received the donors in the evening
at a magnificent feast. Late at night, when the guests had all taken
leave, and the servants had retired, the host lingered to put away
some of the presents. As he leaned over a drawer, with his back
toward the thief, the latter looked over the beam to take a final

survey of the room before the lights should be put out. And as
he did so his head cast a shadow on the floor.

The host betrayed no sign of having observed the moving
shadow, but he called a servant and bade him bring the choicest
food and lay the table for a single guest. When this was done,
he dismissed the servant for the night. Then turning toward the
beam on which the thief lay, and making obeisance as to a noble

guest, he said, "Will the gentleman who is on the roof-beam now come down and partake of refreshments?"

As there was nothing else he could reasonably do, the thief descended, and was led to the table by his host who served him while he ate. When he had finished his repast his host gave him a bag of silver coins, begged him to make good use of them, and dismissed him courteously from his door.

Tens of years passed, and brought the eightieth birthday of the host. His honors had increased, and his descendants were many. During the day costly gifts were sent to him by friends who were all invited to sup with him that evening. His grandson received the presents at his door and brought them to his apartment. Towards nightfall his grandson came to him with a priceless gem, and said that it had been brought by a stranger who would not tell his name but insisted upon seeing the master of the house.

The stranger was admitted to the old man's room, where he expressed great joy in seeing his host alive and in health. The host did not recognize his guest, and excusing himself by a plea of failing sight, inquired his name. The guest replied that he was a sincere friend, an honest man, and rich enough to bring many such gifts as the priceless gem. The host replied that he could not accept gifts without knowing to whom he thus put himself under obligation; and that unless he knew his name, he could not invite him to sup with him that evening in the great hall.

Then the visitor suggested that his host might invite him by saying, "Will the gentleman who was on the roof-beam partake of refreshments?" And he told how he, the thief, had, under the influence of his host's gentleness, repented of evil. He had used the coins given to him for foreign trade and he had prospered, practicing truth and mercy.

He stayed to banquet with the other guests, and among them all, none were more happy than he and his benevolent host.

The History of Tom Thumb

In the days of the great King Arthur there lived a mighty magician, called Merlin, the most learned and skillful enchanter the world has ever seen.

This famous magician, who could take any form he pleased, was travelling about as a poor beggar; and being very tired, he stopped at the cottage of a ploughman to rest himself and asked for some food.

The countryman bade him welcome, and his wife, who was a very good-hearted woman, soon brought him some milk in a wooden bowl and some coarse brown bread on a platter.

Merlin was much pleased with the kindness of the ploughman and his wife; but he could not help noticing that though everything was neat and comfortable in the cottage, they both seemed to be very unhappy. He therefore asked them why they were so melancholy, and learned that they were miserable because they had no children.

The poor woman said, with tears in her eyes: "I should be the happiest creature in the world if I had a son. Although he was no bigger than my husband's thumb, I would be satisfied."

Merlin was so much amused with the idea of a boy no bigger than a man's thumb, that he determined to grant the poor woman's wish. Accordingly, in a short time after, the ploughman's wife had a son, who, wonderful to relate! was not a bit bigger than his father's thumb.

The queen of the fairies, wishing to see the little fellow, came in at the window while the mother was sitting up in the bed admiring him. The queen kissed the child, and, giving it the name of Tom Thumb, sent for some of the fairies, who dressed her little godson according to her orders:

> An oak-leaf hat he had for his crown;
> His shirt of web by spiders spun;
> And jacket wove of thistle's down;
> His trowsers were of feathers done.
> His stockings, of apple-rind, they tie
> With eyelash from his mother's eye:
> His shoes were made of mouse's skin,
> Tann'd with the downy hair within.

Tom never grew any longer than his father's thumb, which was only of ordinary size; but as he got older he became very cunning and full of tricks. When he was old enough to play with the boys and had lost all his own cherry-stones, he use to creep into the bags of his playfellows, fill his pockets and, getting out without their noticing him, would again join in the game.

One day, however, as he was coming out of a bag of cherry-stones, where he had been stealing as usual, the boy to whom it belonged chanced to see him. "Ah, ah! my little Tommy," said the boy, "so I have caught you stealing my cherry-stones at last, and you shall be rewarded for your thievish tricks." On saying this, he drew the string tight round his neck, and gave the bag such a hearty shake, that poor little Tom's legs, thighs, and body were sadly bruised. He roared out with pain and begged to be let out, promising never to steal again.

A short time afterwards his mother was making a batter-pudding; and Tom, being very anxious to see how it was made, climbed up to the edge of the bowl. But his foot slipped, and he plumped over head and ears into the batter, without his mother noticing him, who stirred him into the pudding-bag, and put him in the pot to boil.

The batter filled Tom's mouth and prevented him from crying; but, on feeling the hot water, he kicked and struggled so much in the pot, that his mother thought that the pudding was bewitched. Pulling it out of the pot, she threw it outside the door. A poor

tinker, who was passing by, lifted up the pudding; and, putting
it into his budget, he then walked off. As Tom had now got his
mouth cleared of the batter, he then began to cry aloud, which so
frightened the tinker that he flung down the pudding and ran
away. The pudding being broken to pieces by the fall, Tom crept
out covered all over with the batter and walked home. His mother,
who was very sorry to see her darling in such a woeful state, put

him into a teacup and soon washed off the batter, after which she kissed him and laid him in bed.

Soon after the adventure of the pudding, Tom's mother went to milk her cow in the meadow, and she took him along with her. As the wind was very high, for fear of being blown away, she tied him to a thistle with a piece of fine thread. The cow soon observed Tom's oak-leaf hat and, liking the appearance of it, took poor Tom and the thistle at one mouthful. While the cow was chewing the thistle, Tom was afraid of her great teeth, which threatened to crush him in pieces, and he roared out as loud as he could: "Mother, mother!"

"Where are you, Tommy, my dear Tommy?" said his mother.

"Here, mother," replied he, "in the red cow's mouth."

His mother began to cry and wring her hands; but the cow, surprised at the odd noise in her throat, opened her mouth and let Tom drop out. Fortunately his mother caught him in her apron as he was falling to the ground, or he would have been dreadfully hurt. She then put Tom in her bosom and ran home with him.

Tom's father made him a whip of barley straw to drive the cattle with, and having one day gone into the fields, Tom slipped a foot and rolled into the furrow. A raven, which was flying above, picked him up and flew with him over the sea and there dropped him.

A large fish swallowed Tom the moment he fell into the sea, which was soon after caught, and bought for the table of King Arthur. When they opened the fish in order to cook it, every one was astonished at finding such a little boy, and Tom was quite delighted at being free again. They carried him to the king, who made Tom his dwarf, and he soon grew a great favorite at court; for by his tricks and gambols he not only amused the king and queen but also all the Knights of the Round Table.

It is said that when the king rode out on horseback, he often took Tom along with him; and if a shower came on, Tom used to creep into his majesty's waist coat pocket, where he slept till the rain was over.

King Arthur one day asked Tom about his parents, wishing to

know if they were as small as he was, and whether they were well off. Tom told the king that his father and mother were as tall as anybody about the court, but in rather poor circumstances. On hearing this, the king carried Tom to his treasury, the place where he kept all his money, and told him to take as much money as he could carry home to his parents, which made the poor little fellow caper with joy. Tom went immediately to procure a purse, which was made of a water-bubble, and then returned to the treasury, where he received a silver three-penny-piece to put into it.

Our little hero had some difficulty in lifting the burden upon his back; but he at last succeeded in getting it placed to his mind, and set forward on his journey. However, without meeting with any accident and after resting himself more than a hundred times by the way, in two days and two nights he reached his father's house in safety.

Tom had traveled forty-eight hours with the huge silver-piece on his back and was almost tired to death, when his mother ran out to meet him and carried him into the house. But he soon returned to court.

As Tom's clothes had suffered much in the batter-pudding and the inside of the fish, his majesty ordered him a new suit of clothes, and to be mounted as a knight on a mouse.

It was certainly very diverting to see Tom in this dress and mounted on the mouse, as he rode out a-hunting with the king and nobility, who were all ready to expire with laughter at Tom and his fine prancing charger.

The king was so charmed with his talk that he ordered a little chair to be made, in order that Tom might sit upon his table, and also a palace of gold, a span high, with a door an inch wide, to live in. He also gave him a coach, drawn by six small mice.

The queen was so enraged at the honors conferred on Sir Thomas that she resolved to ruin him and told the king that the little knight had been saucy to her.

The king sent for Tom in great haste; but being fully aware of the danger of royal anger, he crept into an empty snail-shell, where he lay for a long time until he was almost starved with hunger.

But at last he ventured to peep out, and seeing a fine large butterfly on the ground near the place of his concealment, he got close
to it and, jumping astride on it, was carried up into the air. The
butterfly flew with him from tree to tree and from field to field, and
at last returned to the court, where the king and nobility all strove
to catch him. At last poor Tom fell from his seat into a watering
pot in which he was almost drowned.

When the queen saw him, she was in a rage, and said he should
be beheaded; and he was put into a mouse trap until the time of
his execution.

However, a cat, observing something alive in the trap, patted
it about till the wires broke and set Thomas at liberty.

The king received Tom again into favor, which he did not live
to enjoy, for a large spider one day attacked him; and although he
drew his sword and fought well, yet the spider's poisonous breath
at last overcame him.

> He fell dead on the ground where he stood,
> And the spider suck'd every drop of his blood.

King Arthur and his whole court were so sorry at the loss of
their little favorite that they went into mourning and raised a fine
white marble monument over his grave with the following
epitaph:

> Here lies Tom Thumb, King Arthur's knight,
> Who died by a spider's cruel bite.
> He was well known in Arthur's court,
> Where he afforded gallant sport;
> He rode a tilt and tournament,
> And on a mouse a-hunting went.
> Alive he filled the court with mirth;
> His death to sorrow soon gave birth.
> Wipe, wipe your eyes, and shake your head
> And cry—Alas! Tom Thumb is dead!

From *English Fairy Tales*, edited by Joseph Jacobs.

The Brownie of Blednock

by ELIZABETH GRIERSON

The idea of a tiny busy creature, like a brownie or an elf, working for people without any thought of reward is common in many folk tales, and you probably remember it in the famous old story called The Elves and the Shoemaker. *The kindly and miraculously helpful Aiken-Drum in this charming Scottish folk tale objects even more strongly than do most brownies to being paid in any way for his services. For according to tradition, he must then immediately leave his village friends.*

Did you ever hear how a Brownie came to the village of Blednock and was frightened away again?

It was one November evening, just when the milking was done and before the children were put to bed. The people of the village were standing by their doorsteps talking about their bad harvest and the turnips, and what chances there were of a good price for their cattle at the coming fair.

All at once the queerest humming noise seemed to come up from the riverside. It came nearer and nearer, and all the good people stopped talking and began to look down the road. And, indeed, it was no wonder that they stared, for there, coming up the middle of the highway, was the strangest little creature that human eyes had ever seen.

He looked like a wee, wee man. He had a long blue beard which almost touched the ground. His legs were twisted, his knees knocked together as he walked, and his arms were so long that his hands trailed in the mud as he came along. He seemed to be humming something over and over. As he came nearer, the good people of the village could make out the words:

> "Have ye work for Aiken-Drum?
> Any work for Aiken-Drum?"

Oh, how frightened the people were! The children screamed and hid their faces in their mothers' gowns and the milkmaids threw down the pails of milk they were carrying. Even the dogs crept in behind the doors, whining and hiding their tails between their legs. Some of the men who were not too frightened to look the wee man in the face laughed and hooted at him.

"Did you ever see such eyes?" cried one.

"His mouth is so big he could swallow the moon and never even notice it," said the other.

"Look at his long blue beard!" said a third.

And still the poor little man came slowly up the road, crying:

> "Have ye work for Aiken-Drum?
> Any work for Aiken-Drum?"

Good Grannie Duncan, the kindest old woman in the village, called out at last: "He's just a Brownie, a simple, kindly Brownie. I've heard tell of Brownies before. Many a long day's work will they do for the people who treat them well."

Gathering courage from her words, all the village folk crowded around the little man. When they were close to him, they saw that his face was kind and gentle and that his tiny eyes had a merry twinkle in them.

"Strange little creature," said an old man, "tell us what you want and where you came from?"

"I cannot well tell thee whence I came," said the wee man. "My country is a nameless land and is very different from this land of yours. For there we all learn to serve, while here everyone wishes to be served. When there is no work for us to do at home, we sometimes set out to visit thy land to see if there is any work

we can do there. If thou wilt, I will stay here awhile. I do not wish anyone to wait on me, and I want no wages, nor clothes, nor bedding. All I ask for is a corner of the barn to sleep in, and a bowl of broth set down on the floor at bedtime. If no one meddles with me, I shall be ready to help anyone who needs me. I'll gather your sheep on the hill. I'll take in the harvest by moonlight. I'll sing your bairns to sleep in their cradles. You'll find that the bairns all love Aiken-Drum. And, good housewives, I'll churn for you and bake your bread on a busy day. The men folk, too, may find me useful when there is corn to thrash, or untamed colts in the stables, or when the waters are out in flood."

No one knew quite what to say in answer to the little creature's strange request. It was an unheard-of thing for anyone to come and offer his services for nothing. Some thought it could not be true; others said it were better to have nothing to do with the little creature.

Then up spoke good Grannie Duncan again:

"He's but a Brownie, I tell you, a harmless Brownie. Many a story I've heard in my young days about the work that a Brownie can do, if he be treated well and let alone. Have we not all been complaining about bad times, small wages, and the hard work we all have to do? And now, when a workman comes ready to your hand, you will have nothing to do with him just because he is strange looking. And I've heard that a Brownie can stalk a whole ten-acre field in a single night! Shame on you, say I!"

"A ten-acre field in a single night!" cried out all the men of the village at once. "A ten-acre field!" repeated one. "And in a single night!" added another. That settled the matter. The miller at once offered the Brownie a corner of his barn to sleep in, and good Grannie Duncan promised to make him some broth at bedtime and to send her grandchild, wee Janie, down to the barn with it every evening. Then all the people of the village said, "Goodnight," and went to their homes. But they were careful to look over their shoulder once in a while, for fear that the strange little man was following them.

But if they were afraid of him that night, they had a very different story to tell about him before a week had passed. Whatever he was or wherever he came from, he was the most wonderful little worker that these people had ever known. And the strange thing was that he did most of the work at night. Village folk came from all parts of the countryside to catch a glimpse of this queer little worker, but they were never successful, for he was never to be seen when one looked for him. They might have gone to the miller's barn twenty times a day, and twenty times a day they would have found nothing but a heap of straw and an empty broth bowl.

But whenever there was work to be done, whether it was a tired child to be sung to, or a house to be made tidy, or a batch of bread to be worked up, or a flock of sheep to be gathered together on a stormy night, Aiken-Drum always knew of it and appeared ready to help just at the right time.

Many a time some poor mother who had been up all night with a crying child would sit down with it on her lap in front of the fire in the morning and fall asleep. When she awoke she would find that Aiken-Drum had made a visit to her house; for the floor would be scrubbed and the dishes washed, the fire made up and the kettle put on to boil. But the little Brownie would have slipped away as if he were afraid of being thanked.

The little children were the only ones who ever saw him when he was not working, and, oh, how they loved him! When school was out you could see them away down by the stream crowding around the little dark brown figure, and you could hear the sound of low, sweet singing; for Aiken-Drum knew all the songs that children love well.

By and by the name of Aiken-Drum came to be a household word among the good people of the village, for, although they seldom saw him near at hand, they loved him like one of their own people.

And he would never have gone away if everyone in the village had remembered what good Grannie Duncan told them about Brownies. "A Brownie works for love," she had said to them over and over again. "He will not work for pay. If anyone tries to pay him, the wee creature's feelings will be hurt, and he will vanish in the night."

But a good man of the village and his wife forgot all that had been said, and one day they planned to make something for Aiken-Drum.

"He should not work for nothing," said the good man.

"He has already worn out his coat and trousers slaving for us," said his wife.

So one day they made him a little pair of green trousers and a little brown coat. That night the two good people laid a parcel by the side of the bowl of broth in the miller's barn.

In the middle of the night someone heard the Brownie saying to himself, "A nice pair of green trousers and a little brown coat for me. I can come here no more till one of the children of this village travels the world over and finds me first."

So this strange little creature had to go away. He vanished in the night as any Brownie is sure to do if someone tries to pay him.

And all the good people of Blednock talked of the kind deeds of the little strange man who came one evening into their midst, and they wondered and wondered if he would ever come back to them again.

Gudbrand on the Hill-side

Once on a time in Norway there was a man whose name was Gudbrand; he had a farm which lay far, far away, upon a hill-side, and so they called him Gudbrand on the Hill-side.

Now, you must know this man and his goodwife lived so happily together, and understood one another so well, that all the husband did the wife thought so well done, there was nothing like it in the world, and she was always glad whatever he turned his hand to. The farm was their own land, and they had a hundred dollars lying at the bottom of their chest, and two cows tethered up in a stall in their farmyard.

So one day his wife said to Gudbrand,

"Do you know, dear, I think we ought to take one of our cows into town and sell it; that's what I think. For then we shall have some money in hand, and such well-to-do people as we ought to have ready money like the rest of the world. As for the hundred dollars at the bottom of the chest yonder, we can't make a hole in them, and I'm sure I don't know what we want with more than one cow. Besides, we shall gain a little in another way, for then I shall get off with only looking after one cow, instead of having, as now, to feed and litter and water two."

Well, Gudbrand thought his wife talked right good sense, so he set off at once with the cow on his way to town to sell her; but when he got to the town, there was no one who would buy his cow.

"Well! well! never mind," said Gudbrand, "at the worst, I can only go back home again with my cow. I've both stable and tether for her, I should think, and the road is no farther out than in." And with that he began to toddle home with his cow.

But when he had gone a bit of the way, a man met him who had a horse to sell, so Gudbrand thought 'twas better to have a horse than a cow, so he swopped with the man. A little farther on, he met a man walking along, and driving a fat pig before him, and he thought it better to have a fat pig than a horse, so he swopped with the man. After that he went a little farther, and a man met him with a goat; so he thought it better to have a goat than a pig, and he swopped with the man that owned the goat.

Then he went on a good bit till he met a man who had a sheep, and he swopped with him too, for he thought it always better to have a sheep than a goat. After a while he met a man with a goose, and he swopped away the sheep for the goose. And when he had walked a long, long time, he met a man with a cock, and he swopped with him, for he thought in this wise, "'Tis surely better to have a cock than a goose." Then he went on till the day was far spent, and he began to get very hungry, so he sold the cock for a shilling, and bought food with the money, for, thought Gudbrand on the Hill-side, "'Tis always better to save one's life than to have a cock."

After that he went on home till he reached his nearest neighbour's house, where he turned in.

"Well," said the owner of the house, "how did things go with you in town?"

"Rather so so," said Gudbrand. "I can't praise my luck, nor do I blame it either." And with that he told the whole story from first to last.

"Ah!" said his friend, "you'll get nicely hauled over the coals, that one can see, when you get home to your wife. Heaven help you, I wouldn't stand in your shoes for something."

"Well!" said Gudbrand on the Hill-side, "I think things might have gone worse with me. But now, whether I have done wrong or not, I have so kind a goodwife, she never has a word to say against anything that I do."

"Oh!" answered his neighbour, "I hear what you say, but I don't believe it for all that."

"Shall we lay a bet upon it?" asked Gudbrand on the Hill-side. "I have a hundred dollars at the bottom of my chest at home. Will you lay as many against them?"

Yes, the friend was ready to bet. So Gudbrand stayed there till evening, when it began to get dark, and then they went together to his house, and the neighbour was to stand outside the door and listen, while the man went in to see his wife.

"Good evening!" said Gudbrand.

"Good evening!" said the goodwife. "Oh! is that you? Now, God be praised!"

Yes, it was he. So the wife asked how things had gone with him in town.

"Oh! only so so," answered Gudbrand; "not much to brag of. When I got to the town there was no one who would buy the cow, so you must know I swopped it away for a horse."

"For a horse!" said his wife; "well, that is good of you; thanks with all my heart. We are so well-to-do that we may drive to church, just as well as all other people. And if we choose to keep a horse we have a right to get one, I should think. So run out, child, and put up the horse."

"Ah!" said Gudbrand, "but you see I've not got the horse after all; for when I got a bit farther on the road, I swopped it away for a pig."

"Think of that, now!" said the wife; "you did just as I should have done myself; a thousand thanks! Now I can have a bit of bacon in the house to set before people when they come to see me, that I can. What do we want with a horse? People would only say we had got so proud that we couldn't walk to church. Go out, child, and put up the pig in the stye."

"But I've not got the pig either," said Gudbrand, "for when I got a little farther on, I swopped it away for a milch goat."

"Bless us!" cried his wife, "how well you manage everything! Now I think it over, what should I do with a pig? People would only point at us and say, 'Yonder they eat up all they have got.' No! now I have got a goat, and I shall have milk and cheese, and keep the goat too. Run out, child, and put up the goat."

"Nay, but I haven't got the goat either," said Gudbrand, "for a little farther on I swopped it away, and got a fine sheep instead."

"You don't say so!" cried his wife; "why you do everything to please me, just as if I had been with you. What do we want with a goat? If I had it I should lose half my time in climbing up the hills to get it down. No! if I have a sheep, I shall have both wool and clothing, and fresh meat in the house. Run out, child, and put up the sheep."

"But I haven't got the sheep any more than the rest," said Gudbrand, "for when I had gone a bit farther, I swopped it away for a goose."

"Thank you! thank you! with all my heart!" cried his wife. "What should I do with a sheep? I have no spinning-wheel, nor carding-comb, nor should I care to worry myself with cutting, and shaping, and sewing clothes. We can buy clothes now, as we have always done. And now I shall have roast goose, which I have longed for so often and, besides, down to stuff my little pillow with. Run out, child, and put up the goose."

"Ah!" said Gudbrand, "but I haven't the goose either; for when I had gone a bit farther I swopped it away for a cock."

"Dear me!" cried his wife, "how you think of everything! Just as I should have done myself! A cock! Think of that! Why, it's as good as an eight-day clock, for every morning the cock crows at four o'clock, and we shall be able to stir our stumps in good time. What should we do with a goose? I don't know how to cook it; and as for my pillow, I can stuff it with cotton-grass. Run out, child, and put up the cock."

"But, after all, I haven't got the cock," said Gudbrand, "for when I had gone a bit farther, I got as hungry as a hunter, so I was forced to sell the cock for a shilling, for fear I should starve."

"Now, God be praised that you did so!" cried his wife. "Whatever you do, you do it always just after my own heart. What should we do with a cock? We are our own masters, I should think, and can lie a-bed in the morning as long as we like. Heaven be thanked that I have got you safe back again! You do everything so well that I want neither cock nor goose, neither pigs nor kine."

Then Gudbrand opened the door and said,

"Well, what do you say now? Have I won the hundred dollars?" and his neighbour was forced to allow that he had.

From *Popular Tales from the Norse*, edited by Peter C. Asbjörnsen and Jörgen Moe.

Whittington and His Cat

In the reign of the famous King Edward III there was a little boy called Dick Whittington, whose father and mother died when he was very young. As poor Dick was not old enough to work, he was very badly off; he got but little for his dinner, and sometimes nothing at all for his breakfast. For the people who lived in the village were very poor indeed, and could not spare him much more than the parings of potatoes, and now and then a hard crust of bread.

Now Dick had heard many, many very strange things about the great city called London. For the country people at that time thought that folks in London were all fine gentlemen and ladies; and that there was singing and music there all day long; and that the streets were all paved with gold.

One day a large waggon and eight horses, all with bells at their heads, drove through the village while Dick was standing by the sign-post. He thought that this waggon must be going to the fine town of London. So he took courage, and asked the waggoner to let him walk with him by the side of the waggon. As soon as the waggoner heard that poor Dick had no father or mother, and saw by his ragged clothes that he could not be worse off than he was, he told him he might go if he would. So off they set together.

So Dick got safe to London, and was in such a hurry to see the fine streets paved all over with gold, that he did not even stay to thank the kind waggoner; but ran off as fast as his legs would carry him, through many of the streets, thinking every moment to come to those that were paved with gold. For Dick had seen a guinea three times in his own little village, and remembered what a deal of money it brought in change. So he thought he had nothing to

do but to take up some little bits of the pavement, and should then have as much money as he could wish for.

Poor Dick ran till he was tired, and had quite forgot his friend the waggoner. But at last, finding it grow dark, and that every way he turned he saw nothing but dirt instead of gold, he sat down in a dark corner and cried himself to sleep.

Little Dick was all night in the streets; and next morning, being very hungry, he got up and walked about, and asked everybody he met to give him a halfpenny to keep him from starving. But nobody stayed to answer him, and only two or three gave him a halfpenny; so that the poor boy was soon quite weak and faint for the want of victuals.

In this distress he asked charity of several people and one of them said crossly: "Go to work for an idle rogue." "That I will," said Dick, "I will go to work for you, if you will let me." But the man only cursed at him and went on.

At last a good-natured looking gentleman saw how hungry he looked. "Why don't you go to work, my lad?" said he to Dick. "That I would, but I do not know how to get any," answered Dick. "If you are willing, come along with me," said the gentleman, and took him to a hay field, where Dick worked briskly, and lived merrily till the hay was made.

After this he found himself as badly off as before; and being almost starved again, he laid himself down at the door of Mr. Fitzwarren, a rich merchant. Here he was soon seen by the cook-maid, who was an ill-tempered creature, and happened just then to be very busy dressing dinner for her master and mistress. So she called out to poor Dick: "What business have you there, you lazy rogue? There is nothing else but beggars; if you do not take yourself away, we will see how you will like a sousing of some dishwater. I have some here hot enough to make you jump."

Just at that time Mr. Fitzwarren himself came home to dinner; and when he saw a dirty ragged boy lying at the door, he said to him: "Why do you lie there, my boy? You seem old enough to work; I am afraid you are inclined to be lazy."

"No, indeed, sir," said Dick to him, "that is not the case, for I would work with all my heart, but I do not know anybody, and I believe I am very sick for the want of food."

"Poor fellow, get up; let me see what ails you."

Dick now tried to rise, but was obliged to lie down again, being too weak to stand, for he had not eaten any food for three days, and was no longer able to run about and beg a halfpenny of people in the street. So the kind merchant ordered him to be taken into the house, and have a good dinner given him, and be kept to do what work he was able to do for the cook.

Little Dick would have lived very happy in this good family if it had not been for the ill-natured cook. She used to say: "You are under me, so look sharp; clean the spit and the dripping-pan, make the fires, wind up the jack, and do all the scullery work nimbly, or——" and she would shake the ladle at him. Besides, she was so fond of basting, that when she had no meat to baste, she would baste poor Dick's head and shoulders with a broom, or anything else that happened to fall in her way. At last her ill-usage of him was told to Alice, Mr. Fitzwarren's daughter, who told the cook she should be turned away if she did not treat him more kindly.

The behaviour of the cook was now a little better; but besides this, Dick had another hardship to get over. His bed stood in a garret, where there were so many holes in the floor and the walls that every night he was tormented with rats and mice. A gentleman having given Dick a penny for cleaning his shoes, he thought he would buy a cat with it. The next day he saw a girl with a cat, and asked her, "Will you let me have that cat for a penny?" The girl said: "Yes, that I will, master, though she is an excellent mouser."

Dick hid his cat in the garret, and always took care to carry a part of his dinner to her. And in a short time he had no more trouble with the rats and mice, but slept quite soundly every night.

Soon after this, his master had a ship ready to sail; and as it was the custom that all his servants should have some chance for good fortune as well as himself, he called them all into the parlour and asked them what they would send out.

They all had something that they were willing to venture except poor Dick, who had neither money nor goods, and therefore could send nothing. For this reason he did not come into the parlour with the rest; but Miss Alice guessed what was the matter and ordered him to be called in. She then said: "I will lay down some money for him, from my own purse." But her father told her: "This will not do, for it must be something of his own."

When poor Dick heard this, he said: "I have nothing but a cat which I bought for a penny some time since of a little girl."

"Fetch your cat then, my lad," said Mr. Fitzwarren, "and let her go."

Dick went upstairs and brought down poor puss, with tears in his eyes, and gave her to the captain; "For," he said, "I shall now be kept awake all night by the rats and mice." All the company laughed at Dick's odd venture; and Miss Alice, who felt pity for him, gave him some money to buy another cat.

This, and many other marks of kindness shown him by Miss Alice, made the ill-tempered cook jealous of poor Dick, and she began to use him more cruelly than ever, and always made game of him for sending his cat to sea. She asked him, "Do you think your cat will sell for as much money as would buy a stick to beat you?"

At last poor Dick could not bear this usage any longer, and he thought he would run away from his place. So he packed up his few things, and started very early in the morning, on All-hallows Day, the first of November. He walked as far as Halloway, and there sat down on a stone, which to this day is called "Whittington's Stone," and began to think to himself which road he should take.

While he was thinking what he should do, the Bells of Bow Church, which at that time were only six, began to ring, and at their sound seemed to say to him:

"Turn again, Whittington,
Thrice Lord Mayor of London."

"Lord Mayor of London!" said he to himself. "Why, to be sure,

I would put up with almost anything now, to be Lord Mayor of London, and ride in a fine coach, when I grow to be a man! Well, I will go back, and think nothing of the cuffing and scolding of the old cook, if I am to be Lord Mayor of London at last."

Dick went back, and was lucky enough to get into the house, and set about his work, before the old cook came downstairs.

We must now follow Mrs. Puss to the coast of Africa. The ship with the cat on board was a long time at sea; and was at last driven by the winds on a part of the coast of Barbary, where the only people were the Moors, unknown to the English. The people came in great numbers to see the sailors, because they were of different colour to themselves, and treated them civilly; and, when they became better acquainted, were very eager to buy the fine things that the ship was loaded with.

When the captain saw this, he sent patterns of the best things he had to the king of the country, who was so much pleased with them that he sent for the captain to the palace. Here they were placed, as it is the custom of the country, on rich carpets flowered with gold and silver. The king and queen were seated at the upper end of the room, and a number of dishes were brought in for dinner. They had not sat long, when a vast number of rats and mice rushed in, and devoured all the meat in an instant. The captain wondered at this, and asked if these vermin were not unpleasant.

"Oh yes," said they, "very offensive, and the king would give half his treasure to be freed of them. For they not only destroy his dinner, as you see, but they assault him in his chamber, and even in bed, so that he is obliged to be watched while he is sleeping, for fear of them."

The captain jumped for joy; he remembered poor Whittington and his cat, and told the king he had a creature on board the ship that would despatch all these vermin immediately. The king jumped so high at the joy which the news gave him, that his turban dropped off his head. "Bring this creature to me," says he; "vermin are dreadful in a court, and if she will perform what you say, I will load your ship with gold and jewels in exchange for her."

The captain, who knew his business, took this opportunity to set forth the merits of Mrs. Puss. He told his majesty: "It is not very convenient to part with her, as, when she is gone, the rats and mice may destroy the goods in the ship—but to oblige your majesty, I will fetch her."

"Run, run!" said the queen; "I am impatient to see the dear creature."

Away went the captain to the ship, while another dinner was got ready. He put Puss under his arm, and arrived at the place just in time to see the table full of rats. When the cat saw them, she did not wait for bidding, but jumped out of the captain's arms, and in a few minutes laid almost all the rats and mice dead at her feet. The rest of them in their fright scampered away to their holes.

The king was quite charmed to get rid so easily of such plagues, and the queen desired that the creature who had done them so great a kindness might be brought to her, that she might look at her. Upon which the captain called: "Pussy, pussy, pussy!" and she came to him. He then presented her to the queen, who started back and was afraid to touch a creature who had made such a havoc among the rats and mice. However, when the captain stroked the cat and called: "Pussy, pussy," the queen also touched her and cried: "Putty, putty," for she had not learned English. He then put her down on the queen's lap, where she purred and played with her majesty's hand, and then purred herself to sleep.

The king, having seen the exploits of Mrs. Puss, and being informed that her kittens would stock the whole country, and keep it free from rats, bargained with the captain for the whole ship's cargo, and gave him ten times as much for the cat as all the rest amounted to.

The captain then took leave of the royal party, and set sail with a fair wind for England, and after a happy voyage arrived safe in London.

One morning, early, Mr. Fitzwarren had just come to his counting-house and seated himself at the desk to count over the cash and settle the business for the day when somebody came tap, tap, at the door. "Who's there?" said Mr. Fitzwarren. "A friend," answered the other; "I come to bring you good news of your ship

Unicorn." The merchant, bustling up in such a hurry that he forgot his gout, opened the door, and who should he see waiting but the captain and agent, with a cabinet of jewels and a bill of lading. When he looked at this the merchant lifted up his eyes and thanked Heaven for sending him such a prosperous voyage.

They then told the story of the cat, and showed the rich present that the king and queen had sent for her to poor Dick. As soon as the merchant heard this, he called out to his servants:

> "Go send him in, and tell him of his fame;
> Pray call him Mr. Whittington by name."

Mr. Fitzwarren now showed himself to be a good man; for when some of his servants said so great a treasure was too much for Dick, he answered: "God forbid I should deprive him of the value of a single penny. It is his own, and he shall have it to a farthing."

He then sent for Dick, who at that time was scouring pots for the cook and was quite dirty. He would have excused himself from coming into the counting-house, saying, "The room is swept, and my shoes are dirty and full of hobnails." But the merchant ordered him to come in.

Mr. Fitzwarren ordered a chair to be set for him, and so he began to think they were making game of him, and at the same time said to them: "Do not play tricks with a poor simple boy, but let me go down again, if you please, to my work."

"Indeed, Mr. Whittington," said the merchant, "we are all quite in earnest with you, and I most heartily rejoice in the news that these gentlemen have brought you. The captain has sold your cat to the King of Barbary, and brought you in return for her more riches than I possess in the whole world; and I wish you may long enjoy them!"

Mr. Fitzwarren then told the men to open the great treasure they had brought with them, and said: "Mr. Whittington has nothing to do but to put it in some place of safety."

Poor Dick hardly knew how to behave himself for joy. He begged his master to take what part of it he pleased, since he owed it all to his kindness. "No, no," answered Mr. Fitzwarren, "this is all your own; and I have no doubt but you will use it well."

Dick next asked his mistress, and then Miss Alice, to accept a part of his good fortune; but they would not, and at the same time told him they felt great joy at his good success. But this poor fellow was too kind-hearted to keep it all to himself. So he made a present to the captain, the mate, and the rest of Mr. Fitzwarren's servants, and even to the ill-natured old cook.

After this Mr. Fitzwarren advised him to send for a proper tailor, and get himself dressed like a gentleman; and told him he was welcome to live in his house till he could provide himself with a better.

When Whittington's face was washed, his hair curled, his hat cocked, and he was dressed in a nice suit of clothes, he was as handsome and genteel as any young man who visited at Mr. Fitzwarren's. So that Miss Alice, who had once been so kind to him, and thought of him with pity, now looked upon him as fit to be her sweetheart; and the more so, no doubt, because Whittington was now always thinking what he could do to oblige her, and making her the prettiest presents that could be.

Mr. Fitzwarren soon saw their love for each other, and proposed to join them in marriage; and to this they both readily agreed. A day for the wedding was soon fixed; and they were attended to church by the Lord Mayor, the court of aldermen, the sheriffs, and a great number of the richest merchants in London whom they afterwards treated with a very rich feast.

History tells us that Mr. Whittington and his lady lived in great splendour, and were very happy. They had several children. He was Sheriff of London, thrice Lord Mayor, and received the honour of knighthood by Henry V.

After the conquest of France, he entertained his king and queen at dinner so grandly that the king said: "Never had prince such a subject." When Sir Richard heard this, he said: "Never had subject such a prince."

The figure of Sir Richard Whittington with his cat in his arms, carved in stone, was to be seen till the year 1780 over the archway of the old prison at Newgate, which he built for criminals.

From *English Fairy Tales*, edited by Joseph Jacobs.

The Fisherman and His Wife

by JAKOB *and* WILHELM GRIMM

There was once upon a time a Fisherman who lived with his wife in a miserable hovel close by the sea, and every day he went out fishing. And once as he was sitting with his rod, looking at the clear water, his line suddenly went down, far down below, and when he drew it up again, he brought out a large Flounder. Then the Flounder said to him, "Hark, you Fisherman, I pray you, let me live, I am no Flounder really, but an enchanted prince. What good will it do you to kill me? I should not be good to eat, put me in the water again, and let me go."

"Come," said the Fisherman, "there is no need for so many words about it—a fish that can talk I should certainly let go, anyhow." With that he put him back again into the clear water, and the Flounder went to the bottom, leaving a long streak of blood behind him. Then the Fisherman got up and went home to his wife in the hovel.

"Husband," said the woman, "have you caught nothing today?" "No," said the man, "I did catch a Flounder, who said he was an enchanted prince, so I let him go again." "Did you not wish for anything first?" said the woman. "No," said the man; "what should I wish for?" "Ah," said the woman, "it is surely hard to have to live always in this dirty hovel; you might have wished for a small cottage for us. Go back and call him. Tell him we want to have a small cottage, he will certainly give us that." "Ah," said the man, "why should I go there again?" "Why," said the woman, "you did catch him, and you let him go again; he is sure to do it. Go at once." The man still did not quite like to go, but did not like to oppose his wife either, and went to the sea.

When he got there the sea was all green and yellow, and no longer so smooth; so he stood and said,

> "Oh, fish of the sea,
> Come listen to me,
> For, Isobel, my wife,
> The plague of my life,
> Has sent me to beg a boon of thee."

Then the Flounder came swimming to him and said: "Well, what does she want then?" "Ah," said the man, "I did catch you, and my wife says I really ought to have wished for something. She does not like to live in a wretched hovel any longer; she would like to have a cottage." "Go, then," said the Flounder, "she has it already."

When the man went home, his wife was no longer in the hovel, but instead of it there stood a small cottage, and she was sitting on a bench before the door. Then she took him by the hand and said to him, "Just come inside. Look, now isn't this a great deal better?"

So they went in, and there was a small porch, and a pretty little parlour and bedroom, and a kitchen and pantry, with the best of furniture, and fitted up with the most beautiful things made of tin and brass, whatsoever was wanted. And behind the cottage there was a small yard, with hens and ducks, and a little garden with flowers and fruit. "Look," said the wife, "is not that nice!" "Yes," said the husband, "and so we must always think it—now we will live quite contented." "We will think about that," said the wife. With that they ate something and went to bed.

Everything went well for a week or a fortnight, and then the woman said, "Hark you, husband, this cottage is far too small for us, and the garden and yard are little; the Flounder might just as well have given us a larger house. I should like to live in a great stone castle. Go to the Flounder, and tell him to give us a castle."

"Ah, wife," said the man, "the cottage is quite good enough; why should we live in a castle?" "What!" said the woman; "just go there, the Flounder can always do that." "No, wife," said the man, "the Flounder has just given us the cottage, I do not like to go back so soon, it might make him angry." "Go," said the woman, "he can do it quite easily, and will be glad to do it; just you go to him."

The man's heart grew heavy, and he would not go. He said to himself, "It is not right," and yet he went. And when he came to the sea the water was quite purple and dark-blue, and grey and thick, and no longer so green and yellow, but it was still quiet. And he stood there and said,

> "Oh, fish of the sea,
> Come listen to me,
> For, Isobel, my wife,
> The plague of my life,
> Has sent me to beg a boon of thee."

"Well, what does she want, then?" said the Flounder. "Alas," said the man, half scared, "she wants to live in a great stone castle." "Go to it, then, she is standing before the door," said the Flounder.

Then the man went away, intending to go home, but when he got there, he found a great stone palace, and his wife was just standing on the steps going in, and she took him by the hand and said: "Come in." So he went in with her, and in the castle was a great hall paved with marble, and many servants, who flung wide the doors; and the walls were all bright with beautiful hangings, and in the rooms were chairs and tables of pure gold, and crystal chandeliers hung from the ceiling, and all the rooms and bedrooms had carpets, and food and wine of the very best were standing on all the tables, so that they nearly broke down beneath it. Behind the house, too, there was a great court-yard, with stables for horses and cows, and the very best of carriages; there was a magnificent large garden, too, with the most beautiful flowers and fruit-trees, and a park quite half a mile long, in which were stags, deer, and hares, and everything that could be desired.

"Come," said the woman, "isn't that beautiful?" "Yes, indeed," said the man, "now let it be; and we will live in this beautiful castle and be content." "We will consider about that," said the woman, "and sleep upon it." Thereupon they went to bed.

Next morning the wife awoke first, and it was just daybreak, and from her bed she saw the beautiful country lying before her.

Her husband was still stretching himself, so she poked him in the side with her elbow, and said, "Get up, husband, and just peep out of the window. Look you, couldn't we be the King over all that land? Go to the Flounder, we will be the King." "Ah, wife," said the man, "why should we be King? I do not want to be King." "Well," said the wife, "if you won't be King, I will; go to the Flounder, for I will be King." "Ah, wife," said the man, "why do you want to be King? I do not like to say that to him." "Why not?" said the woman; "go to him this instant; I must be King!"

So the man went, and was quite unhappy because his wife wished to be King. "It is not right; it is not right," thought he. He did not wish to go, but yet he went.

And when he came to the sea, it was quite dark-grey, and the water heaved up from below, and smelt putrid. Then he went and stood by it, and said,

> "Oh, fish of the sea,
> Come listen to me,
> For, Isobel, my wife,
> The plague of my life,
> Has sent me to beg a boon of thee."

"Well, what does she want, then?" said the Flounder. "Alas," said the man, "she wants to be King." "Go to her; she is King already."

So the man went, and when he came to the palace, the castle had become much larger, and had a great tower and magnificent ornaments, and the sentinel was standing before the door, and there were numbers of soldiers with kettledrums and trumpets. And when he went inside the house, everything was of real marble and gold, with velvet covers and great golden tassels. Then the doors of the hall were opened, and there was the court in all its splendour, and his wife was sitting on a high throne of gold and diamonds, with a great crown of gold on her head, and a sceptre of pure gold and jewels in her hand, and on both sides of her stood her maids-in-waiting in a row, each of them always one head shorter than the last.

Then he went and stood before her, and said: "Ah, wife, and now you are King." "Yes," said the woman, "now I am King." So he stood and looked at her, and when he had looked at her thus for some time, he said, "And now that you are King, let all else be, now we will wish for nothing more."

"No, husband," said the woman, quite anxiously, "I find time passes very heavily, I can bear it no longer, go to the Flounder—I am King, but I must be Pope, too."

"Oh, wife," said the unhappy man, "what will you not wish for? You cannot be Pope; there is but one in Christendom; he cannot make you Pope." "Husband," said she, "I will be Pope, go immediately, I must be Pope this very day." "No, wife," said the man, "I do not like to say that to him; that would not do, it is too much. The Flounder can't make you Pope." "Husband," said she, "what nonsense! if he can make a king, he can make a pope. Go to him directly. I am King, and you are nothing but my husband; will you go at once?"

Then he was afraid and went; but he was quite faint, and shivered and shook, and his knees and legs trembled. And a high wind blew over the land, and the clouds flew, and towards evening all grew dark, and the leaves fell from the trees, and the water rose and roared as if it were boiling, and splashed upon the shore; and in the distance he saw ships which were firing guns in their sore need, pitching and tossing on the waves. And yet in the midst of the sky there was still a small bit of blue, though on every side it was as red as in a heavy storm. So, full of despair, he went and stood in much fear and said,

> "Oh, fish of the sea,
> Come listen to me,
> For, Isobel, my wife,
> The plague of my life,
> Has sent me to beg a boon of thee."

"Well, what does she want, now?" said the Flounder. "Alas,"

said the man, "she wants to be Pope." "Go to her then," said the
Flounder; "she is Pope already."

So he went, and when he got there, he saw what seemed to be
a large church surrounded by palaces. He pushed his way through
the crowd. Inside, however, everything was lighted up with thousands and thousands of candles, and his wife was clad in gold,
and she was sitting on a much higher throne, and had three great
golden crowns on, and round about her there was much ecclesi-
astical splendour; and on both sides of her was a row of candles
the largest of which was as tall as the very tallest tower, down
to the very smallest kitchen candle, and all the emperors and kings
were on their knees before her, kissing her shoe.

"Wife," said the man, and looked attentively at her, "are you
now Pope?" "Yes," said she, "I am Pope." So he stood and looked
at her, and it was just as if he was looking at the bright sun.
When he had stood looking at her thus for a short time, he said:
"Ah, wife, if you are Pope, do let well alone!" But she looked as
stiff as a post, and did not move or show any signs of life. Then
said he, "Wife, now that you are Pope, be satisfied, you cannot
become anything greater now." "I will consider about that," said
the woman. Thereupon they both went to bed, but she was not
satisfied, and greediness let her have no sleep, for she was continually thinking what there was left for her to be.

The man slept well and soundly, for he had run about a great
deal during the day; but the woman could not fall asleep at all,
and flung herself from one side to the other the whole night
through, thinking always what more was left for her to be, but
unable to call to mind anything else. At length the sun began to
rise, and when the woman saw the red of dawn, she sat up in bed
and looked at it. And when, through the window, she saw the
sun thus rising, she said, "Cannot I, too, order the sun and moon
to rise?"

"Husband," she said, poking him in the ribs with her elbows,
"wake up! go to the Flounder, for I wish to be even as God is."
The man was still half asleep, but he was so horrified that he
fell out of bed. He thought he must have heard amiss, and rubbed

his eyes, and said, "Alas, wife, what are you saying?" "Husband," said she, "if I can't order the sun and moon to rise, and have to look on and see the sun and moon rising, I can't bear it. I shall not know what it is to have another happy hour, unless I can make them rise myself." Then she looked at him so terribly that a shudder ran over him, and said, "Go at once; I wish to be like unto God."

"Alas, wife," said the man, falling on his knees before her, "the Flounder cannot do that; he can make a king and a pope; I beseech you, go on as you are, and be Pope." Then she fell into a rage, and her hair flew wildly about her head, and she cried, "I will not endure this, I'll not bear it any longer; will you go this instant?" Then he put on his trousers and ran away like a madman. But outside a great storm was raging, and blowing so hard that he could scarcely keep his feet; houses and trees toppled over, the mountains trembled, rocks rolled into the sea, the sky was pitch black, and it thundered and lightened, and the sea came in with black waves as high as church-towers and mountains, and all with crests of white foam at the top. Then he cried, but could not hear his own words,

> "Oh, fish of the sea,
> Come listen to me,
> For, Isobel, my wife,
> The plague of my life,
> Has sent me to beg a boon of thee."

"Well, what does she want, then?" said the Flounder. "Alas," said he, "she wants to be like unto God." "Go to her, and you will find her back again in the dirty hovel." And there they are still living to this day.

Uncle Remus

OLD MR. RABBIT, HE'S A GOOD FISHERMAN

by JOEL CHANDLER HARRIS

The author of the Uncle Remus stories heard them told and sung by the Negroes who lived on the Georgia plantation where he was a printer. He had a wonderful ear for language and he set down these folk tales—which had probably been brought over from Africa—in all the richness of the negro dialect. He then re-told them with zest and gaiety through the character of old Uncle Remus, who is pictured as telling them to a little boy who lives on the same plantation. These animal stories have been enormously popular, but nowadays many children find them too hard to read on account of the dialect. Those lucky enough to have them read aloud by someone who can handle the dialect will get the most enjoyment out of them. The next best thing is to read them out loud yourself, because sounding the words makes them easier to understand than just looking at them. In any case, they are too good to miss.

The hero of this tale, as of many others of the Uncle Remus stories, is Brer Rabbit. Although one of the weaker animals, he usually manages to get the better of his bigger neighbors by playing tricks on them. He delights especially in outsmarting his old enemy, Brer Fox, as he does here, with the two buckets in the well.

"Brer Rabbit and Brer Fox was like some children what I knows," said Uncle Remus, regarding the little boy, who had come to hear another story, with an affectation of great solemnity. "Both of

'em was always after one another, a prankin' an' a pestrin'
'round. But Brer Rabbit did have some peace, 'cause Brer Fox
done got skittish 'bout puttin' the clamps on Brer Rabbit.

"One day, when Brer Rabbit, an' Brer Fox, an' Brer Coon, an'
Brer B'ar, an' a whole lot of 'em was clearin' up a new-groun' fer
to plant 'em a roastin'-ear patch, the sun commence to git sorta
hot, an' Brer Rabbit he got tired. But he didn't let on, 'cause he
was afear'd the balance of 'em would call him lazy. He jus' keep
on totin' off trash an' pilin' up brush, 'til by-an'-by he holler out
that he gotta brier in his han'—an' then he take an' slip off, an'
hunt fer a cool place fer to rest. He look 'round fer a spell, an'
after a while he come acrost a well with a bucket hangin' in it.

" 'Dat *look* cool,' says Brer Rabbit, says he, 'an' cool I 'spect
she is. I'll jus' git right in der an' take me a nap.' An' with dat he
jump in the bucket he did. But he ain't hardly started to fix hisself
comfortable than the bucket start to go down in the well.

"Wasn't the Rabbit scared, Uncle Remus?" asked the little boy.

"Honey, they ain't never been no worser skeer'd beast since
the world begin than this here same Brer Rabbit. He was fairly
shakin' all over. He know where he come from, but he *didn't* know
where he was goin'. Pretty soon he feel the bucket hit the water,
an' der she sat an' floated. But Brer Rabbit he keep mighty still,
'cause he didn't know what minute was goin' to be his last. He
jus' lay there in the bucket an' he shook an' he shiver.

"Now Brer Fox he always got one eye on Brer Rabbit, an' when
he see that scamp sneak off from the new-ground, Brer Fox he
sneak right after him. He know Brer Rabbit was up to some
projeck er other, an' Brer Fox he took an' creep off to watch him.
Brer Fox he see Brer Rabbit come to the well an' stop, an' then
he see him jump in the bucket, an' then—lo an' behold—he see
him go down right outa sight. Well, sir, Brer Fox was the most
astonish Fox that you ever laid eyes on. He sat out there in the
bushes an' he study an' he study, but he don't make no head nor
tails to this kind of business. Then he says to hisself, says he:

" 'Well, if this don't bang my times,' says he, 'then Joe's dead
an' Sal's a widder. Right down there in that well is where Brer

Rabbit keep his money hid. An' if it ain't that, then he done gone an' 'scovered a gold-mine. An' if it ain't that, then I'm agoin' to see what it *is* in there,' says he.

"Brer Fox he creep up a little nigher, he did, an' he listen, but he don't hear no fuss. An' he keep on creepin' an' gittin' nigher, an' yit he don't hear nothin' down in the well. By-an'-by he git right up close an' peep down, but he don't see nothin' and he don't hear nothin'.

"Now all this time Brer Rabbit he mighty nigh skeer'd outa his skin. He fear'd to move 'cause the bucket might keel right over an' spill him out in the water. An' while he down there sayin' his prayers over like a train o' cars running down a track, old Brer Fox he holler out:

" 'Heyo, Brer Rabbit! Who you visitin' down there?' says he.

" 'Who? Me? Oh, I'm jus' a fishin', Brer Fox,' says Brer Rabbit, says he. 'I jus' say to myself that I'd sorta surprise you all with a mess of fish for dinner, an' so here I is, an' there's the fishes. I'm a fishin' for suckers, Brer Fox,' says Brer Rabbit, says he.

" 'Is they many of 'em down there, Brer Rabbit?' says Brer Fox, says he.

" 'Lots of 'em, Brer Fox. Scores an' scores of 'em. The water is jus' natcherly 'live with 'em. Come down an' help me haul 'em in, Brer Fox,' says Brer Rabbit, says he.

" 'How I goin' to git down, Brer Rabbit?'

" 'Jump in the other bucket hangin' up there, Brer Fox. It'll fetch you down all safe an' sound.'

"Brer Rabbit he talk so happy an' talk so sweet that Brer Fox he jump right in the bucket, he did. An' as he went down, o' course his weight pull Brer Rabbit up. When they pass one another at the half-way place, Brer Rabbit he sing out:

" 'Good-by, Brer Fox, take keer o' your clothes,
     For this is the way the world goes;
     Some goes up an' some goes down,
     You'll git to the bottom all safe an' sound.'

"Soon as Brer Rabbit got out, he gallop right off an' told the folks what the well belong to that Brer Fox was down in there mudyin' up the drinkin' water. An' then he gallop back to the well an' holler down to Brer Fox:

> " 'Here come a man with a great big gun—
> When he haul you up, you jump an' run.' "

"What then, Uncle Remus?" asked the little boy, as the old man paused.

"In jus' about half a hour, honey, both of 'em was back in the new-ground workin' like they never hear of no well—'ceptin' that every now an' then Brer Rabbit he'd bust out in a laugh, an' old Brer Fox he'd git a spell o' the dry grins."

Original spelling slightly adapted.

The Jolly Tailor Who Became King

by LUCIA M. BORSKI *and* KATE B. MILLER

Once upon a time, in the town of Taidaraida, in Poland, there lived a merry little Tailor, Mr. Joseph Nitechka. He was a very thin man and had a small beard of one hundred and thirty-six hairs.

All tailors are thin, reminding one of a needle and thread, but Mr. Nitechka was the thinnest of all, for he could pass through the eye of his own needle. He was so thin that he could eat nothing but noodles, for they were the only thing which could pass down his throat. But for all this, he was a very happy man, and a handsome one, too, particularly on holidays when he braided his beard.

Now Mr. Nitechka would have lived very happily in Taidaraida had it not been for a Gypsy. She happened to be in the town when she cut her foot. In her trouble she went to the Tailor, who darned the skin so carefully and so neatly that not a scar could be seen. The Gypsy was so grateful that she read Nitechka's future from his hand:

"If you leave this town on a Sunday and walk always Westward, you will reach a place where you will be chosen King!"

Nitechka laughed at this. But that very night he dreamt that he indeed became a King, and that from great prosperity he grew so fat that he looked like an immense barrel. Upon waking he thought:

"Maybe it is true? Who knows? Get up, Mr. Nitechka, and go West."

He took a bundle with a hundred needles and a thousand miles
of thread, a thimble, an iron, and a pair of very big scissors, and
started out to find the West. He asked first one and then another
in the town of Taidaraida where the West was. But no one knew.
Finally he asked an old man, a hundred and six years old, who
upon thinking awhile said:

"West must be there where the sun sets."

This seemed so wise to Nitechka that he went that way. But
he had not gone far when a gust of wind blew across the field—
not a very strong gust—but, because Mr. Nitechka was so exceedingly thin, just strong enough to carry him off.

The Tailor flew through the air, laughing heartily at such a
ride. Soon, however, the wind became tired and let him down to
earth. He was much bewildered and did not come to his senses
until someone shouted:

"What is this?"

Mr. Nitechka looked around and saw that he was in a wheat
field and that the wind had thrown him right into the arms of a
Scarecrow. The Scarecrow was very elegant in a blue jacket and
a broken stovepipe hat, and his trousers were only a bit torn. He
had two sticks for feet and also sticks for hands.

Nitechka took off his little cap, bowed very low, saying in his
thin voice:

"My regards to the honorable Sir. I beg your pardon if I stepped
on your foot. I am Mr. Nitechka, the Tailor."

"I am very much pleased to meet such a charming man," answered the Scarecrow. "I am Count Scarecrow and my coat of
arms is Four Sticks. I watch the sparrows here so that they will
not steal wheat, but I give little heed to them. I am uncommonly
courageous and would like to fight only with lions and tigers, but
this year they very seldom come to eat the wheat. Where are you
going, Mr. Nitechka?"

Nitechka bowed again and hopped three times as he was very
polite and he knew that well-bred men thus greeted each other.

"Where do I go, Mr. Count? I am going Westward to a place
where I will become King."

"Is it possible?"

"Of course! I was born to be a King. And perhaps you, Mr. Count, would like to go with me; it will be merrier."

"All right," answered the Scarecrow. "I am already weary of being here. But please, Mr. Nitechka, mend my clothes a bit, because I might like to marry someone on the way; and so I should be neat and handsome."

"With great pleasure!" said Nitechka. He went to work, and

in an hour the Scarecrow had a beautiful suit and a hat almost like new. The sparrows in the field laughed at him a little, but he paid no attention to them as he walked with great dignity with Mr. Nitechka.

On the way the two became great friends. They generally slept in a wheat field, the Tailor tying himself to the Scarecrow with a piece of thread so that the wind could not carry him off again. And when dogs fell upon them, the Scarecrow, who was very brave because of his profession, tore out his foot and threw it after them. Then he tied it again to his body.

Once in the evening they spied a light through the trees.

"Let us go there; maybe they will let us pass the night," said Nitechka.

"By all means, let us do them the honor," answered Count Scarecrow.

As they drew nearer they saw that it was a strange house because it could walk. It stood on four feet and was turning around.

"The owner of the house must be a gay man," whispered the Tailor. "He dances all the time."

They waited until the door came round to them and then went into the house. It was indeed a very strange house. Although it was summer, immense logs of wood burned in the stove, and on the fire sat a nobleman warming himself. From time to time he took a glowing coal in his hands and swallowed it with great pleasure. Upon noticing the travelers, he went over to them, bowed and said:

"Is it not Mr. Nitechka and Count Scarecrow?"

They were speechless with astonishment to think that he should know them, but said nothing. Mr. Nitechka hopped up three times and Count Scarecrow took off his hat.

The nobleman continued:

"Stay with me for supper and tomorrow you may go your way. I will call my wife, my daughter, and my other relatives."

He clapped his hands and suddenly a large company appeared. The host's daughter was very beautiful, but when she laughed, it was as if a horse had neighed in a meadow. She took an instant liking to Nitechka and told him she would very much like to have him for her husband. They sat down to supper, Nitechka and Count Scarecrow on a bench, and all the others on iron pots filled with glowing coals.

"Do not wonder, dear Sirs," the host said, "that we sit thus, for our family always feels very cold."

They served soup in a big caldron and Nitechka was just putting his spoon to his lips, when Count Scarecrow pulled his coat and whispered:

"Mr. Nitechka, don't eat, for this is hot pitch!"

So pretending that they liked the soup, they spilt it under the table. Then a strange looking servant brought a new dish of rats in a black sauce, and later he served fried locust, lob-worms with parmesan cheese like noodles, and, for dessert, old, bad eggs. Nitechka and Count Scarecrow threw everything under the table, becoming more and more frightened.

All at once the host said:

"Do you know, Mr. Nitechka, that the King has just died in Pacanów?"

"Where is Pacanów, is it far?" asked the Tailor.

"A crow can fly to that town in two days. And do you know they are seeking a King there, and he who marries my daughter will become King?"

The girl neighed like an old horse at this and threw her arms around Nitechka's neck.

"Let's run away!" murmured Count Scarecrow.

"But I can't find the door. There is no help," replied Nitechka.

Soon, however, the whole family became very gay, and presently the host said:

"We will drink to your health and sing merrily. Mr. Nitechka, do you know a song?"

"Yes, indeed," said Nitechka, "and a very nice one."

Saying this, he whispered to Count Scarecrow:

"Watch, brother, and when the door is behind us, shout!"

Then he got up, took off his cap and in his thin little voice began to sing the only song he knew.

"Sing praises to the Holy Virgin,
Sing praises to Her Wondrous Name!"

At the mention of the Virgin, the whole family rose to their feet, and ran around the room, sprawling and shouting and cursing. Nitechka said nothing, but simply continued his song. He could feel the house running somewhere with them, and so he sang and sang like the thinnest pipe in the organ. When he had finished the song, he began to sing it over again. At that moment everything disappeared, and only a terrible wind blew.

Terrified, Nitechka and Count Scarecrow found themselves alone in a huge meadow. Then they gave thanks for their delivery and Nitechka said:

"They were awful devils, but we overpowered them."

"I frightened them so much," boasted Count Scarecrow.

They continued their way toward Pacanów, where dwelt the famous smiths who shoe the goats, a beautiful old town, where the King had died. When after seven days of adventures they reached Pacanów, they were greatly astonished. All around the town it was sunshiny and pleasant; but over Pacanów the rain poured from the sky as from a bucket.

"I won't go in there," said the Scarecrow, "because my hat will get wet."

"And even I do not wish to become King of such a wet kingdom," said the Tailor.

Just then the townspeople spied them and rushed toward them, led by the Burgomaster riding on a shod goat.

"Dear Sirs," they said, "maybe you can help us."

"And what has happened to you?" asked Nitechka.

"Deluge and destruction threaten us. Our King died a week ago, and since that time a terrible rain has come down upon our gorgeous town. We can't even make fires in our houses, because so much water runs through the chimneys. We will perish, honorable Sirs!"

"It is too bad," said Nitechka very wisely.

"Oh, very bad! And we are most sorry for the late King's daughter, as the poor thing can't stop crying and this causes even more water."

"That makes it still worse," replied Nitechka, still more wisely.

"Help us, help us!" continued the Burgomaster. "Do you know the immeasurable reward the Princess promised to the one who stops the rain? She promised to marry him and then he will become King."

"Truly?" cried Nitechka. "Count Scarecrow, let's go to the town. We ought to try to help them."

They were led through the terrible rain to the Princess, who upon seeing Nitechka, cried out:

"Oh, what a handsome youth!"

He hopped three times and said:

"Is it true, Princess, that you will marry the one who stops the rain?"

"I vowed I would."

"And if I do it?"

"I will keep my promise."

"And I shall become a King?"

"You will, O beautiful youth."

"Very well," answered the Tailor. "I am going to stop the rain."

So saying he nodded to Count Scarecrow and they left the Princess.

The whole population, full of hope, gathered around them. Nitechka and the Scarecrow stood under an umbrella and whispered to each other.

"Listen, Scarecrow, what shall we do to make the rain stop falling?"

"We have to bring back pleasant weather."

"But how?"

"Ha! Let's think!"

But for three days they thought and the rain fell and fell and fell. Suddenly Nitechka gave a cry of joy like a goat's bleating.

"I know where the rain comes from!"

"Where from?"

"From the sky!"

"Eh!" grumbled the Scarecrow. "I know that too. Surely it doesn't fall from the bottom to the top, but the other way around."

"Yes," said Nitechka, "but why does it fall over the town only, and not elsewhere?"

"Because elsewhere is nice weather."

"You're stupid, Mr. Count," said the Tailor. "But tell me, how long has it rained?"

"They say since the King died."

"So you see! Now I know everything! The King was so great and mighty that when he died and went to Heaven he made a huge hole in the sky."

"Oh, oh, true!"

"Through the hole the rain poured and it will pour until the end of the world if the hole isn't sewed up!"

Count Scarecrow looked at him in amazement.

"In all my life I have never seen such a wise Tailor," said he.

They rejoiced greatly, went to the Burgomaster, and ordered him to tell the townspeople that Mr. Joseph Nitechka, a citizen of the town of Taidaraida, promised to stop the rain.

"Long live Mr. Nitechka! Long may he live!" shouted the whole town.

Then Nitechka ordered them to bring all the ladders in the town, tie them together, and lean them against the sky. He took a hundred needles and, threading one, went up the ladders. Count Scarecrow stayed at the bottom and unwound the spool on which there was a hundred miles of thread.

When Nitechka got to the very top he saw that there was a huge hole in the sky, a hole as big as the town. A torn piece of the sky hung down, and through this hole the water poured.

So he went to work and sewed and sewed for two days. His fingers grew stiff and he became very tired but he did not stop. When he had finished sewing he pressed out the sky with the iron and then, exhausted, went down the ladders.

Once more the sun shone over Pacanów. Count Scarecrow almost went mad with joy, as did all the other inhabitants of the town. The Princess wiped her eyes that were almost cried out,

and throwing herself on Nitechka's neck, kissed him affectionately.

Nitechka was very happy. He looked around, and there were
the Burgomaster and Councilmen bringing him a golden scepter
and a gorgeous crown and shouting:

"Long live King Nitechka! Long live he! Long live he! And let
him be the Princess' husband and let him reign happily!"

So the merry little Tailor reigned happily for a long time, and
the rain never fell in his kingdom. In his good fortune Nitechka
did not forget his old friend, Count Scarecrow, but he appointed
him the Great Warden of the Kingdom to drive away the sparrows
from the royal head.

The Boy Who Drew Cats

by LAFCADIO HEARN

A long, long time ago, in a small country village in Japan, there lived a poor farmer and his wife, who were very good people. They had a number of children, and found it very hard to feed them all. The elder son was strong enough when only fourteen years old to help his father; and the little girls learned to help their mother almost as soon as they could walk.

But the youngest child, a little boy, did not seem to be fit for hard work. He was very clever—cleverer than all his brothers and sisters; but he was quite weak and small, and people said he could never grow very big. So his parents thought it would be better for him to become a priest than to become a farmer. They took him with them to the village temple one day, and asked the good old priest who lived there, if he would have their little boy for his attendant, and teach him all that a priest ought to know.

The old man spoke kindly to the lad, and asked him some hard questions. So clever were the answers that the priest agreed to take the little fellow into the temple as an acolyte, and to educate him for the priesthood.

The boy learned quickly what the old priest taught him, and was very obedient in most things. But he had one fault. He liked to draw cats during study hours, and to draw cats even where cats ought not to have been drawn at all.

Whenever he found himself alone, he drew cats. He drew them on the margins of the priest's books, and on all the screens of the temple, and on the walls, and on the pillars. Several times the priest told him this was not right; but he did not stop drawing cats. He drew them because he could not really help it. He had what is called "the genius of an *artist*," and just for that reason he was not quite fit to be an acolyte; a good acolyte should study books.

One day after he had drawn some very clever pictures of cats upon a paper screen, the old priest said to him severely: "My boy, you must go away from this temple at once. You will never make a good priest, but perhaps you will become a great artist. Now let me give you a last piece of advice, and be sure you never forget it. *Avoid large places at night; keep to small!*"

The boy did not know what the priest meant by saying, "*Avoid large places; keep to small.*" He thought and thought, while he was tying up his little bundle of clothes to go away. But he could not understand those words, and he was afraid to speak to the priest any more, except to say good-by.

He left the temple very sorrowfully, and began to wonder what he should do. If he went straight home he felt sure his father would punish him for having been disobedient to the priest: so he was afraid to go home. All at once he remembered that at the next village, twelve miles away, there was a very big temple. He had heard there were several priests at that temple; and he made up his mind to go to them and ask them to take him for their acolyte.

Now that big temple was closed up but the boy did not know this fact. The reason it had been closed up was that a goblin had frightened the priests away, and had taken possession of the place. Some brave warriors had afterward gone to the temple at night to kill the goblin; but they had never been seen alive again. Nobody had ever told these things to the boy—so he walked all the way to the village hoping to be kindly treated by the priests.

When he got to the village it was already dark, and all the people were in bed; but he saw the big temple on a hill at the other end of the principal street, and he saw there was a light in the temple. People who tell the story say the goblin used to make that light, in order to tempt lonely travelers to ask for shelter. The boy went at once to the temple and knocked. There was no sound inside. He knocked and knocked again; but still nobody came. At last he pushed gently at the door, and was quite glad to find that it had not been fastened. So he went in, and saw a lamp burning —but no priest.

He thought some priest would be sure to come very soon, and he sat down and waited. Then he noticed that everything in the temple was gray with dust, and thickly spun over with cobwebs. So he thought to himself that the priests would certainly like to have an acolyte, to keep the place clean. He wondered why they had allowed everything to get so dusty. What most pleased him, however, were some big white screens, good to paint cats upon. Though he was tired, he looked at once for a writing-box, and found one, and ground some ink, and began to paint cats.

He painted a great many cats upon the screens; and then he began to feel very, very sleepy. He was just on the point of lying down to sleep beside one of the screens, when he suddenly remembered the words, "Avoid large places; keep to small!"

The temple was very large; he was all alone; and as he thought of these words—though he could not quite understand them— he began to feel for the first time a little afraid; and he resolved to look for a *small place* in which to sleep. He found a little cabinet, with a sliding door, and went into it, and shut himself up. Then he lay down and fell fast asleep.

Very late in the night he was awakened by a most terrible noise —a noise of fighting and screaming. It was so dreadful that he was afraid even to look through a chink of the little cabinet: he lay very still, holding his breath for fright. The light that had been in the temple went out; but the awful sounds continued, and became more awful, and all the temple shook. After a long time silence came; but the boy was still afraid to move. He did not move until the light of the morning sun shone into the cabinet through the chinks of the little door.

Then he got out of his hiding-place very cautiously, and looked about. The first thing he saw was that all the floor of the temple

was covered with blood. And then he saw, lying dead, in the middle of it, an enormous, monstrous rat—a goblin-rat—bigger than a cow!

But who or what could have killed it? There was no man or other creature to be seen. Suddenly the boy observed that the mouths of all the cats he had drawn the night before were red and wet with blood. Then he knew that the goblin had been killed by the cats which he had drawn. And then also, for the first time, he understood why the wise old priest had said to him, "*Avoid large places at night; keep to small.*"

Afterward that boy became a very famous artist. Some of the cats which he drew are still shown to travelers in Japan.

Some Boys and Girls . . .

Adventures of Real Children

Rufus M.

by ELEANOR ESTES

The three books about the Moffat family—The Moffats, The
Middle Moffats, *and* Rufus M. *are about a jolly and lovable group
of children who make and solve their own problems with very
funny results. This chapter shows Rufus, who is the youngest in
the family and has just turned seven, as he uses the usual Moffat
energy and ingenuity to get what he wants, in this case, his first
library card. Eleanor Estes herself was a children's librarian in
New Haven, and her experiences with young book borrowers
probably gave her the inspiration for this hilarious encounter between Rufus and "the library lady."*

Rufus M. That's the way Rufus wrote his name on his heavy
arithmetic paper and on his blue-lined spelling paper. Rufus M.
went on one side of the paper. His age, seven, went on the other.
Rufus had not learned to write his name in school, though that
is one place for learning to write. He had not learned to write his
name at home either, though that is another place for learning
to write. The place where he had learned to write his name was
the library, long ago before he ever went to school at all. This is
the way it happened.

One day when Rufus had been riding his scooter up and down
the street, being the motorman, the conductor, the passengers, the
steam, and the whistle of a locomotive, he came home and found
Joey, Jane, and Sylvie, all reading in the front yard. Joey and Jane

were sitting on the steps of the porch and Sylvie was sprawled in the hammock, a book in one hand, a chocolate-covered peppermint in the other.

Rufus stood with one bare foot on his scooter and one on the grass and watched them. Sylvie read the fastest. This was natural since she was the oldest. But Joey turned the pages almost as fast and Jane went lickety-cut on the good parts. They were all reading books and he couldn't even read yet. These books they were reading were library books. The library must be open today. It wasn't open every day, just a few days a week.

"I want to go to the library," said Rufus. "And get a book," he added.

"We all just came home from there," said Jane, while Joey and Sylvie merely went on reading as though Rufus had said nothing. "Besides," she added, "why do you want a book anyway? You can't even read yet."

This was true and it made Rufus mad. He liked to do everything that they did. He even liked to sew if they were sewing. He never thought whether sewing was for girls only or not. When he saw Jane sewing, he asked Mama to let him sew too. So Mama tied a thread to the head of a pin and Rufus poked that in and out of a piece of goods. That's the way he sewed. It looked like what Jane was doing and Rufus was convinced that he was sewing too, though he could not see much sense in it.

Now here were the other Moffats, all with books from the library. And there were three more books stacked up on the porch that looked like big people's books without pictures. They were for Mama, no doubt. This meant that he was the only one here who did not have a book.

"I want a book from the library," said Rufus. A flick of the page as Sylvie turned it over was all the answer he got. It seemed to Rufus as though even Catherine-the-cat gave him a scornful glance because he could not read yet and did not have a book.

Rufus turned his scooter around and went out of the yard. Just wait! Read? Why, soon he'd read as fast if not faster than they did. Reading looked easy. It was just flipping pages. Who couldn't do that?

Rufus thought that it was not hard to get a book out of the library. All you did was go in, look for a book that you liked, give it to the lady to punch, and come home with it. He knew where the library was, for he had often gone there with Jane and some of the others. While Jane went off to the shelves to find a book, he and Joey played the game of Find the Duke in the Palmer Cox Brownie books. This was a game that the two boys had made up. They would turn the pages of one of the Brownie books, any of them, and try to be the first to spot the duke, the brownie in the tall hat. The library lady thought that this was a noisy game, and she wished they would not play it there. Rufus hoped to bring a Brownie book home now.

"Toot-toot!" he sang to clear the way. Straight down Elm Street was the way to the library; the same way that led to Sunday School, and Rufus knew it well. He liked sidewalks that were white the best, for he could go the fastest on these.

"Toot-toot!" Rufus hurried down the street. When he arrived at the library, he hid his scooter in the pine trees that grew under the windows beside the steps. Christmas trees, Rufus called them. The ground was covered with brown pine needles and they were soft to walk upon. Rufus always went into the library the same way. He climbed the stairs, encircled the light on the granite arm of the steps, and marched into the library.

Rufus stepped carefully on the strips of rubber matting that led to the desk. This matting looked like dirty licorice. But it wasn't licorice. He knew because once, when Sylvie had brought him here when he was scarcely more than three, he had tasted a torn corner of it. It was not good to eat.

The library lady was sitting at the desk playing with some cards. Rufus stepped off the matting. The cool, shiny floor felt good to his bare feet. He went over to the shelves and luckily did find one of the big Palmer Cox Brownie books there. It would be fun to play the game of Find the Duke at home. Until now he had played it only in the library. Maybe Jane or Joey would play it with him right now. He laughed out loud at the thought.

"Sh-sh-sh, quiet," said the lady at the desk.

Rufus clapped his chubby fist over his mouth. Goodness! He had forgotten where he was. Do not laugh or talk out loud in the library. He knew these rules. Well, he didn't want to stay here any longer today anyway. He wanted to read at home with the others. He took the book to the lady to punch.

She didn't punch it, though. She took it and she put it on the table behind her and then she started to play cards again.

"That's my book," said Rufus.

"Do you have a card?" the lady asked.

Rufus felt in his pockets. Sometimes he carried around an old playing card or two. Today he didn't have one.

"No," he said.

"You'll have to have a card to get a book."

"I'll go and get one," said Rufus.

The lady put down her cards. "I mean a library card," she explained kindly. "It looks to me as though you are too little to have a library card. Do you have one?"

"No," said Rufus. "I'd like to, though."

"I'm afraid you're too little," said the lady. "You have to write your name to get one. Can you do that?"

Rufus nodded his head confidently. Writing. Lines up and down. He'd seen that done. And the letters that Mama had tied in bundles in the closet under the stairs were covered with writing. Of course he could write.

"Well, let's see your hands," said the lady.

Rufus obligingly showed this lady his hands, but she did not like the looks of them. She cringed and clasped her head as though the sight hurt her.

"Oh," she gasped. "You'll just have to go home and wash them before we can ever think about joining the library and borrowing books."

This was a complication upon which Rufus had not reckoned. However, all it meant was a slight delay. He'd wash his hands and then he'd get the book. He turned and went out of the library, found his scooter safe among the Christmas trees, and pushed it home. He surprised Mama by asking to have his hands washed. When this was done, he mounted his scooter again and returned all the long way to the library. It was not just a little trip to the library. It was a long one. A long one and a hot one on a day like this. But he didn't notice that. All he was bent on was getting his book and taking it home and reading with the others on the front porch. They were all still there, brushing flies away and reading.

Again Rufus hid his scooter in the pine trees, encircled the light, and went in.

"Hello," he said.

"Well," said the lady. "How are they now?"

Rufus had forgotten he had had to wash his hands. He thought she was referring to the other Moffats. "Fine," he said.

"Let me see them," she said, and she held up her hands.

Oh! His hands! Well, they were all right, thought Rufus, for Mama had just washed them. He showed them to the lady. There was a silence while she studied them. Then she shook her head. She still did not like them.

"Ts, ts, ts!" she said. "They'll have to be cleaner than that."

Rufus looked at his hands. Supposing he went all the way home and washed them again, she still might not like them. However, if that is what she wanted, he would have to do that before he could get the Brownie book . . . and he started for the door.

"Well, now, let's see what we can do," said the lady. "I know what," she said. "It's against the rules, but perhaps we can wash them in here." And she led Rufus into a little room that smelled of paste where lots of new books and old books were stacked up. In one corner was a little round sink and Rufus washed his hands again. They they returned to the desk. The lady got a chair and put a newspaper on it. She made Rufus stand on this because he was not big enough to write at the desk otherwise.

Then the lady put a piece of paper covered with a lot of printing in front of Rufus, dipped a pen in the inkwell and gave it to him.

"All right," she said. "Here's your application. Write your name here."

All the writing Rufus had ever done before had been on big pieces of brown wrapping paper with lots of room on them. Rufus had often covered those great sheets of paper with his own kind of writing at home. Lines up and down.

But on this paper there wasn't much space. It was already covered with writing. However, there was a tiny little empty space and that was where Rufus must write his name, the lady said. So, little space or not, Rufus confidently grasped the pen with his left hand and dug it into the paper. He was not accustomed to pens, having always worked with pencils until now, and he made a great many holes and blots and scratches.

"Gracious," said the lady. "Don't bear down so hard! And why don't you hold it in your right hand?" she asked, moving the pen back into his right hand.

Rufus started again scraping his lines up and down and all over the page, this time using his right hand. Wherever there was an empty space he wrote. He even wrote over some of the print for good measure. Then he waited for the lady, who had gone off to get a book for some man, to come back and look.

"Oh," she said, as she settled herself in her swivel chair, "is that the way you write? Well . . . it's nice, but what does it say?"

"Says Rufus Moffat. My name."

Apparently these lines up and down did not spell Rufus Moffat to this lady. She shook her head.

"It's nice," she repeated. "Very nice. But nobody but you knows what it says. You have to learn to write your name better than that before you can join the library."

Rufus was silent. He had come to the library all by himself, gone back home to wash his hands, and come back because he wanted to take books home and read them the way the others did. He had worked hard. He did not like to think he might have to go home without a book.

The library lady looked at him a moment and then she said

quickly before he could get himself all the way off the big chair, "maybe you can *print* your name."

Rufus looked at her hopefully. He thought he could write better than he could print, for his writing certainly looked to him exactly like all grown people's writing. Still he'd try to print if that was what she wanted.

The lady printed some letters on the top of a piece of paper. "There," she said. "That's your name. Copy it ten times and then we'll try it on another application."

Rufus worked hard. He worked so hard the knuckles showed white on his brown fist. He worked for a long, long time, now with his right hand and now with his left. Sometimes a boy or girl came in, looked over his shoulder and watched, but he paid no attention. From time to time the lady studied his work and she said, "That's fine. That's fine." At last she said, "Well, maybe now we can try." And she gave him another application.

All Rufus could get, with his large generous letters, in that tiny little space where he was supposed to print his name, was R–U–F. The other letters he scattered here and there on the card. The lady did not like this either. She gave him still another blank. Rufus tried to print smaller and this time he got RUFUS in the space, and also he crowded an M at the end. Since he was doing so well now, the lady herself printed the *offat* part of Moffat on the next line.

"This will have to do," she said. "Now take this home and ask your mother to sign it on the other side. Bring it back on Thursday and you'll get your card."

Rufus's face was shiny and streaked with dirt where he had rubbed it. He never knew there was all this work to getting a book. The other Moffats just came in and got books. Well, maybe they had had to do this once too.

Rufus held his hard-earned application in one hand and steered his scooter with the other. When he reached home, Joey, Jane, and Sylvie were not around any longer. Mama signed his card for him, saying, "My! So you've learned how to write!"

"Print," corrected Rufus.

Mama kissed Rufus and he went back out. The lady had said to come back on Thursday, but he wanted a book today. When the other Moffats came home, he'd be sitting on the top step of the porch, reading. That would surprise them. He smiled to himself as he made his way to the library for the third time.

Once his application blew away. Fortunately it landed in a thistle bush and did not get very torn. The rest of the way Rufus clutched it carefully. He climbed the granite steps to the library again, only to find that the big round dark brown doors were closed. Rufus tried to open them, but he couldn't. He knocked at the door, even kicked it with his foot, but there was no answer. He pounded on the door, but nobody came.

A big boy strode past with his newspapers. "Hey, kid," he said to Rufus, "library's closed!" And off he went, whistling.

Rufus looked after him. The fellow said the library was closed. How could it have closed so fast? He had been here such a little while ago. The lady must still be here. He did want his Brownie book. If only he could see in, he might see the lady and get his book. The windows were high up, but they had very wide sills. Rufus was a wonderful climber. He could shinny up trees and poles faster than anybody on the block. Faster than Joey. Now, helping himself up by means of one of the pine trees that grew close to the building, and by sticking his toes in the ivy and rough places in the bricks, he scrambled up the wall. He hoisted himself up on one of the sills and sat there. He peered in. It was dark inside, for the shades had been drawn almost all the way down.

"Library lady!" he called, and he knocked on the window-pane. There was no answer. He put his hands on each side of his face to shield his eyes, and he looked in for a long, long time. He could not believe that she had left. Rufus was resolved to get a book. He had lost track of the number of times he had been back and forth from home to the library, and the library home. Maybe the lady was in the cellar. He climbed down, stubbing his big toe on the bricks as he did so. He stooped down beside one of the low dirt-spattered cellar windows. He couldn't see in. He lay flat on the ground, wiped one spot clean on the window, picked up a few pieces of coal from the sill and put them in his pocket for Mama.

"Hey, lady," he called.

He gave the cellar window a little push. It wasn't locked, so he opened it a little and looked in. All he could see was a high pile of coal reaching up to this window. Of course he didn't put any of that coal in his pocket, for that would be stealing.

"Hey, lady," he yelled again. His voice echoed in the cellar, but the library lady did not answer. He called out, "Hey, lady," every

few seconds, but all that answered him was an echo. He pushed
the window open a little wider. All of a sudden it swung wide open
and Rufus slid in, right on top of the coal pile, and crash, clatter,
bang! He slid to the bottom, making a great racket.

A little light shone through the dusty windows, but on the
whole it was very dark and spooky down here and Rufus really
wished that he was back on the outside looking in. However,
since he was in the library, why not go upstairs quick, get the
Brownie book, and go home? The window had banged shut, but
he thought he could climb up the coal pile, pull the window up,
and get out. He certainly hoped he could, anyway. Supposing he
couldn't and he had to stay in this cellar! Well, that he would not
think about. He looked around in the dusky light and saw a staircase across the cellar. Luckily his application was still good. It
was torn and dirty but it still had his name on it, RUFUS M, and
that was the important part. He'd leave this on the desk in exchange for the Brownie book.

Rufus cautiously made his way over to the steps, but he stopped
halfway across the cellar. Somebody had opened the door at the
top of the stairs. He couldn't see who it was, but he did see the
light reflected and that's how he knew that somebody had opened
the door. It must be the lady. He was just going to say, "Hey,
lady," when he thought, "Gee, maybe it isn't the lady. Maybe it's
a spooky thing."

Then the light went away, the door was closed, and Rufus was
left in the dark again. He didn't like it down here. He started to
go back to the coal pile to get out of this place. Then he felt of his
application. What a lot of work he had done to get a book and
now that he was this near to getting one, should he give up? No.
Anyway, if it was the lady up there, he knew her and she knew
him and neither one of them was scared of the other. And Mama
always said there's no such thing as a spooky thing.

So Rufus bravely made his way again to the stairs. He tiptoed
up them. The door at the head was not closed tightly. He pushed
it open and found himself right in the library. But goodness!

There in the little sink room right opposite him was the library lady!

Rufus stared at her in silence. The library lady was eating. Rufus had never seen her do anything before but play cards, punch books, and carry great piles of them around. Now she was eating. Mama said not to stare at anybody while they were eating. Still Rufus didn't know the library lady ate, so it was hard for him not to look at her.

She had a little gas stove in there. She could cook there. She was reading a book at the same time that she was eating. Sylvie could do that too. This lady did not see him.

"Hey, lady," said Rufus.

The librarian jumped up out of her seat. "Was that you in the cellar? I thought I heard somebody. Goodness, young man! I thought you had gone home long ago."

Rufus didn't say anything. He just stood there. He had gone home and he had come back lots of times. He had the whole thing in his mind; the coming and going, and going and coming, and sliding down the coal pile, but he did not know where to begin, how to tell it.

"Didn't you know the library is closed now?" she demanded, coming across the floor with firm steps.

Rufus remained silent. No, he hadn't known it. The fellow had told him, but he hadn't believed him. Now he could see for himself that the library was closed so the library lady could eat. If the lady would let him take his book, he'd go home and stay there. He'd play the game of Find the Duke with Jane. He hopefully held out his card with his name on it.

"Here this is," he said.

But the lady acted as though she didn't even see it. She led Rufus over to the door.

"All right now," she said. "Out with you!" But just as she opened the door the sound of water boiling over on the stove struck their ears, and back she raced to her little room.

"Gracious!" she exclaimed. "What a day!"

Before the door could close on him, Rufus followed her in and sat down on the edge of a chair. The lady thought he had gone and started to sip her tea. Rufus watched her quietly, waiting for her to finish.

After a while the lady brushed the crumbs off her lap. And then she washed her hands and the dishes in the little sink where Rufus had washed his hands. In a library a lady could eat and could wash. Maybe she slept here, too. Maybe she lived here.

"Do you live here?" Rufus asked her.

"Mercy on us!" exclaimed the lady. "Where'd you come from? Didn't I send you home? No, I don't live here and neither do you. Come now, out with you, young man. I mean it." The lady called all boys "young man" and all girls "Susie." She came out of the little room and she opened the big brown door again. "There," she said. "Come back on Thursday."

Rufus's eyes filled up with tears.

"Here's this," he said again, holding up his application in a last desperate attempt. But the lady shook her head. Rufus went slowly down the steps, felt around in the bushes for his scooter, and with drooping spirits he mounted it. Then for the second time that day, the library lady changed her mind.

"Oh, well," she said, "come back here, young man. I'm not supposed to do business when the library's closed, but I see we'll have to make an exception."

So Rufus rubbed his sooty hands over his face, hid his scooter in the bushes again, climbed the granite steps, and, without circling the light, he went back in and gave the lady his application.

The lady took it gingerly. "My, it's dirty," she said. "You really ought to sign another one."

"And go home with it?" asked Rufus. He really didn't believe this was possible. He wiped his hot face on his sleeve and looked looked up at the lady in exhaustion. What he was thinking was: All right. If he had to sign another one, all right. But would she just please stay open until he got back?

However, this was not necessary. The lady said, "Well, now, I'll try to clean this old one up. But remember, young man, always have everything clean—your hands, your book, everything, when you come to the library."

Rufus nodded solemnly. "My feet too," he assured her.

Then the lady made Rufus wash his hands again. They really were very bad this time, for he had been in a coal pile, and now at last she gave Rufus the book he wanted—one of the Palmer Cox Brownie books. This one was *The Brownies in the Philippines*.

And Rufus went home.

When he reached home, he showed Mama his book. She smiled at him, and gave his cheek a pat. She thought it was fine that he had gone to the library and joined all by himself and taken out a book. And she thought it was fine when Rufus sat down at the kitchen table, was busy and quiet for a long, long time, and then showed her what he had done.

He had printed RUFUS M. That was what he had done. And that's the way he learned to sign his name. And that's the way he always did sign his name for a long, long time.

Heidi

by JOHANNA SPYRI

When her Aunt Dete takes Heidi to her grandfather's, the little girl is not sorry because Dete had resented the job of taking care of her dead sister's child. Heidi wastes no time in making a useful place for herself in her grandfather's cottage and a warm place in his heart. Peter the goatherd and everyone else who comes in contact with the sweet and spirited girl are quickly won over. Johanna Spyri decided to write this story of Swiss mountain life because she was anxious to earn money to help the orphans after the Franco-Prussian War. The book succeeded beyond her wildest hopes, mainly because the personality of Heidi is so genuine and moving that children all over the world have been able to identify themselves with this lonely and brave little girl. Created more than 75 years ago, Heidi still remains the most beloved child in fiction.

After Dete had left, the old man sat down on his bench again, blowing great clouds of smoke from his pipe, while he looked fixedly on the ground, and was silent.

Heidi looked about in the greatest delight, discovered the goat-shed and peeped in, but finding nothing, pursued her investigations. At last she went behind the hut to look at the old pines.

The wind was sighing and moaning in the branches, and the topmost bough swayed to and fro. Heidi stood listening, but the wind lulled, and she went on again until she came to where her grandfather sat as she had left him. Planting herself directly in front of the old man, she put her little hands behind her, and looked fixedly at him. After a few moments he raised his head and asked, as the child continued to stand motionless before him, "What will you do now?"

"I want to see what you have in there, in the hut," said Heidi.

"Well, take up your bundle of clothes and follow me." Her grandfather rose to enter the dwelling.

"I don't want them any more," said the child.

He turned, at these words, to examine the little girl, whose black eyes were dancing with eagerness to know what the hut contained.

"At least she is not wanting in intelligence," he said half aloud, then louder, "Why shall you not need them, my child?"

"I want to go about like the goats," said Heidi, "they have such light legs."

"You shall do that," replied her grandfather, "but bring in the bundle, and we will put it into the cupboard." She raised the bundle as he bade her; he opened the door, and they entered the large room which made up the entire hut.

In one corner was the bed, in another a big kettle hung over the hearth. There was also a table and a chair. In the wall was a big door, which the grandfather opened. It was the cupboard. There hung his clothes; on the shelves were shirts, stockings, handkerchiefs, cups, plates, saucers, and glasses; above was the smoked meat, cheese, a round loaf of bread—in short, all that was needed for daily use. While he held the door open, Heidi stepped up with her bundle, which she stuffed in behind her grandfather's things, as far out of sight as possible. After this she looked carefully about the room, saying, "But where shall I sleep, Grandfather?"

"Wherever you like," was his answer.

This pleased the little girl. She ran about the room, searching every corner, to find the place that would best suit her. Opposite her grandfather's bed was a ladder, that led into the hayloft. Up this ran Heidi, and found it strewn with fresh, sweet-smelling hay, while from a round hole in the rafters one could look far, far away into the valley.

"Oh, I must sleep here! It really is beautiful," cried the child. "Come up!" she called to the old man. "Come up, and see how beautiful it is here."

"I know all about it," he answered from below.

"I am making my bed here," said Heidi again, while she worked busily away, "but you must come up, and bring me a sheet. There must be a sheet on the bed to lie on."

"Well, well," replied her grandfather. He went to the cupboard, searched about, and at last pulled out from under his shirts a long, coarse linen cloth that was certainly something like a sheet.

He then mounted the ladder with it; and behold! there was a dear little bed all piled up with hay, and where the head was to lie was raised quite high, and so arranged that the occupant could look directly through the open hole.

"That is well done," said the old man. "Now we must put on the sheet; but stop a bit." He took more hay, piling the bed up till it was twice as thick as Heidi had made it, that she might not feel the floor through the hay. "Now bring me the sheet."

Heidi seized the sheet, but could hardly lift it, the linen was so heavy—and that was good, for the hay could not penetrate such thick stuff—and now they both spread this sheet over the hay. As it was much too long for such a little bed, Heidi busily tucked it well under. Now it was a charming resting-place to look at, and the child stood in admiration of it for a long time, thoughtfully. "We have forgotten one thing, Grandfather," said she at last.

"What is that?"

"A coverlid, to be sure, for when one goes to bed, one must creep in between the sheet and the coverlid."

"Do you think so?" said he. "I fear I have none."

"Oh, then, no matter!" said Heidi. "I can get more hay instead." She ran to fetch some, but her grandfather stopped her.

"Wait a moment," he said. He descended the ladder, and went over to his bed; then, climbing up again, placed a heavy linen sack on the floor, saying, "Is not this better than hay?"

Heidi strove with might and main to spread out the sack, but her little hands could not manage the heavy stuff. With her grandfather's help, however, it was soon arranged; and then the bed looked so nice and firm, that Heidi stood entranced in admiration, and exclaimed, "This is a beautiful coverlid, and a perfect bed! I wish it were night, Grandfather, that I might lie down."

"I think, however, that we could eat something first. What do you think?" asked the old man.

Heidi had been so much interested about her bed that she had forgotten everything else. Now she remembered, and felt suddenly very hungry. She had eaten nothing since breakfast, when she had a piece of bread and a little weak coffee, and had since made a long journey. Heidi replied heartily to her grandfather's question, "Yes, I think so, indeed."

"Well, go down then, since we agree," said the old man, and followed his grandchild down the ladder. He went over to the fireplace, removed the big kettle, hung a smaller one in its place on the chain, seated himself on the three-legged stool with a round seat before him, and blew the fire till there was a blaze, and the kettle began to boil. Next, he held a long iron fork over the fire, with a big piece of cheese on it, which he turned slowly round and round till it was of a golden yellow.

Heidi watched him with keen interest; but suddenly an idea came into her head, and she sprang away to the cupboard, then back to the table, and again many times. When her grandfather came with the pot, and the roasted cheese on the fork, there already lay the round loaf, two plates, two knives, all neatly arranged. For Heidi had noticed everything in the cupboard, and she knew what was needed for the table.

"Now, this is nice that you can think of things yourself," said the old man, and put the cheese upon the bread. "But there is something more needed still."

Heidi saw how invitingly the pot was steaming, and dashed to the cupboard again. Only one mug could she find, but did not remain long in perplexity. Two glasses stood at the back of the cupboard; in an instant the child was back again, with a glass and the mug.

"That is right. You are very helpful. But where will you sit?" said he, for he sat on the only high stool himself. Like an arrow the child was at the fireplace, brought the little three-legged stool back again, and sat down.

"Well, you have a seat, at any rate," said the grandfather, "but rather low down. You would be rather too short, even on mine, to reach the table. But you must have something to eat at once, so begin."

He stood up, filled the mug with milk, set it upon the high stool, drew the latter up to Heidi so that she had a table to herself, and sitting on the corner of the table began his dinner, bidding her also to eat.

Heidi seized her little mug, and drank and drank without once stopping, for all the thirst of her journey seemed to rise up at once. Then she drew a long breath—for in her eagerness to drink, she had not been able to stop to breathe—and set down her mug.

"Does the milk taste good?" asked her grandfather.

"I never drank such good milk," said the child.

"Then you must have more," said he, and filled the mug again quite to the top, and placed it before the child, who was eating her bread, spread thickly with the hot cheese, which was like butter from the heat, and tasted delicious. She now and then drank her milk and looked meanwhile perfectly happy.

When they had finished eating, the old man went out to the goats' house, and put things to rights there, while Heidi observed him carefully, how he first swept everything up with the broom, then strewed fresh straw about for the animals to sleep upon. He then went to the wood pile near-by, cut round sticks of the right size, cut a board to the right shape, bored holes in it, stuck the sticks in, and had soon a stool like his own, only higher. Heidi watched him at this work, speechless with wonder.

"What do you call this, Heidi?" asked he.

"That is my stool, because it is so high. How quickly you have made it!" said the little one, in the greatest wonder and admiration.

"She knows what she sees. She has her eyes in the right place," remarked the old man to himself, as he moved round the hut, and drove a nail here, or made something fast there, going with his hammer and nails and pieces of wood from one place to another, finding constantly something to do or to mend. Heidi followed him step by step, watching everything that he did with unflagging attention, for all that happened interested her very much.

At last it was evening. The wind began to sigh through the old trees. As it blew harder, all the branches swayed back and forth. Heidi felt the sounds not only in her ears, but in her heart; and she was so happy, so happy, she ran out under the pines, and sprang and leaped for joy, as if she had found the greatest pleasure imaginable.

Her grandfather meanwhile stood in the doorway, and watched the child.

Suddenly a shrill whistle was heard. Heidi stopped her jumping, and the old man went out. Down from the mountain streamed the goats, one after the other, and Peter was in their midst.

With a joyous shout Heidi vanished into the midst of the flock, to greet her old friends of the morning, one and all.

When they reached the hut, they all stopped; and from out the herd came two beautiful slender goats, one white and one brown. They went to the old man, and licked his hands, for he held a little salt for them every evening when they came home. Peter vanished with the rest. Heidi stroked the goats gently, one after the other, then ran to the other side, and did the same. She was as joyful as possible over the charming creatures.

"Are they both ours, Grandfather? Will they go into our stall? Will they always stay here with us?" Heidi poured out her questions in her excitement, her grandfather having hardly a chance to repeat a continual, "Yes, yes, child," now and then.

When the goats had licked up all the salt, her grandfather said, "Go fetch your little mug and some bread."

Heidi obeyed, and he milked the goats into the mug, into which he cut bits of bread, and said, "Now eat your supper and then go to bed. Dete left another bundle for you. There are your night-

gowns, and so on, in it. You will find them in the cupboard. I must put up the goats now. Go, and sleep soundly."

"Good-night, Grandfather, good-night," shouted Heidi after him, as he disappeared with the goats. "What are their names?"

"The white one is called Schwänli, the other Bärli." [Little Swan and Little Bear]

"Good-night, Schwänli; good-night, Bärli," shouted the child at the top of her voice to the goats, who were already going into their stall.

The little girl sat down on the bench to eat her bread and milk, but the wind was so strong that it almost blew her off her seat; so she ate as fast as she could, went into the cottage, climbed up to her bed, and was soon fast asleep. Indeed, she slept all night as comfortably as a princess.

Not long after, but before it was quite dark, the old man also went to bed, for he was always up by sunrise, and that was very early in summer on the mountain. During the night the wind arose. It blew so hard that the hut shook, and the beams all cracked. The wind roared and moaned through the big chimney as if in anguish. In the old pine tree, too, it blew a blast that broke the old branches off as if in anger. In the midst of it all the old man rose, saying to himself, "The child will be afraid."

He mounted the ladder and went softly into Heidi's chamber. The moon was shining brightly in the clear sky, but in a moment the driving clouds flew across, and everything was dark. In another moment she shone clearly forth, through the round hole in the roof, and her beams fell on Heidi's bed. The little one slept with rosy red cheeks under her heavy covering, quiet and peaceful, with one round arm under her head, and certainly dreaming of something that made her happy, for her little face beamed with contentment. Her grandfather stood long, looking at the lonely, sleeping child, until the clouds again obscured the moon. Then he turned and went down the ladder.

The Story of a Bad Boy

THE ADVENTURES OF A FOURTH

by THOMAS BAILEY ALDRICH

This is the true story of the author's happy boyhood in a typical New England town called "Rivermouth," which is actually Portsmouth, New Hampshire. Tom was not really a bad boy, just full enough of fun and high spirits to make his escapades good reading. For a whole week before the old-fashioned Fourth of July celebration described here, there had been very little studying done at school because the boys could think of nothing except Roman candles, rockets, pin-wheels and gunpowder. Even in the classroom their pockets bulged with fire crackers and "if a boy whipped out his handkerchief without proper precaution, he was sure to let off two or three torpedoes."

Great were the bustle and confusion on the square. By the way, I don't know why they called this large open space a square, unless because it was an oval—an oval formed by the confluence of half a dozen streets, now thronged by crowds of smartly dressed towns-people and country folks; for Rivermouth on the Fourth was the centre of attraction to the inhabitants of the neighboring villages.

On one side of the Square were twenty or thirty booths arranged in a semi-circle, gay with little flags and seductive with lemonade, ginger-beer, and seed-cakes. Here and there were tables at which would be purchased the smaller sort of fireworks, such as pin-wheels, serpents, double-headers, and punk warranted not to go out. Many of the adjacent houses made a pretty display of bunting, and across each of the streets opening on the Square was an arch of spruce and evergreen, blossoming all over with patriotic mottoes and paper roses.

It was a noisy, merry, bewildering scene as we came upon the ground. The incessant rattle of small arms, the booming of the twelve-pounder firing on the Mill Dam, and the silvery clangor of the church-bells ringing simultaneously—not to mention an ambitious brass-band that was blowing itself to pieces on a balcony —were enough to drive one distracted. We amused ourselves for an hour or two, darting in and out among the crowd and setting off our crackers. At one o'clock the Honorable Hezekiah Elkins mounted a platform in the middle of the Square and delivered an oration to which his "feller-citizens" didn't pay much attention, having all they could do to dodge the squibs that were set loose upon them by mischievous boys stationed on the surrounding housetops.

Our little party which had picked up recruits here and there, not being swayed by eloquence, withdrew to a booth on the outskirts of the crowd, where we regaled ourselves with root beer at two cents a glass. I recollect being much struck by the placard surmounting the tent:

> ROOT BEER
> SOLD HERE

It seemed to me the perfection of pith and poetry. What could be more terse? Not a word to spare, and yet everything fully expressed. Rhyme and rhythm faultless. It was a delightful poet who made those verses. As for the beer itself—that, I think, must have been made from the root of all evil! A single glass of it insured an uninterrupted pain for twenty-four hours.

The influence of my liberality working on Charley Marden— for it was I who paid for the beer—he presently invited us all to take an ice cream with him at Pettingil's saloon. Pettingil was the Delmonico of Rivermouth. He furnished ices and confectionery for aristocratic balls and parties, and didn't disdain to officiate as leader of the orchestra at the same time; for Pettingil played on the violin, as Pepper Whitcomb described it, "like Old Scratch."

Pettingil's confectionery store was on the corner of Willow and High streets. The saloon, separated from the shop by a flight of three steps leading to a door hung with faded red drapery, had about it an air of mystery and seclusion quite delightful. Four windows, also draped, faced the side street, affording an unobstructed view of Marm Hatch's back yard, where a number of inexplicable garments on a clothes line were always to be seen careering in the wind.

There was a lull just then in the ice cream business, it being dinner-time, and we found the saloon unoccupied. When we had seated ourselves around the largest marble-topped table, Charley Marden in a manly voice ordered twelve sixpenny ice creams, "strawberry and verneller mixed."

It was a magnificent sight, those twelve chilly glasses entering the room on a waiter, the red and white custard rising from each glass like a church steeple, and the spoon handle shooting up from the apex like a spire. I doubt if a person of the nicest palate could have distinguished, with his eyes shut, which was the vanilla and which the strawberry; but if I could at this moment obtain a cream tasting as that did, I would give five dollars for a very small quantity.

We fell to with a will, and so evenly balanced were our capabilities that we finished our creams together, the spoons clinking in the glasses like one spoon.

"Let's have some more!" cried Charley Marden, with the air of Aladdin ordering up a fresh hogshead of pearls and rubies. "Tom Bailey, tell Pettingil to send in another round."

Could I credit my ears? I looked at him to see if he were in earnest. He meant it. In a moment I was leaning over the counter giving directions for a second supply. Thinking it would make no difference to such a gorgeous young sybarite as Marden, I took the liberty of ordering ninepenny creams this time.

On returning to the saloon, what was my horror at finding it empty!

There were the twelve cloudy glasses, standing in a circle on the sticky marble slab, and not a boy to be seen. A pair of hands letting go their hold on the window-sill outside explained matters. I had been made a victim.

I couldn't stay and face Pettingil, whose peppery temper was well known among the boys. I hadn't a cent in the world to appease him. What should I do? I heard the clink of approaching glasses—the ninepenny creams. I rushed to the nearest window. It was only five feet to the ground. I threw myself out as if I had been an old hat.

Landing on my feet, I fled breathlessly down High Street, through Willow, and was turning into Brierwood Place when the sound of several voices, calling to me in distress, stopped my progress.

"Look out, you fool! the mine! the mine!" yelled the warning voices.

Several men and boys were standing at the head of the street, making insane gestures to me to avoid something. But I saw no mine, only in the middle of the road in front of me was a common flour-barrel, which, as I gazed at it, suddenly rose into the air with a terrific explosion. I felt myself thrown violently off my feet. I remember nothing else, excepting that, as I went up, I caught a momentary glimpse of Ezra Wingate leering through his shop-window like an avenging spirit.

The mine that had wrought me woe was not properly a mine at all, but merely a few ounces of powder placed under an empty keg or barrel and fired with a slow-match. Boys who didn't happen to have pistols or cannon generally burnt their powder in this fashion.

For an account of what followed I am indebted to hearsay, for I was insensible when the people picked me up and carried me home on a shutter borrowed from the proprietor of Pettingil's saloon. I was supposed to be killed, but happily (happily for me at least) I was merely stunned. I lay in a semi-unconscious state

until eight o'clock that night, when I attempted to speak. Miss Abigail, who watched by the bedside, put her ear down to my lips and was saluted with these remarkable words:

"Strawberry and verneller mixed!"

"Mercy on us! What is the boy saying?" cried Miss Abigail.

"ROOTBEERSOLDHERE!"

Hans Brinker, or the Silver Skates

HANS AND GRETEL FIND A FRIEND

by MARY MAPES DODGE

This story about a brother and sister in Holland was one of the first books written about children in a foreign country and it is still one of the best and most popular. The author is an American, but when she was travelling in Holland with her children and asked for the best boy's book about Holland, the librarian gave her a copy of her own book, Hans Brinker. Boys and girls love this book, however, not so much for its true picture of Dutch life and the exciting ice-skate races, as for the appealing characters of Hans and Gretel. They are so gay and uncomplaining in spite of their poverty, and the scenes between the poor brother and sister and the rich children are packed with true emotion.

At noon our young friends poured forth from the schoolhouse intent upon having an hour's practicing upon the canal.

They had skated but a few moments when Carl Schummel said mockingly to Hilda:

"There's a pretty pair just coming upon the ice! The little rag-pickers! Their skates must have been a present from the king direct."

"They are patient creatures," said Hilda, gently. "It must have been hard to learn to skate upon such queer affairs. They are very poor peasants, you see. The boy has probably made the skates himself."

Carl was somewhat abashed.

"Patient they may be, but, as for skating, they start off pretty well only to finish with a jerk. They could move well to your new staccato piece I think."

Hilda laughed pleasantly and left him. After joining a small detachment of the racers, and sailing past every one of them, she halted beside Gretel who, with eager eyes, had been watching the sport.

"What is your name, little girl?"

"Gretel, my lady," answered the child, somewhat awed by Hilda's rank, though they were nearly of the same age, "and my brother is called Hans."

"Hans is a stout fellow," said Hilda, cheerily, "and seems to have a warm stove somewhere within him, but you look cold. You should wear more clothing, little one."

Gretel, who had nothing else to wear, tried to laugh as she answered:

"I am not so very little. I am past twelve years old."

"Oh, I beg your pardon. You see I am nearly fourteen, and so large for my age that other girls seem small to me, but that is nothing. Perhaps you will shoot up far above me yet; not unless you dress more warmly, though—shivering girls never grow."

Hans flushed as he saw tears rising in Gretel's eyes.

"My sister has not complained of the cold; but this is bitter weather they say——" and he looked sadly upon Gretel.

"It is nothing," said Gretel, "I am often warm—too warm when I am skating. You are good, jufvrouw, to think of it."

"No, no," answered Hilda, quite angry at herself. "I am careless, cruel; but I meant no harm. I wanted to ask you—I mean— if——" and here Hilda, coming to the point of her errand, faltered before the poorly clad but noble-looking children she wished to serve.

"What is it, young lady?" exclaimed Hans eagerly. "If there is any service I can do? any——"

"Oh! no, no," laughed Hilda, shaking off her embarrassment, "I only wished to speak to you about the grand race. Why do you not join it? You both can skate well, and the ranks are free. Anyone may enter for the prize."

Gretel looked wistfully at Hans, who tugging at his cap, answered respectfully:

"Ah, jufvrouw, even if we could enter, we could skate only a few strokes with the rest. Our skates are hard wood, you see," holding up the sole of his foot, "but they soon become damp, and then they stick and trip us."

Gretel's eyes twinkled with fun as she thought of Hans' mishap in the morning, but she blushed as she faltered out timidly:

"Oh no, we can't join; but may we be there, my lady, on the great day to look on?"

"Certainly," answered Hilda, looking kindly into the two earnest faces, and wishing from her heart that she had not spent so much of her monthly allowance for lace and finery. She had but eight kwartjes left, and they would buy but one pair of skates, at the furthest.

Looking down with a sigh at the two pair of feet so very different in size, she asked:

"Which of you is the better skater?"

"Gretel," replied Hans, promptly.

"Hans," answered Gretel, in the same breath. Hilda smiled.

"I cannot buy you each a pair of skates, or even one good pair; but here are eight kwartjes. Decide between you which stands the best chance of winning the race, and buy the skates accordingly. I wish I had enough to buy better ones—good-bye!" and, with a nod and a smile, Hilda, after handing the money to the electrified Hans, glided swiftly away to rejoin her companions.

"Jufvrouw! jufvrouw von Gleck!" called Hans in a loud tone, stumbling after her as well as he could, for one of his skate strings was untied.

Hilda turned, and with one hand raised to shield her eyes from the sun, seemed to him to be floating through the air, nearer and nearer.

"We cannot take this money," panted Hans, "though we know your goodness in giving it."

"Why not indeed?" asked Hilda flushing.

"Because," replied Hans, bowing like a clown, but looking with the eye of a prince at the queenly girl, "we have not earned it."

Hilda was quick-witted. She had noticed a pretty wooden chain upon Gretel's neck.

"Carve me a chain, Hans, like the one your sister wears."

"That I will, lady, with all my heart, we have white-wood in the house, fine as ivory; you shall have one tomorrow," and Hans hastily tried to return the money.

"No, no," said Hilda, decidedly. "That sum will be but a poor price for the chain," and off she darted, outstripping the fleetest among the skaters.

Hans sent a long, bewildered gaze after her; it was useless, he felt, to make any further resistance.

"It is right," he muttered, half to himself, half to his faithful shadow, Gretel, "I must work hard every minute, and sit up half the night if the mother will let me burn a candle; but the chain shall be finished. We may keep the money, Gretel."

"What a good little lady!" cried Gretel clapping her hands with delight. "Oh! Hans, was it for nothing the stork settled on our roof last summer? Do you remember how the mother said it would bring us luck, and how she cried when Janzoon Kolp shot him? And she said it would bring him trouble. But the luck has come to us at last! Now, Hans, if Mother sends us to town tomorrow you can buy the skates in the market-place."

Hans shook his head. "The young lady would have given us the money to buy skates; but if I earn it, Gretel, it shall be spent for wool. You must have a warm jacket."

"Oh!" cried Gretel, in real dismay, "not buy the skates! Why I am not often cold! Mother says the blood runs up and down in poor children's veins humming 'I must keep 'em warm! I must keep 'em warm.'"

"Oh, Hans," she continued with something like a sob, "don't say you won't buy the skates, it makes me feel just like crying—besides, I want to be cold—I mean I'm real, awful warm—so now!"

Hans looked up hurriedly. He had a true Dutch horror of tears, or emotion of any kind, and most of all, he dreaded to see his sister's blue eyes overflowing.

"Now mind," cried Gretel, seeing her advantage, "I'll feel awful if you give up the skates. I don't want them. I'm not such a stingy as that; but I want you to have them, and then when I get bigger they'll do for me—oh-h—count the pieces, Hans. Did ever you see so many!"

Hans turned the money thoughtfully in his palm. Never in all his life had he longed so intensely for a pair of skates, for he had known of the race and had, boylike, fairly ached for a chance to test his powers with the other children. He felt confident that with a good pair of steel runners, he could readily distance most of the boys on the canal. Then, too, Gretel's argument was so plausible. On the other hand, he knew that she, with her strong but lithe little frame, needed but a week's practice on good runners, to make her a better skater than Rychie Korbes or even Katrinka Flack. As soon as this last thought flashed upon him his resolve was made. If Gretel would not have the jacket, she should have the skates.

"No, Gretel," he answered at last, "I can wait. Some day I may have money enough saved to buy a fine pair. You shall have these."

Gretel's eyes sparkled; but in another instant she insisted, rather faintly:

"The young lady gave the money to you, Hans. I'd be real bad to take it."

Hans shook his head, resolutely, as he trudged on, causing his sister to half skip and half walk in her effort to keep beside him; by this time they had taken off their wooden "rockers," and were hastening home to tell their mother the good news.

"Oh! I know!" cried Gretel, in a sprightly tone. "You can do this. You can get a pair a little too small for you, and too big for me, and we can take turns and use them. Won't that be fine?" and Gretel clapped her hands again.

Poor Hans! This was a strong temptation, but he pushed it away from him.

"Nonsense, Gretel. You could never get on with a big pair. You

stumbled about with these, like a blind chicken, before I curved off the ends. No, you must have a pair to fit exactly, and you must practice every chance you can get, until the 20th comes. My little Gretel shall win the silver skates."

Gretel could not help laughing with delight at the very idea.

"Hans! Gretel!" called out a familiar voice.

"Coming, Mother!" and they hastened toward the cottage, Hans still shaking the pieces of silver in his hand.

On the following day, there was not a prouder nor a happier boy in all Holland than Hans Brinker as he watched his sister, with many a dexterous sweep, flying in and out among the skaters who at sundown thronged the canal. A warm jacket had been given her by the kind-hearted Hilda, and the burst-out shoes had been cobbled into decency by Dame Brinker. As the little creature darted backward and forward, flushed with enjoyment, and quite unconscious of the many wondering glances bent upon her, earth turned suddenly into Fairyland, while "Hans, dear, good Hans!" echoed itself over and over again in her grateful heart.

"By den donder!" exclaimed Peter van Holp to Carl Schummel, "but that little one in the red jacket and patched petticoat skates well. Gunst! she has toes on her heels, and eyes in the back of her head! See her! It will be a joke if she gets in the race and beats Katrinka Flack, after all."

"Hush! not so loud!" returned Carl, rather sneeringly. "That little lady in rags is the special pet of Hilda van Gleck. Those shining skates are her gift, if I make no mistake."

"So! so!" exclaimed Peter, with a radiant smile, for Hilda was his best friend. "She has been at her good work there, too!" And Mynheer van Holp, after cutting a double 8 on the ice, to say nothing of a huge P, then a jump, and an H, glided onward until he found himself beside Hilda.

Hand in hand, they skated together, laughingly at first, then staidly talking in a low tone.

Strange to say, Peter van Holp soon arrived at a sudden conviction that his little sister needed a wooden chain just like Hilda's.

Two days afterward, on Saint Nicholas' Eve, Hans, having burned three candle-ends and cut his thumb into the bargain, stood in the market-place at Amsterdam, buying another pair of skates.

In the Garden

by ELIZABETH COATSWORTH

Violets, daffodils,
Roses and thorn
Were all in the garden
Before you were born.
Daffodils, violets,
Green thorn and roses
Your grandchildren's children
Will hold to their noses.

He Prayeth Best

by SAMUEL TAYLOR COLERIDGE

He prayeth best who loveth best
All things both great and small;
For the dear God who loveth us,
He made and loveth all.

The Bastable Children

THE TREASURE SEEKERS

by E. NESBIT

The "I" who tells this story is one of six Bastable children, four boys and two girls, who live in a suburb near London. In the chapter before this one, they learn that their father has lost his money and they are now very poor. So they plan a way to help him out financially. Because they believe that "people who dig for treasure always find it," they begin to dig right in their own garden, with the results described below. The Bastable children have lively imaginations—fed on much reading of fairy tales—and enormous energy, and they manage to make delightful adventures out of the everyday things that happen to them as they search for treasure. In the end, they do find a sort of treasure, though it comes to them, not by magic, but through their own generosity and kindness towards their uncle from India, whom they had mistaken for a poor man, but he really had a fortune.

I am afraid the last chapter was rather dull. It is always dull in books when people talk and talk, and don't do anything, but I was obliged to put it in, or else you wouldn't have understood all the rest. The best part of books is when things are happening. That is the best part of real things too. That is why I shall not tell you in this story about all the days when nothing happened. You will not catch me saying, "thus the sad days passed slowly by" —or "the years rolled on their weary course," or "time went on"— because it is silly; of course time goes on, whether you say so or not. So I shall just tell you the nice, interesting parts—and in between, you will understand that we had our meals and got up and went to bed, and dull things like that. It would be sickening to write all that down, though of course it happens. I said so to Albert-next-door's uncle, who writes books, and he said "Quite right, that's what we call selection, a necessity of true art." And he is very clever indeed. So you see.

I have often thought that if the people who write books for children knew a little more, it would be better. I shall not tell you anything about us except what I should like to know about, if I was reading the story and you were writing it. Albert's uncle says I ought to have put this in the preface, but I never read prefaces, and it is not much good writing things just for people to skip. I wonder other authors have never thought of this.

Well, when we had agreed to dig for treasure we all went down into the cellar and lighted the gas. Oswald would have liked to dig there, but it is stone flags. We looked among the old boxes and broken chairs and fenders and empty bottles and things, and at last we found the spades we had to dig in the sand with when we went to the seaside three years ago. They are not silly, babyish, wooden spades, that split if you look at them, but good iron, with a blue mark across the top of the iron part, and yellow wooden handles. We wasted a little time getting them dusted, because the girls wouldn't dig with spades that had cobwebs on them. Girls would never do for African explorers or anything like that, they are too beastly particular.

It was no use doing the thing by halves. We marked out a sort of square in the mouldy part of the garden, about three yards across, and began to dig. But we found nothing except worms and stones—and the ground was very hard.

So we thought we'd try another part of the garden, and we found a place in the big round flower bed, where the ground was much softer. We thought we'd make a smaller hole to begin with, and it was much better. We dug and dug and dug, and it was jolly hard work! We got very hot digging, but we found nothing.

Presently Albert-next-door looked over the wall. We do not like him very much, but we let him play with us sometimes, because his father is dead, and you must not be unkind to orphans, even if their mothers are alive. Albert is always very tidy. He wears frilly collars and velvet knickerbockers. I can't think how he can bear to.

So we said, "Hullo!"

And he said, "What are you up to?"

"We're digging for treasure," said Alice; "an ancient parchment revealed to us the place of concealment. Come over and help us. When we have dug deep enough we shall find a great pot of red clay, full of gold and precious jewels."

Albert-next-door only sniggered and said, "What silly nonsense!" He cannot play properly at all. It is very strange, because he has a very nice uncle. You see, Albert-next-door doesn't care for reading, and he has not read nearly so many books as we and he is very foolish and ignorant, but it cannot be helped, and you just have to put up with it when you want him to do anything. Besides, it is wrong to be angry with people for not being so clever as you are yourself. It is not always their fault.

So Oswald said, "Come and dig! Then you shall share the treasure when we've found it."

But he said, "I shan't—I don't like digging—and I'm just going in to my tea."

"Come along and dig, there's a good boy," Alice said. "You can use my spade. It's much the best—"

So he came along and dug, and when once he was over the wall we kept him at it, and we worked as well, of course, and the hole got deep. Pincher worked too—he is our dog and he is very good at digging. He digs for rats in the dustbin sometimes, and gets very dirty. But we love our dog, even when his face wants washing.

"I expect we shall have to make a tunnel," Oswald said, "to reach the rich treasure." So he jumped into the hole and began to dig at one side. After that we took it in turns to dig at the tunnel, and Pincher was most useful in scraping the earth out of the tunnel—he does it with his back feet when you say "Rats!", and he digs with his front ones, and burrows with his nose as well.

At last the tunnel was nearly a yard long, and big enough to creep along to find the treasure, if only it had been a bit longer. Now it was Albert's turn to go in and dig, but he funked it.

"Take your turn like a man," said Oswald—nobody can say that Oswald doesn't take his turn like a man. But Albert wouldn't. So we had to make him, because it was only fair.

"It's quite easy," Alice said, "you just crawl in and dig with your hands. Then when you come out, we can scrape out what you've done, with the spades. Come—be a man. You won't notice it being dark in the tunnel if you shut your eyes tight. We've all been in except Dora—and she doesn't like worms."

"I don't like worms neither." Albert-next-door said this; but we remembered how he had picked a fat red and black worm up in his fingers, and thrown it at Dora only the day before.

So we put him in.

But he would not go in head first, the proper way, and dig with his hands as we had done, and though Oswald was angry at the time, for he hates snivellers, yet afterwards he owned that perhaps it was just as well. You should never be afraid to own that perhaps you were mistaken—but it is cowardly to do it unless you are quite sure you are in the wrong.

"Let me go in feet first," said Albert-next-door. "I'll dig with my boots—I will truly, honour bright."

So we let him go in feet first—and he did it very slowly and at last he was in, and only his head sticking out into the hole; and all the rest of him in the tunnel.

"Now dig with your boots," said Oswald, "and, Alice, do catch hold of Pincher, he'll be digging again in another minute, and perhaps it would be uncomfortable for Albert, if Pincher threw the mould into his eyes."

You should always try to think of these little things. Thinking of other people's comfort makes them like you. Alice held Pincher, and we all shouted, "Kick! dig with your feet, for all you're worth!"

So Albert-next-door began to dig with his feet, and we stood on the ground over him, waiting—and all in a minute the ground gave way, and we tumbled together in a heap; and when we got up there was a little shallow hollow where we had been standing and Albert-next-door was underneath, stuck quite fast, because the roof of the tunnel had tumbled in on him. He is a horribly unlucky boy to have anything to do with.

It was dreadful the way he cried and screamed, though he had to own, it didn't hurt, only it was rather heavy and he couldn't move his legs. We would have dug him out all right enough, in time, but he screamed so we were afraid the police would come, so Dicky climbed over the wall, to tell the cook there, to tell Albert-next-door's uncle he had been buried by mistake, and to come and help dig him out.

Dicky was a long time gone. We wondered what had become of him, and all the while the screaming went on and on, for we had taken the loose earth off Albert's face, so that he could scream quite easily and comfortably.

Presently Dicky came back and Albert-next-door's uncle came with him. He has very long legs, and his hair is light and his face is brown. He has been to sea, but now he writes books. I like him.

He told his nephew to stow it, so Albert did, and then he asked him if he was hurt—and Albert had to say he wasn't, for though he is a coward and very unlucky, he is not a liar like some boys are.

"This promises to be a protracted if agreeable task," said Albert-next-door's uncle, rubbing his hands and looking at the hole with Albert's head in it. "I will get another spade." So he fetched the big spade out of the next door garden tool-shed, and began to dig his nephew out.

"Mind you keep very still," he said, "or I might chunk a bit out of you with the spade." Then after a little while he said:

"I confess that I am not absolutely insensible to the dramatic interest of the situation. My curiosity is excited. I own that I should like to know how my nephew happened to be buried. But don't tell me if you'd rather not. I suppose no force was used?"

"Only moral force," said Alice. They used to talk a lot about moral force at the High School where she went, and in case you don't know what it means, I'll tell you that it is making people do

what they don't want to, just by slanging them, or laughing at them, or promising them things if they're good.

"Only moral force, eh?" said Albert-next-door's uncle. "Well?"

"Well," Dora said, "I'm very sorry it happened to Albert—I'd rather it had been one of us. It would have been my turn to go into the tunnel, only I don't like worms, so they let me off. You see we were digging for treasure."

"Yes," said Alice, "and I think we were just coming to the underground passage that leads to the secret hoard, when the tunnel fell in on Albert. He is so unlucky," and she sighed.

Then Albert-next-door began to scream again and his uncle wiped his face—his own face, not Albert's—with his silk handkerchief, and then he put it in his trousers pocket. It seems a strange place to put a handkerchief, but he had his coat and waistcoat off, and I suppose he wanted the handkerchief handy. Digging is warm work.

He told Albert-next-door to drop it, or he wouldn't proceed further in the matter, so Albert stopped screaming, and presently his uncle finished digging him out. Albert did look so funny, with his hair all dusty and his velvet suit covered with mould and his face muddy with earth and crying.

We all said how sorry we were, but he wouldn't say a word back to us. He was most awfully sick to think he'd been the one buried, when it might just as well have been one of us. I felt myself that it was hard lines.

"So you were digging for treasure," said Albert-next-door's uncle, wiping his face again with his handkerchief. "Well, I fear that your chances of success are small. I have made a careful study of the whole subject. What I don't know about buried treasure is not worth knowing. And I never knew more than one coin buried in any one garden—and that is generally—Hullo—what's that?"

He pointed to something in the hole he had just dragged Albert out of. Oswald picked it up. It was a half-crown. We looked at each other, speechless with surprise and delight, like in books.

"Well, that's lucky, at all events," said Albert-next-door's uncle. "Let's see, that's fivepence each for you."

"It's fourpence—something; I can't do fractions," said Dicky; "there are seven of us, you see."

"Oh, you count Albert as one of yourselves on this occasion, eh?"

"Of course," said Alice; "and I say, he was buried after all. Why shouldn't we let him have the odd somethings, and we'll have fourpence each."

We all agreed to this, and told Albert-next-door we would bring his share as soon as we could get the half-crown changed. He cheered up a little at that and his uncle wiped his face again—he did look hot—and began to put on his coat and waistcoat.

When he had done it he stooped and picked up something. He held it up, and you will hardly believe it, but it is quite true—it was another half-crown!

"To think that there should be two!" he said; "in all my experience of buried treasure I never heard of such a thing!"

I wish Albert-next-door's uncle would come treasure-seeking with us regularly; he must have very sharp eyes: for Dora says she was looking just the minute before at the very place where the second half-crown was picked up from, and she never saw it.

Travel

by ROBERT LOUIS STEVENSON

I should like to rise and go
Where the golden apples grow;—
Where below another sky
Parrot islands anchored lie,
And, watched by cockatoos and goats,
Lonely Crusoes building boats;—
Where in sunshine reaching out
Eastern cities, miles about,
Are with mosque and minaret
Among sandy gardens set,
And the rich goods from near and far
Hang for sale in the bazaar;—
Where the Great Wall round China goes,
And on one side the desert blows,
And with bell and voice and drum,
Cities on the other hum;—
Where are forests, hot as fire,
Wide as England, tall as a spire,

Full of apes and cocoa-nuts
And the Negro hunters' huts;—
Where the knotty crocodile
Lies and blinks in the Nile,
And the red flamingo flies
Hunting fish before his eyes;—
Where in jungles, near and far,
Man-devouring tigers are,
Lying close and giving ear
Lest the hunt be drawing near,
Or a comer-by be seen
Swinging in a palanquin;—
Where among the desert sands
Some deserted city stands,
All its children, sweep and prince,
Grown to manhood ages since,
Not a foot in street or house,
Not a stir of child or mouse,
And when kindly falls the night,
In all the town no spark of light.
There I'll come when I'm a man
With a camel caravan;
Light a fire in the gloom
Of some dusty dining-room;
See the pictures on the walls,
Heroes, fights, and festivals;
And in a corner find the toys
Of the old Egyptian boys.

The Good Master

COUSIN KATE FROM BUDAPEST

by KATE SEREDY

Kate does not always behave quite so badly as she does in this opening chapter. Under the loving yet firm guidance of "the good master," as Jancsi's father is called, the little city girl from Budapest learns to take her place on the ranch. She even succeeds in rounding up some wild horses and preventing a stampede. For this story of life on a large horse farm in Hungary, Kate Seredy has used the recollections of her own childhood spent there. The descriptions of how the country people live on the Hungarian plains, their festivals, fairs, and legends are vivid and authentic. But what has probably made this book so exceedingly popular is the personal development of Kate, the headstrong resentful girl who blossoms into a fine dependable person who can appreciate the goodness of daily farm life and the warm and affectionate atmosphere of her new home. And The Good Master *is also full of spirited adventures that the two cousins enjoy on the ranch.*

Jancsi was up bright and early that morning and at work milking the cows. He was so excited he couldn't stay in bed. For today Cousin Kate was coming. She was the only cousin he had, and she was a city girl. A real city girl from Budapest. Ever since the letter came from his uncle, Jancsi had been the proudest boy on the big Hungarian plain. He was the only boy in the neighborhood who had a cousin in the city. And she was coming today, to stay for a long time. Father had told Jancsi what was in the letter. It said that Kate had had the measles last winter. Jancsi had never had the measles—he thought it must be something wonderful to have. And she was delicate, the letter said, too, so she was coming to the country. A *delicate* city cousin, who had had the *measles*— that was something.

If it were only Sunday, they would go to church and he could tell everybody about her. Sunday was the only time when Jancsi saw anyone outside his own family. Father had a ranch, with thousands of sheep, horses, cows, and pigs. He had chickens and ducks and geese; he even had donkeys, but he didn't have enough children to suit Jancsi. It got so lonesome for poor Jancsi, he would have given ten horses for a brother. He had it all figured out—he would give a donkey for even a sister. Not horses, just a donkey.

The ranch was miles and miles from the village. It was too far to walk, and they were too busy to drive on weekdays. So, although Jancsi was ten years old and quite a man if you asked his opinion, he had never been to school, and he did not know how to read or write. The ranch was the only reality to him—the world outside was just a fairy story. Mother knew lots of fairy stories about dragons and golden-haired princesses who lived in glittering castles. Jancsi thought that houses in Budapest were made of gold and had diamond windows. All the city people rode around on pure white horses and wore silk gowns. Cousin Kate would have golden curls, rosy cheeks, big blue eyes; she would wear a white silk flowing gown, and her voice would be like honey. Now—Jancsi is off in dreamland—some day a dragon will capture her, and it will be up to Jancsi to go to the rescue. He is clad in green velvet, red boots, riding a coal-black steed. Here comes the dragon! Jancsi pulls out his golden sword, and one-two-three heads are at his feet! All good dragons have twelve perfectly hideous heads. Four— slash, five—swish goes his sword——

"Mo-o-o-o!" bellowed something close to him. And crash-bang went Jancsi together with the milking-stool. He sat and blinked. Máli, the mottled cow, looked at him with reproachful eyes.

Reality closed around the hero—oh yes, here he was in the barn, milking the cow.

"Jancsi! Ja-a-ncsi-i! Hurry up with the milk or you'll be late for the train!" It was his mother's voice calling from the house. He scrambled to his feet, scowled at Máli, and picking up the full pails made his way back to the kitchen. Mother took the milk from him. "I'll strain it today, Jancsi. You eat your breakfast and get dressed. And get a good scrub—why, you're all full of mud!"

Jancsi kept his back out of Mother's sight—the seat of his white pants would need explaining. He gulped down his bread and milk. Then, backing out of the kitchen, he ran to the well. He filled a wooden bucket with the icy water and, stripping off his clothes, stepped into it. With great splutters and groans he scrubbed himself, using sand on the most disgraceful spots. Then he took a bit of salt from a mug and scrubbed his teeth with his fingers. Squirting out the salty water, he set a new long-distance record; he even paused long enough to gaze at it admiringly and mark the spot with a stone. "Can spit almost as far as Father," he muttered with pride.

He ran back to the house. His very best Sunday clothes were all laid out on the bench, near the big white stove—his embroidered shirt, the wide pleated pants, his shiny black boots, his round hat with the bunch of flowers. He put them on. Mother wasn't in the kitchen. He went to the bedroom. No Mother in the bedroom. But on the windowsill, glittering in the sunshine, was a green bottle. He gazed at it for a while, torn between desire and discipline. It was too much for him. Tiptoeing to the window, he took the bottle and the little red comb next to it. It was perfumed hair oil—and only *men* used perfumed hair oil! He put a little on his hair. Then a little more, and still more, until his hair looked as if it were made of black enamel. Then with a sigh of satisfaction he put on his hat and strutted out. He heard the wagon—time to go!

When he saw the wagon drive up to the door, he gave a whoop of joy. Father had harnessed his four black horses with the very best brass-studded harness. Each horse had a big bunch of geraniums fastened to the headband, and long streamers of gayly colored ribbons floated in the breeze. He jumped up next to Father, and off they went down the long poplar-lined lane leading to the main road.

It was early April, and fields and pastures were a fresh pale green. The poplars stood like solemn sentinels, whispering to the wind. Father was a man of few words; men never spoke, he believed, unless they had something important to say. Gossip was only for the womenfolks. Jancsi was quiet, too, busy with his own thoughts. He was going to the town for the first time in his life—he would see a train. Trains were a mystery to him. One of the shepherds had told him trains were fire-eating dragons; they roared, and snorted black smoke. "They pull little houses; people go from one place to another in the little houses. And trains kill everybody who gets in their way." Jancsi wondered if he could hitch their own house to one of these dragons. Then he could go and see the world. But he would take his dog Peti, he'd take his favorite horse, he'd take Máli, the cow . . . No, he scowled and rubbed his side, remembering this morning. No, he wouldn't take Máli. Deeply absorbed in deciding whom he would take with him, he hardly noticed how fast they were traveling. Soon they left the open country and entered the long village street. The village was always interesting to him, so he began to look around. Father turned to him. "I'll stop at the store to buy some tobacco. You hold the reins, Jancsi." Jancsi slid over to Father's seat and grabbed the reins. He sat there, head up, shoulders erect, looking straight ahead. Just then a village boy walked by. He stopped and looked at Jancsi with open admiration.

"Hey! You driving *alone?*"

Jancsi gulped and replied evasively: "Going to fetch my cousin from the train. She comes from Budapest." Then, unable to keep from gossiping like womenfolks, he blurted out his news: "She had the measles and is delicate and her name is Kate! She'll live with us!"

Father came down the store steps, stuffing his pipe. Jancsi prayed for a miracle. If the boy would only go away or if Father would only let him drive . . . !

The miracle came. Father walked around the wagon and, getting up next to Jancsi, said: "Let's see how you handle wagon and four!"

So they left the boy staring after them openmouthed. Jancsi drove through the village like a king in a golden coach. The clouds of white dust around the horses' hoofs were like stardust to him. The glittering hoofs were made of diamonds. Everything looked new and beautiful to him today. The endless rows of snow-white houses with their gayly painted doors and shutters were like pearls in a row. The geraniums in the windows were a brighter red than ever. The church seemed taller, the grass greener. He flipped his whip impatiently at the barking dogs and almost rode over a flock of honking geese slowly plodding across the street. Then they were in the open country again. It was almost noon; the spring sun beat down on the shimmering fields. They passed a long fence. Horses were grazing placidly in the pasture.

"Good horseflesh," remarked Father. "See how meek they look now, but it's a man's job to stay on one of those beasts."

"I can get on one and stay on it, Father. Those aren't worse than your own horses."

"Think you can, Son?"

"I *know* I can!" asserted Jancsi hastily, forgetting that this would call for explanations. He was not yet allowed to ride unbroken horses.

"You *know* you can?" said Father, reaching for his pocket knife. Jancsi watched him in shocked silence. He knew he was in for it, but somehow he didn't mind. After the pocket knife came a little round stick of wood with many cross-marks cut into it. It was the score pad. One notch was cut in for each sin Jancsi committed, and after a while it was crossed out. But the "after a while" usually included moments Jancsi didn't like to remember. Holding knife and stick in his hands, Father looked at Jancsi. Jancsi looked far, far ahead. Suddenly Father laughed and, putting away the "score," slapped Jancsi on the back.

"You're no worse than I was at your age, Son. You'll make a good rancher."

Jancsi heaved a sigh of relief. This was a man's world, and he was accepted!

Father pointed ahead. "See those houses and chimneys? That's the town and the station." Jancsi was all eyes and ears now. Soon the wagon was rattling on the cobbled street. They passed lots of buildings, and there were a great many people walking around. Father told him where to stop and, after the horses were hitched to a post, said: "Well done, boy!" This made Jancsi feel still better. Praises from Father were few and far between, but they were all the more satisfying.

Walking through the station building, they came to the platform. "Those long shiny snakes are rails, Son; the train travels on them. It'll be here soon now."

Jancsi heard a great rumbling, snorting, and pounding in the distance. He felt the platform shake under his feet. Casting a frightened look at his father, he saw that Father wasn't afraid, so it must be all right. Then he saw a black monster rushing around the curve. It must be the dragon. It had an immense eye glittering in the sunshine. Vicious-looking black teeth, close to the ground. And black smoke poured out of its head. Then it gave a shrill scream, blew white smoke out of its ears, and came to a groaning halt. Men jumped down, opened the doors of the funny little black houses. Jancsi waited with eyes round and shiny like big black cherries. He expected to see people in silks and velvets, glorious people. But not one of them had good clothes on; they were just everyday people dressed in drab grays and browns. Then he heard someone shouting: "Márton Nagy! Is Márton Nagy here?"

Father yelled back: "Here! Márton Nagy!" A man hurried toward them, dragging a little girl with him. Just any kind of little girl, with plain black hair, a smudgy face, and skinny legs.

"Well, thank goodness you're here," said the man, wiping his forehead. "Here, take this—this imp, this unspeakable little devil —take her and welcome." He pushed the girl to Father. "Never again in my life will I take care of girls. I'm a self-respecting railroad guard. I handle anything from baggage to canaries, but I'd

rather travel with a bag of screaming monkeys than her, any time."
He gave her a final push. "Here's your uncle, he'll take care of you
now. G'bye and—good luck to you, Mister Nagy!"

All this tirade left Jancsi and Father speechless. Here was Kate,
looking as meek as Moses, but evidently something was wrong
with her. Father bent down and said: "Well, Kate, I am your
Uncle Márton and this is Jancsi, your cousin. We'll take you home
now."

Cousin Kate looked up. Her dirty little face broke into a grin.
"Oh, but you look funny!" she cried. "And I thought my cousin
was a boy, and she's nothing but a girl!"

"But, Kate," said Father, "can't you see he's a boy?"

"I only see that she has skirts on and an embroidered blouse.
Nobody's wearing embroidered blouses this season, they're out of
style!"

Jancsi just began to realize that this dirty, skinny little girl in
the plain blue dress was his cousin. He felt cheated—that was bad
enough—but she called Father "funny" and said he was a *girl*—
that was really too much! With fists clenched, chin stuck out, he
advanced toward Kate. "I am a girl, am I? . . . I'm funny, am I?
. . . I'll show you!"

Kate was ready. She dropped her bag, took a threatening step
toward Jancsi. They were face to face now, tense, poised like two
little bantam roosters, ready to settle the argument on the spot.
Suddenly Father's hearty laugh broke the tension. "You two little
monkeys," he cried, "now I'll tell you that you are both funny!
Stop this nonsense, both of you. Jancsi! Gentlemen don't fight
girls. Come on, we'll go home."

He grabbed their hands and, still laughing, walked to the bag-
gage-room. Jancsi and Kate had no choice, they had to go, but at
least they could make faces at each other behind his back. The
fight was not over, it was just put off for the moment.

When they reached the wagon, there was more trouble. Kate
declared that since the wagon had no top, she'd get a sunstroke.
It didn't have cushions on the seat, so she'd break to pieces. She
told Father to "phone" for a "taxicab."

"I'll wash your mouth out with soap, if you swear at *my* father!" cried Jancsi. "Phone" and "taxicab" sounded like swearing to him.

"She wasn't swearing, Jancsi," said Father; "she is just talking city language. 'Phone' is a little black box, you can talk into it, and people many miles away hear you. 'Taxicab' is a horseless wagon city people travel in." He turned to Kate. "We haven't any taxi-cabs here, Kate, so come on, hop on the seat."

Kate shook her head. "I will not. Ride in this old wagon indeed! Why, everybody will laugh at me."

Father's patience was wearing out. He just grabbed Kate under the arms and lifted her into the seat before she knew what had happened. "Come on, Son, we can't waste the whole day. You sit on the outside so she won't fall off." They both got on the wagon. Kate almost disappeared between them. Father was a very big man, and Jancsi a big husky boy for his age. But what Kate lacked in size, she made up in temper. When she realized what had happened, she turned into a miniature whirlwind. She kicked and screamed, she pinched Jancsi, she squirmed like a "bag of screaming monkeys."

"Father, the man was right, she's a bag of screaming monkeys!" said Jancsi, half angry, half amused, holding on to Kate.

Father was busy holding the horses in check. They were respectable farm horses, not used to the unpleasant sounds Kate managed to make. Soon they left the town and were traveling at a fast clip on the country road. Little by little Kate subsided. The long trip in the train and all the excitement were beginning to wear her out. She looked around. She saw the great Hungarian plain unfold before her eyes. Something in her was touched by the solemn beauty of it. Its immense grassy expanses unbroken by mountains or trees, shimmering under the spring sun. The dark blue sky, cloudless, like an inverted blue bowl. Herds of grazing sheep, like patches of snow. No sound, save the soft thud of the horses' hoofs on the white dusty road, and now and then the distant tinkle of sheep's bells, or the eerie sound of a shepherd's flute, the tilinkó. At times these plains, called the "puszta," are the very essence of timeless calm. At times the puszta wakes up and resembles an ocean in a storm. Clouds, so low it seems you can reach up and touch them, gather above. Hot winds roar over the waving grass. Frightened herds stampede, bellowing and crying. But calm or stormy, it is magnificent. Its people are truly children of the soil, they are like the puszta itself. Good-natured, calm, smiling, they, like the plain, can be aroused to violent emotions.

Kate did not know all this, but she was touched by the greatness and calm of it. She was very quiet now. Jancsi looked at her and touched Father's shoulder. They smiled at each other—she seemed asleep. Jancsi felt almost sorry for her now, she was so little and thin, so funny with her dirty little face. "Like a kitten," he thought, "the poor little kitten I found after the storm." He moved, to give her more room. She leaned heavily against him, her head nodding. He didn't see her face now, didn't see the slow impish grin, the awakening mischief in her eyes. He moved a little more, balancing on the edge of the seat. "Poor little kitten," he thought again—and "poor little kitten" suddenly gave him a hearty push which sent him off the wagon like a bag of flour. He landed in the dusty road, resembling a bag of flour indeed. He hurt something awful where he landed; it was the same spot Máli the cow had kicked that morning. Through the dust he saw the wagon come to a stop.

Father jumped down and, reaching Jancsi, began to feel his arms and legs for broken bones. "You great big baby," he scolded, "you want to ride wild horses? Can't even stay on a wagon!"

"Hey! Hey! Father! Stop Kate! Look, Father!" Jancsi yelled, struggling away from Father.

There was Kate, standing bolt upright on the seat, reins and whip in hand. She was grinning from ear to ear.

"Pushed you off, didn't I, little girl? Catch me if you can!" She whipped the horses, screaming at them: "Gee, git up, git up!" This was too much for one day even for the horses. They lunged forward, and broke into a wild gallop.

Father, shocked speechless for a moment, grabbed Jancsi by the arm.

"Come on, Son, we've got to catch this screaming monkey before the horses break their legs, or she breaks her neck!"

They ran, panting and choking in the hot dust. The wagon was almost out of sight now.

"Got-to-get-horses!" panted Father.

"We-could-catch-two from the herd here!" choked Jancsi, pointing to the herd they had passed that morning.

They jumped the fence and were among the surprised horses before the animals became alarmed.

"Run with the horse, Son," cried Father. "Run with it, grab its mane, and *swing!*"

Exciting moments followed. They were used to horses, but this was hard business, without rope or halter. Jancsi singled out a young chestnut horse. The animal reared, shied, baring his teeth, and started to run. But Jancsi's hands were already clutching his mane. The horse broke into a wild run, Jancsi clinging to him for dear life. He was carried like a piece of cloth, almost flying beside the horse. With a supreme effort he pulled himself up. Clutching his legs around the animal's neck, he reached forward to pull its nose down. Horse and rider were a mass of plunging, snorting animation. Jancsi was dizzy, but he gritted his teeth and hung on.

Then he heard Father's voice through the tumult. "Let him run and guide with your knees. Come on, 'csikós,' you're a real son of mine!"

Slowly the horse quieted down. Jancsi pulled him around and headed for the fence. Father was riding a big mare, waving to him to follow. Soon they were traveling side by side—hot, dirty, exhausted, and, judging by Father's face, madder than hornets.

They rode through the village without stopping to ask questions. The poplars on the ranch road whizzed past them. There was the house now! There was Mother, at the gate, waving madly with one hand. With her other hand she was clutching the blue skirts of a dancing, struggling little imp—a dirty, disheveled, but grinning little girl—Cousin Kate from Budapest!

Of Heroes, Gods, and the Beginnings of Things . . .

Legends
and
Myths

King Arthur and His Noble Knights

THE MARVEL OF THE SWORD

by MARY MACLEOD

The hundreds of stories that have come down to us about King Arthur and his Knights of the Round Table are the main basis of our ideas about the life of chivalry during the Middle Ages. Even those who have not read the Arthurian legends know something about what King Arthur and his court represent. They have become symbols of high-minded greatness and the brave deeds that were done in England in the long ago. But the legends themselves are too thrilling for you to miss—they give a fascinating picture of the knightly manners of such romantic figures as Sir Launcelot, the brave, Galahad, the pure, and Gawaine, the courteous, and of the mysterious enchantments practiced by Merlin the Magician. Nowhere are the qualities of idealism, devotion to duty, honor and loyalty more vividly shown than in the tales about King Arthur and his noble knights.

When Uther Pendragon, King of England, died, the country for a long while stood in great danger, for every lord that was mighty gathered his forces, and many wished to be King. For King Uther's own son, Prince Arthur, who should have succeeded him, was but a child, and Merlin, the mighty magician, had hidden him away.

Now a strange thing had happened at Arthur's birth, and this was how it was.

Some time before, Merlin had done Uther a great service, on condition that the King should grant him whatever he wished for.

This the King swore a solemn oath to do. Then Merlin made him promise that when his child was born it should be delivered to Merlin to bring up as he chose, for this would be to the child's own great advantage. The King had given his promise so he was obliged to agree. Then Merlin said he knew a very true and faithful man, one of King Uther's lords, by name Sir Ector, who had large possessions in many parts of England and Wales, and that the child should be given to him to bring up.

On the night the baby was born, while it was still unchristened, King Uther commanded two knights and two ladies to take it, wrapped in a cloth of gold, and deliver it to a poor man whom they would find waiting at the postern gate of the Castle. This poor man was Merlin in disguise, although they did not know it. So the child was delivered unto Merlin and he carried him to Sir Ector, and made a holy man christen him, and named him Arthur. And Sir Ector's wife cherished him as her own child.

Within two years King Uther fell sick of a great malady, and for three days and three nights he was speechless. All the Barons were in much sorrow, and asked Merlin what was best to be done.

"There is no remedy," said Merlin, "God will have His Will. But look ye all, Barons, come before King Uther tomorrow, and God will make him speak."

So the next day Merlin and all the Barons came before the King, and Merlin said aloud to King Uther:

"Sir, after your days shall your son Arthur be King of this realm and all that belongs to it?"

Then Uther Pendragon turned to him and said in hearing of them all:

"I give my son Arthur God's blessing and mine, and bid him pray for my soul, and righteously and honorably claim the Crown, on forfeiture of my blessing."

And with that, King Uther died.

But Arthur was still only a baby, not two years old, and Merlin knew it would be no use yet to proclaim him King. For there were many powerful nobles in England in those days, who were all trying to get the kingdom for themselves, and perhaps they would kill the little Prince. So there was much strife and debate in the land for a long time.

When several years had passed, Merlin went to the Archbishop of Canterbury and counseled him to send for all the lords of the realm, and all the gentlemen of arms, that they should come to London at Christmas, and for this cause—that a miracle would show who should be rightly King of the realm. So all the lords and gentlemen made themselves ready, and came to London, and long before dawn on Christmas Day they were all gathered in the great church of St. Paul's to pray.

When the first service was over, there was seen in the church-yard a large stone, four-square, like marble, and in the midst of it was an anvil of steel, a foot high. Into this was stuck by the point a beautiful sword, with naked blade, and there were letters written in gold about the sword, which said thus:

"Whoso pulleth this sword out of this stone and anvil is rightly King of all England."

Then the people marveled, and told it to the Archbishop.

"I command," said the Archbishop, "that you keep within the church, and pray unto God still and that no man touch the sword till the service is over."

So when the prayers in church were over, all the lords went to behold the stone and the sword; and when they read the writing some of them—such as wished to be King—tried to pull the sword out of the anvil. But not one could make it stir.

"The man is not here that shall achieve the sword," said the Archbishop, "but doubt not God will make him known. But let us provide ten knights, men of good fame, to keep guard over the sword."

So it was ordained, and proclamation was made that everyone who wished might try to win the sword. And upon New Year's Day the Barons arranged to have a great tournament, in which all knights who would joust or tourney might take a part. This was ordained to bring together the Lords and Commons, for the Archbishop trusted that on that day it would be made known who should win the sword.

HOW ARTHUR WAS CROWNED KING

On New Year's Day, after church, the Barons rode to the field, some to joust, and some to tourney, and so it happened that Sir Ector, who had large estates near London, came also to the tournament. And with him rode Sir Kay, his son, with young Arthur, his foster brother.

As they rode, Sir Kay found he had lost his sword, for he had left it at his father's lodging, so he begged young Arthur to go and fetch it for him.

"That will I gladly," said the boy, and he rode fast away.

But when he came to the house, he found no one at home to give him the sword, for everyone had gone to see the jousting. Then Arthur was angry and said to himself:

"I will ride to the churchyard, and take the sword with me that sticketh in the stone, for my brother, Sir Kay, shall not be without a sword this day."

When he came to the churchyard he alighted, and tied his horse to the stile, and went to the tent. But he found there no knights, who should have been guarding the sword, for they were all away at the joust. Seizing the sword by the handle he lightly and fiercely pulled it out of the stone, then took his horse and rode his way, till he came to Sir Kay his brother to whom he delivered the sword.

As soon as Sir Kay saw it, he knew well it was the sword of the Stone, so he rode to his father Sir Ector, and said:

"Sir, lo, here is the sword of the Stone, wherefore I must be King of this land."

When Sir Ector saw the sword he turned back, and came to the church, and there they all three alighted and went into the church, and he made his son swear truly how he got the sword.

"By my brother Arthur," said Sir Kay, "for he brought it to me."

"How did you get this sword?" said Sir Ector to Arthur.

And the boy told him.

"Now," said Sir Ector, "I understand you must be King of this land."

"Wherefore I?" said Arthur; "and for what cause?"

"Sir," said Ector, "because God will have it so; for never man could draw out this sword but he that shall rightly be King. Now let me see whether you can put the sword there as it was, and pull it out again."

"There is no difficulty," said Arthur, and he put it back into the stone.

Then Sir Ector tried to pull out the sword, and failed; and Sir Kay also pulled with all his might, but it would not move.

"Now you shall try," said Sir Ector to Arthur.

"I will, well," said Arthur, and pulled the sword out easily.

At this Sir Ector and Sir Kay knelt down on the ground before him.

"Alas," said Arthur, "mine own dear father and brother, why do you kneel to me?"

"Nay, nay, my lord Arthur, it is not so; I was never your father, nor of your blood. But I know well you are of higher blood than I thought you were."

Then Sir Ector told him all, how he had taken him to bring up, and by whose command; and how he had received him from Merlin. And when he understood that Ector was not his father, Arthur was deeply grieved.

"Will you be my good gracious lord, when you are King?" asked the knight.

"If not, I should be to blame," said Arthur, "for you are the man in the world to whom I am the most beholden, and my good lady and mother, your wife, who has fostered and kept me as well as her own children. And if ever it be God's will that I be King, as you say, you shall desire of me what I shall do, and I shall not fail you; God forbid I should fail you."

"Sir," said Sir Ector, "I will ask no more of you but that you will make my son, your foster brother Sir Kay, seneschal of all your lands."

"That shall be done," said Arthur, "and by my faith, never man but he shall have that office while he and I live."

Then they went to the Archbishop and told him how the sword was achieved, and by whom.

On Twelfth Day all the Barons came to the Stone in the churchyard, so that any who wished might try to win the sword. But not one of them all could take it out, except Arthur. Many of them therefore were very angry, and said it was a great shame to them and to the country to be governed by a boy not of high blood, for as yet none of them knew that he was the son of King Pendragon. So they agreed to delay the decision till Candlemas, which is the second day of February.

But when Candlemas came, and Arthur once more was the only one who could pull out the sword, they put it off till Easter; and when Easter came, and Arthur again prevailed in presence of them all, they put it off till the Feast of Pentecost.

Then by Merlin's advice the Archbishop summoned some of the best knights that were to be got—such knights as in his own day King Uther Pendragon had best loved and trusted most—and these were appointed to attend young Arthur, and never to leave him night or day till the Feast of Pentecost.

When the great day came, all manner of men once more made the attempt, and once more not one of them all could prevail but Arthur. Before all the Lords and Commons there assembled he pulled out the sword, whereupon all the Commons cried out at once:

"We will have Arthur for our King! We will put him no more in delay, for we all see that it is God's will that he shall be our King, and he who holdeth against it, we will slay him."

And therewith all knelt down at once, both rich and poor, and besought pardon of Arthur, because they had delayed him so long.

And Arthur forgave them, and took the sword in both his hands, and offered it on the altar where the Archbishop was, and so he was made knight by the best man there.

After that, he was crowned at once, and there he swore to his Lords and Commons to be a true King, and to govern with true justice from thenceforth all the days of his life.

Based on Thomas Malory's *Morte d'Arthur.*

The Merry Adventures of Robin Hood

THE GRAND SHOOTING-MATCH AT NOTTINGHAM

by HOWARD PYLE

King Henry II had taunted the Sheriff of Nottingham because he was unable, in spite of his enormous array of men-at-arms, to capture Robin Hood and his little band. So the Sheriff thinks up the scheme of the shooting-match. But of course he does not succeed this time, nor at any other time, in his efforts to catch the bold outlaw. The legends about Robin Hood go back to the 14th century, and ever since that time he has been the favorite hero of the common people—as the best archer in all England, and as a figure of protest against the rich and the privileged; because Robin Hood stole only from the rich so that he could give generously to the poor. What appeals to boys and girls is not only the carefree adventures of the merry band in Sherwood Forest, but the tricky way that Robin Hood always manages to get the better of any enemy, as he does of the Sheriff in this shooting-match.

"Now," thought the Sheriff, "could I but persuade Robin nigh to Nottingham Town so that I could find him, I warrant I would lay hands upon him so stoutly that he would never get away again." Then of a sudden it came to him like a flash that were he to proclaim a great shooting-match and offer some grand prize, Robin Hood might be overpersuaded by his spirit to come to the range. And it was this thought which caused him to cry "Aha!" and smite his palm upon his thigh.

So, as soon as he had returned safely to Nottingham, he sent messengers north and south, and east and west, to proclaim through town, hamlet, and countryside, this grand shooting-match, and every one was bidden that could draw a long bow, and the prize was to be an arrow of pure beaten gold.

When Robin Hood first heard the news of this he was in Lincoln Town, and hastening back to Sherwood Forest he soon called all his merry men about him and spoke to them thus:

"Now hearken, my merry men all, to the news that I have brought from Lincoln Town to-day. Our friend the Sheriff of Nottingham hath proclaimed a shooting-match, and hath sent messengers to tell of it through all the countryside, and the prize is to be a bright golden arrow. Now I fain would have one of us win it, both because of the fairness of the prize and because our sweet friend the Sheriff hath offered it. So we will take our bows and shafts and go there to shoot, for I know right well that merriment will be a-going. What say ye, lads?"

Then young David of Doncaster spoke up and said: "Now listen, I pray thee, good master, unto what I say. I have come straight from our friend Eadom o' the Blue Boar, and there I heard the full news of this same match. But, master, I know from him, and he got it from the Sheriff's man Ralph o' the Scar, that this same knavish Sheriff hath but laid a trap for thee in this shooting-match and wishes nothing so much as to see thee there. So go not, good master, for I know right well he doth seek to entrap thee, but stay within the greenwood lest we all meet dole and woe."

"Now," quoth Robin, "thou art a wise lad and keepest thine ears open and thy mouth shut, as becometh a wise and crafty woodsman. But shall we let it be said that the Sheriff of Nottingham did cow bold Robin Hood and sevenscore as fair archers as are in all merry England? Nay, good David, what thou tellest me maketh me to desire the prize even more than I else should do. But what sayeth our good gossip Swanthold? Is it not 'A hasty man burneth his mouth, and the fool that keepeth his eyes shut falleth into the pit?' Thus he says, truly, therefore we must meet guile with guile. Now some of you clothe yourselves as short-frocked friars, and some as peasants, and some as tinkers, or as beggars, but see that each man taketh a good bow or broadsword, in case need should arise. As for myself, I will shoot for this same golden arrow, and should I win it, we will hang it to the branches of our good greenwood tree for the joy of all the band. How like you the plan, my merry men all?"

Then "Good, good!" cried all the band right heartily.

A fair sight was Nottingham Town on the day of the shooting-match. All along upon the green meadow beneath the town wall stretched a row of benches, one above the other, which were for knight and lady, squire and dame, and rich burghers and their wives; for none but those of rank and quality were to sit there. At the end of the range, near the target, was a raised seat bedecked with ribbons and scarfs and garlands of flowers, for the Sheriff of Nottingham and his dame. The range was twoscore paces broad. At one end stood the target, at the other a tent of striped canvas, from the pole of which fluttered many-colored flags and streamers. In this booth were casks of ale, free to be broached by any of the archers who might wish to quench their thirst.

Across the range from where the seats for the better folk were raised was a railing to keep the poorer people from crowding in front of the target. Already, while it was early, the benches were beginning to fill with people of quality, who kept constantly arriving in little carts, or upon palfreys that curveted gayly to the merry tinkle of silver bells at bridle reins; with these came also the poorer folk, who sat or lay upon the green grass near the railing that kept them from off the range. In the great tent the archers were gathering by twos and threes; some talking loudly of the fair shots each man had made in his day; some looking well to their bows, drawing a string betwixt the fingers to see that there was no fray upon it, or inspecting arrows, shutting one eye and peering down a shaft to see that it was not warped, but straight and true, for neither bow nor shaft should fail at such a time and for such a prize. And never were such a company of yeomen as were gathered at Nottingham Town that day, for the very best archers of merry England had come to this shooting-match. There was Gill o' the Red Cap, the Sheriff's own head archer, and

Diccon Cruikshank of Lincoln Town, and Adam o' the Dell, a man of Tamworth, of threescore years and more, yet hale and lusty still, who in his time had shot in the famous match at Woodstock, and had there beaten that renowned archer, Clym o' the Clough. And many more famous men of the long bow were there, whose names have been handed down to us in goodly ballads of the olden time.

But now all the benches were filled with guests, lord and lady, burgher and dame, when at last the Sheriff himself came with his lady, he riding with stately mien upon his milk-white horse and she upon her brown filly. Upon his head he wore a purple velvet cap, and purple velvet was his robe, all trimmed about with rich ermine; his jerkin and hose were of sea-green silk, and his shoes of black velvet, the pointed toes fastened to his garters with golden chains. A golden chain hung about his neck, and at his collar was a great carbuncle set in red gold. His lady was dressed in blue velvet, all trimmed with swan's down. So they made a gallant sight as they rode along side by side, and all the people shouted from where they crowded across the space from the gentlefolk.

Then when the Sheriff and his dame had sat down, he bade his herald wind upon his silver horn; who thereupon sounded three blasts that came echoing cheerily back from the gray walls of Nottingham. Then the archers stepped forth to their places, while all the folk shouted with a mighty voice, each man calling upon his favorite yeoman. "Red Cap!" cried some. "Cruikshank!" cried others. "Hey for William o' Leslie!" shouted others yet again; while ladies waved silken scarfs to urge each yeoman to do his best.

Then the herald stood forth and loudly proclaimed the rules of the game as follows:

"Shoot each man from yon mark, which is sevenscore yards and ten from the target. One arrow shooteth each man first, and from all the archers shall the ten that shooteth the fairest shafts be chosen for to shoot again. Two arrows shooteth each man of these ten, then shall the three that shoot the fairest shafts be chosen for to shoot again. Three arrows shooteth each man of those three, and to him that shooteth the fairest shafts shall the prize be given."

Then the Sheriff leaned forward, looking keenly among the press of archers to find whether Robin Hood was amongst them. But no one was there clad in Lincoln green, such as was worn by Robin and his band. "Nevertheless," said the Sheriff to himself, "he may still be there, and I miss him among the crowd of other men. But let me see when but ten men shoot, for I wot he will be among the ten, or I know him not."

And now the archers shot, each man in turn, and the good folk never saw such archery as was done that day. Six arrows were within the clout, four within the black, and only two smote the outer ring; so that when the last arrow sped and struck the target, all the people shouted aloud, for it was noble shooting.

And now but ten men were left of all those that had shot before, and of these ten, six were famous throughout the land, and most of the folk gathered there knew them. These six men were Gilbert o' the Red Cap, Adam o' the Dell, Diccon Cruikshank, William o' Leslie, Hubert o' Cloud, and Swithin o' Hertford. Two others were yeomen of merry Yorkshire, another was a tall stranger in blue, who said he came from London Town, and the last was a tattered stranger in scarlet, who wore a patch over one eye.

"Now," quoth the Sheriff to a man-at-arms who stood near him, "seest thou Robin Hood amongst those ten?"

"Nay, that do I not, your worship," answered the man. "Six of them I know right well. Of those Yorkshire yeomen, one is too tall and the other too short for that bold knave. Robin's beard is as yellow as gold, while yon tattered beggar in scarlet hath a beard of brown, besides being blind of one eye. As for the stranger in blue, Robin's shoulders, I ween, are three inches broader than his."

"Then," quoth the Sheriff, smiting his thigh angrily, "yon knave is a coward as well as a rogue, and dares not show his face among good men and true."

Then, after they had rested a short time, those ten stout men stepped forth to shoot again. Each man shot two arrows, and as they shot, not a word was spoken, but all the crowd watched with scarce a breath of sound. But when the last had shot his arrow another great shout arose, while many cast their caps aloft for joy of such marvellous shooting.

And now but three men were left of all those that had shot before. One was Gill o' the Red Cap, one the tattered stranger in scarlet, and one Adam o' the Dell of Tamworth Town. Then all the people called aloud, some crying, "Ho for Gilbert o' the Red Cap!" and some, "Hey for stout Adam o' Tamworth!" But not a single man in the crowd called upon the stranger in scarlet.

"Now, shoot thou well, Gilbert," cried the Sheriff, "and if thine be the best shaft, fivescore broad silver pennies will I give to thee beside the prize."

"Truly I will do my best," quoth Gilbert, right sturdily. "A man cannot do aught but his best, but that will I strive to do this day." So saying, he drew forth a fair smooth arrow with a broad feather and fitted it deftly to the string, then drawing his bow with care he sped the shaft. Straight flew the arrow and lit fairly in the clout, a finger breadth from the centre. "A Gilbert, a Gilbert!" shouted all the crowd; and, "Now, by my faith," cried the Sheriff, smiting his hands together, "that is a shrewd shot."

Then the tattered stranger stepped forth, and all the people laughed as they saw a yellow patch that showed beneath his arm when he raised his elbow to shoot, and also to see him aim with but one eye. He drew the good yew bow quickly, and quickly loosed a shaft; so short was the time that no man could draw a breath betwixt the drawing and the shooting. Yet his arrow lodged nearer the centre than the other by twice the length of a barleycorn.

"Now by all the saints in Paradise!" cried the Sheriff, "that is a lovely shaft in very truth!"

Then Adam o' the Dell shot, carefully and cautiously, and his arrow lodged close beside the stranger's. Then after a short space they all three shot again, and once more each arrow lodged within the clout, but this time Adam o' the Dell's was farthest from the centre, and again the tattered stranger's shot was the best. Then, after another time of rest, they all shot for the third time. This time Gilbert took great heed to his aim, keenly measuring the distance and shooting with shrewdest care. Straight flew the arrow, and all shouted till the very flags that waved in the breeze shook with the sound, and the rooks and daws flew clamoring about the roofs of the old gray tower, for the shaft had lodged close beside the spot that marked the very centre.

"Well done, Gilbert!" cried the Sheriff, right joyously. "Fain am I to believe the prize is thine, and right fairly won. Now, thou ragged knave, let me see thee shoot a better shaft than that."

Naught spake the stranger but took his place, while all was hushed, and no one spoke or even seemed to breathe, so great was the silence for wonder what he would do. Meanwhile, also, quite still stood the stranger holding his bow in his hand, while one could count five. Then he drew his trusty yew, holding it drawn but a moment, then loosed the string. Straight flew the arrow, and so true that it smote a gray goose feather from off Gilbert's shaft, which fell fluttering through the sunlit air as the stranger's arrow lodged close beside his of the red cap, and in the very centre. No one spoke a word for a while and no one shouted, but each man looked into his neighbor's face amazedly.

"Nay," quoth old Adam o' the Dell presently, drawing a long breath and shaking his head as he spoke; "twoscore years and more have I shot shaft, and maybe not all times bad, but I shoot no more this day, for no man can match with yon stranger, whosoe'er he may be." Then he thrust his shaft into his quiver, rattling, and unstrung his bow without another word.

Then the Sheriff came down from his dais and drew near, in all his silks and velvets, to where the tattered stranger stood leaning upon his stout bow, whilst the good folk crowded around to see the man who shot so wondrously well. "Here, good fellow," quoth the Sheriff, "take thou the prize, and well and fairly hast thou won it, I trow. What may be thy name, and whence comest thou?"

"Men do call me Jock o' Teviotdale, and thence am I come," said the stranger.

"Then, by Our Lady, Jock, thou art the fairest archer that e'er mine eyes beheld, and if thou wilt join my service I will clothe thee with a better coat than that thou hast upon thy back. Thou shalt eat and drink of the best, and at every Christmas-tide four-score marks shall be thy wage. I trow thou drawest better bow than that same coward knave, Robin Hood, that dared not show his face here this day. Say, good fellow, wilt thou join my service?"

"Nay, that will I not," quoth the stranger, roughly. "I will be mine own, and no man in all merry England shall be my master."

"Then get thee gone, and a murrain seize thee!" cried the Sheriff, and his voice trembled with anger. "And by my faith and troth I have a good part of mind to have thee beaten for thine insolence!" Then he turned upon his heel and strode away.

It was a right motley company that gathered about the noble greenwood tree in Sherwood's depths that same day. A score and more of barefoot friars were there, and some that looked like tinkers, and some that seemed to be sturdy beggars and rustic peasants; and seated upon a mossy couch was one clad in tattered scarlet, with a patch over one eye; and in his hand he held the golden arrow that was the prize of the great shooting-match. Then, amidst a noise of talking and laughter, he took the patch from off his eye and stripped away the scarlet rags from off his body and showed himself all clothed in fair Lincoln green, and quoth he:

"Easy come these things away, but walnut stain cometh not so speedily from yellow hair." Then all laughed louder than before, for it was Robin Hood himself that had won the prize from the Sheriff's very hands.

Then all sat down to the woodland feast and talked amongst themselves of the merry jest that had been played upon the Sheriff, and of the adventures that had befallen each member of the band in his disguise. But when the feast was done, Robin Hood took Little John apart and said, "Truly am I vexed in my blood, for I heard the Sheriff say to-day, 'Thou shootest better than that coward knave, Robin Hood, that dared not show his face here this day.' I would fain let him know who it was who won the golden arrow from out his hand, and also that I am no coward such as he takes me to be."

Then Little John said, "Good master, take thou me and Will Stutely and we will send yon fat Sheriff news of all this by a messenger such as he doth not expect."

That day the Sheriff sat at meat in the great hall of his house at Nottingham Town. Long tables stood down the hall, at which sat men-at-arms and household servants and good stout villains [farm-servants], in all fourscore and more. There they talked of the day's shooting as they ate their meat and quaffed their ale. The Sheriff sat at the head of the table upon a raised seat under a canopy, and beside him sat his dame.

"By my troth," said he, "I did reckon full roundly that that knave, Robin Hood, would be at the game to-day. I did not think that he was such a coward. But who could that saucy knave be who answered me to my beard so bravely? I wonder that I did not have him beaten; but there was something about him that spoke of other things than rags and tatters."

Then, even as he finished speaking, something fell rattling among the dishes on the table, while those that sat near started up wondering what it might be. After a while one of the men-at-arms gathered courage enough to pick it up and bring it to the Sheriff. Then every one saw that it was a blunted gray goose shaft, with a fine scroll, about the thickness of a goose quill, tied near to its head. The Sheriff opened the scroll and glanced at it, while the veins upon his forehead swelled and his cheeks grew ruddy with rage as he read, for this was what he saw:

Now Heaven bless thy grace this day,
* Say all in sweet Sherwood,*
For thou didst give the prize away
* To merry Robin Hood.*

"Whence came this?" cried the Sheriff in a mighty voice.

"Even through the window, your worship," quoth the man who had handed the shaft to him.

Greek Myths

The word myth in Greek means a story, and the first myths were simply that—stories primitive man made up to explain what was happening around him in the world of nature. These forces were imagined as gods with special powers: Zeus controlling the thunder, Apollo the sun, Poseidon the sea; and the change of season from summer to winter, for example, was explained by Demeter going into mourning for her daughter Persephone who had to descend into the underworld for half of each year. To explain such things as why the spider spins, they invented the story of the proud and unfortunate maiden Arachne. (From her name we get our scientific word for spider, arachnid.) Later the myths or legends about great heroes, that may have had some basis in history, were woven into tales of action and adventure, like the one about Perseus and the Gorgon head.

Because the ancient Greeks had such a wonderfully rich imagination and great love of beauty their stories have always been the most admired and widely known of all European myths. They can be enjoyed solely for their charm, grace, and direct action; but you might also read them as a helpful background for innumerable allusions and symbols you are bound to meet in art and literature. Much of classical and Renaissance art, and many masterpieces of literature cannot be understood without some knowledge of the Greek gods and heroes. In these stories the original Greek names are given first, and the Roman names in parentheses.

ARACHNE

In Lydia there lived a maiden named Arachne who had become so skillful in the art of weaving that the nymphs themselves would leave their play in the woodlands and waters to come and admire her at work. Her work was beautiful, not only when finished, but also beautiful to watch in the doing. As the nymphs surrounding her loom watched her fingering the crude wool, then carding it skillfully till it looked as light and soft as a cloud, or twirling the spindle with unbelievable speed and dexterity, they could not help saying, "Surely Athena herself must have taught you!"

But Arachne denied this. She was so proud that she could not bear to be thought a pupil, even of Athena (Minerva) who was the goddess of wisdom and of all the household arts. "Let Athena try her skill with mine," she boasted. "If she beats me, I will pay the penalty."

When Athena heard this she was very displeased. Assuming the form of an old woman, she came to Arachne and gave her some friendly words of warning. "Maiden," she said, "I have had much experience in these matters, and I can give you some good advice. Challenge any mortal you wish, but never compete with a goddess. On the contrary, I advise you to ask Athena's forgiveness for your wild boast. As she is merciful, she will perhaps pardon you."

Arachne stopped her spinning and looked at the old woman with anger. "Keep your advice," said she, "for your own daughters or handmaidens. For my part, I know what I am talking about and I stand by it. I am not afraid of the goddess. Let her try her skill with mine if she dares."

"She comes," said Athena, and dropping her disguise she stood revealed in her tall majestic form as the goddess with the golden helmet.

The nymphs bent low in homage, and all the bystanders shrank back in fear and reverence. Arachne alone stood unbowed, though a sudden blush reddened her cheek, and then she grew pale. She would not back down, however, on her foolish resolve to compete with Athena.

The contest began. Each took her place and attached the web to the beam, then passed the slender shuttle in and out among the threads. Mortal and goddess worked with great speed, their skillful hands moving swiftly in the excitement of the public competition.

Athena used wools of many contrasting colors which shaded off into one another so subtly that the joining deceived the eye. It was like some marvelous rainbow, formed by sunbeams reflected from the shower, and where, when the colors meet, they seem as one; but at a little distance from the point of contact, they are wholly different. In the central circle of her web, she wove the story of her contest with Poseidon (Neptune), the god of the sea, for the possession of Athens. The first king of that city had promised to dedicate it to the one who produced the gift most useful to mortals. Poseidon gave the horse, but Athena gave the olive, which was judged more useful, and the city was named Athens in her honor. In the four corners of her web Athena wove incidents showing how mortals who had dared to compete with the gods had been punished. These were meant to be a final warning to her rival to give up the contest before it was too late.

Arachne filled her web with stories chosen to belittle the gods. She made light even of the great Zeus (Jupiter), portraying him in his animal disguises—first as a bull, and then as a swan. The subjects she chose were plainly disrespectful, yet they were woven so miraculously, and so close to nature that the bull, for instance, seemed like a living breathing animal. Even Athena herself had to stop for a moment to admire the handiwork.

But the goddess could not withhold her wrath at the girl's insolence. With her shuttle, she struck at the web and tore it to pieces. Then she touched the forehead of Arachne three times. "Live on," she said, "and since you were so vainglorious about your weaving, you shall continue to weave forever."

Then Athena sprinkled some poisonous plant juice on the maiden, and immediately her hair came off, her face disappeared, and her body shrank up and changed into that of a spider. To this day you may see Arachne's descendants still weaving.

Based on *The Age of Fable* by Thomas Bulfinch.

ICARUS AND DAEDALUS

Daedalus was widely known as the most skillful of all men. It was he who had built for King Minos of Crete the famous Labyrinth which had so many winding passages and twisted turnings that no one could ever find his way out of the maze without a magic clue. But the master builder fell out of favor with King Minos and that tyrannical ruler had him shut up in a tower. Though Daedalus managed to escape from this prison, he could not leave the island because King Minos kept a strict watch on the shore, permitting no ship to sail without the most careful search.

Determined to use all his skill and cunning to make his escape, Daedalus waited for his chance. He watched the seagulls along the seashore as they soared off into the air. Suddenly he thought of a plan to win freedom for himself and his young son Icarus who was held captive with him. "Minos may control the land and sea," he said, "but not the regions of the air. We can go that way."

Father and son set to work gathering as many feathers as they could find dropped by the birds along the shore. Then Daedalus fashioned the feathers to a framework, securing the larger ones with thread and the smaller ones with wax; and to the whole he gave a gentle curvature exactly like the wings of a huge bird. When at last the work was done, he fastened the wings to his shoulders, and as they bore him aloft into the air, he practiced moving his arms in birdlike motions until he had learned to fly. Then he made another and smaller pair of wings for his son and patiently taught the boy to fly with him.

The day came when the wind was just right, and everything had been made ready for the escape. In the early morning, Daedalus called his son to him and gave him the final instructions, "Icarus, my son, remember to keep at a moderate height. For if you fly too low the dampness will clog your wings, and if you fly too high the heat of the sun will melt them. Keep near me and you will be safe."

As he fitted the wings to the boy's shoulders, the face of the father was wet with tears and his hands trembled. He kissed the
boy, putting away from him the thought that it might be for the
last time. Then rising in the air, Daedalus flew off, encouraging
his son to follow him, and looking back every few minutes to see
how the boy was managing his wings. As they flew away from

the island of Crete, some shepherds and farmers stopped their work to gaze up at them in astonishment, thinking they surely must be gods.

The two glided smoothly, the boy behind his father, passing Samos and Delos on the left, and Lebynthos on the right. But now Icarus, overjoyed with the ease and freedom of his flight grew too bold. He stopped following his father and began to soar higher and higher towards the sky.

Poor Icarus! The nearness of the blazing sun softened the wax that held the feathers together, and they began to drop off. He grew terrified and fluttered his arms wildly, but there were not enough feathers left to buoy him up. He felt himself falling. Trying desperately to find his father, he called his name, but his voice was submerged in the blue waters of the sea.

When Daedalus saw that his son was no longer following him, he cried out in fear, "Icarus, Icarus, where are you?" There was no answer. At last he saw the feathers floating in the water and found the body of the drowned boy. He buried him on the nearest island which he named Icaria in his memory, and which is still called by that name.

He flew on alone, bitterly lamenting what he had invented, and arrived safely in Sicily. There he built a temple to Apollo and hung up his wings as an offering to the god. And never again did he attempt to fly.

Based on *The Age of Fable* by Thomas Bulfinch.

KING MIDAS AND THE GOLDEN TOUCH

Once upon a time there lived a rich king whose name was Midas, and this king was fonder of gold than of anything else in the world. He thought, foolish man, that the greatest joy would be to amass the greatest pile of golden coins that had ever been heaped together. Thus he gave all his thoughts and time to this one purpose. If he happened to gaze at the gold-tinted clouds of sunset, he would wish that they were real gold, so that they could be put into his strongbox. When his little daughter ran to meet him with a bunch of buttercups, he used to say, "Pooh, pooh, child! If these flowers were really as golden as they look, they would then be worth plucking."

At length Midas had become so possessed with the idea of gold that he could scarcely bear to see or touch any object that was not gold. He made it his custom, therefore, to spend a large part of every day in a dark and gloomy room down in the basement of his palace. After carefully locking the door, he would take a bag of gold coin, or a gold cup, or a heavy gold bar, or a peck of gold dust, and bring them from the dark corners of the room into the one bright and narrow sunbeam that fell from the dungeon-like window. He valued the sunbeam for no other reason than that it helped his treasure to shine. And then he would count over the coins in the bag, toss up the bar and catch it as it came down and sift the gold dust through his fingers.

One day Midas was enjoying himself in his treasure room as usual when he noticed a shadow fall over the heaps of gold. Looking up suddenly, what should he see but the figure of a stranger, standing in the sunbeam. He was a young man with a cheerful face and though his figure blocked the sunshine, a brighter radiance seemed to shine over the piled-up treasure than before.

As Midas knew that he had carefully turned the key in the lock, and that no mortal strength could possibly break into this dungeon, he concluded that this visitor must surely be a god. The stranger gazed about the room and then turned again to Midas.

"You are a wealthy man, friend Midas," he observed. "I doubt whether any other four walls on earth contain so much gold as you have managed to pile up in this room."

"I have done pretty well—pretty well," answered Midas. "But after all it is but a trifle when you think that it has taken me my whole life to get it together. If one could live a thousand years, he might have time to grow really rich."

"What!" exclaimed the stranger. "You are not satisfied?"

Midas shook his head.

"And pray, what would satisfy you?"

Midas paused to think. He had a feeling that this stranger had come here to grant him his wish. He thought and thought, heaping up one pile of gold upon another, without being able to imagine anything big enough. At last a bright idea came to him. Raising his head he looked the radiant stranger in the face.

"Well, Midas," said his visitor, "tell me your wish."

"It is only this," replied Midas. "I am tired of collecting my treasure bit by bit. I wish that everything I touch would be changed into gold."

"The Golden Touch!" exclaimed the stranger. "But are you quite sure that this will satisfy you?"

"How could it fail?" asked Midas.

"And you will never regret the possession of it?"

"I ask nothing else to make me perfectly happy."

"Be it as you wish then," replied the stranger, waving his hands in token of farewell. "Tomorrow, at sunrise, you will find yourself gifted with the Golden Touch."

The figure of the stranger then became exceedingly bright, causing Midas to blink his eyes. When he opened them, his visitor had vanished.

As soon as the first rays of the sun shone through the window, Midas was awake. What was his delight to find the linen fabric of his bed cover, where his hands lay, transformed into what seemed a woven texture of the purest and brightest gold! The Golden Touch had come to him!

Midas started up in a kind of joyful frenzy and ran about the room touching everything within reach. He seized one of the bedposts, and it became immediately a fluted golden column. He hurriedly put on his clothes, and was delighted to see himself in a magnificent suit of gold cloth. As he went downstairs he smiled on seeing the balustrade of the staircase turn into burnished gold. He lifted the door-latch—it was brass only a moment ago, but golden now—and went into the garden. There he found a great number of beautiful roses in full bloom and their fragrance was delicious in the morning breeze.

But Midas knew a way to make them far more precious than

roses had ever been before. So he took great pains, going from bush to bush, to exercise his magic touch on every rose. Soon each individual flower and bud, even the worms at the heart of some of them, had been changed to gold. By the time this work was completed, breakfast was announced, and as the morning air and his exercise had given him an excellent appetite, he hastened into the palace.

His little daughter was not yet at the breakfast table and so he ordered her to be called. To do Midas justice, he dearly loved his daughter, and was therefore very distressed when he heard her coming into the room crying bitterly.

"How now, my little lady," said Midas. "What is the matter with you this bright morning?"

For answer his daughter held out her hand in which was one of the roses that Midas had transformed this morning.

"Beautiful!" exclaimed her father—"And what is there in this magnificent golden rose to make you cry?"

"Oh, Father," sobbed the child, "it is not beautiful, it's ugly! I went into the garden to gather some roses for you, because I know you like them so much. And what do you think has happened? All the beautiful roses that smelled so sweet and had such lovely colors are all spoiled! They're all turned yellow and haven't any more fragrance. What can be the matter with them?"

"Don't cry about it," said Midas, who was ashamed to confess that he himself had brought about the change that made her so unhappy. "Sit down and eat your bread and milk."

Midas meanwhile had lifted a piece of bread to his mouth and was astonished to feel that the instant his lips touched the bread, it hardened into a lump of solid gold. By way of an experiment, he touched one of the delicious looking brook trout on his plate with his finger, and to his horror it immediately turned into a hard gold fish. Almost in despair, he helped himself to a boiled egg, which at once underwent a similar change. "I don't quite see how I am to get any breakfast," he thought to himself, looking enviously at his little daughter eating her bread and milk.

Hoping that by working very quickly he might avoid what he

now felt to be a considerable inconvenience, King Midas next
snatched a smoking hot-cake and attempted to cram it into his
mouth and swallow it in a hurry. But the Golden Touch was
too nimble for him. He found his mouth full, not of mealy pan-
cake, but of solid metal, which so burned his tongue that he
roared aloud. Jumping from the table, he began to stamp around
the room with pain and fright.

"Oh, poor Father!" cried his little daughter, who was of a most affectionate nature, "pray, what is the matter? Have you burnt your mouth?"

"Dear child," groaned Midas, "I don't know what is to become of your poor father!"

The little girl could endure it no longer. With a sweet impulse to comfort him, she ran to Midas and threw her arms affectionately about his knees. He bent down and kissed her, feeling that his little daughter's love was worth a thousand times more than what he had gained by the Golden Touch. "My precious, precious darling," he cried.

But the child made no answer.

Alas, what had he done? The moment his lips touched her forehead, a change had taken place. Her sweet, rosy face took on a glittering yellow color and her soft, tender form grew hard and inflexible in her father's arms. She was no longer a human child, but a golden statue!

Midas began to wring his hands and bemoan his terrible loss. He could neither bear to look at his daughter, nor yet to look away from her. While he was in this tumult of despair, he suddenly saw a stranger standing near the door. Midas bent down his head without speaking, for he recognized the same figure that had appeared to him in the treasure room the day before.

"Well, friend Midas," said the stranger, "pray, how do you succeed with the Golden Touch?"

Midas shook his head. "I am most miserable."

"Miserable indeed!" exclaimed the stranger. "Have you not everything that your heart desired?"

"Gold is not everything," answered Midas. "I have lost all that I really loved. Oh, my child, my dear child!" cried poor Midas wringing his hands. "I would not give that one small dimple in her chin for the power of changing this whole earth into gold!"

"You are wiser than you were, King Midas," said the stranger. "Tell me, do you really wish to rid yourself of this Golden Touch?"

"More than anything in the world!" replied Midas.

"Go then," said the stranger, "and plunge into the river that

runs past the bottom of your garden. Take some of that same water and sprinkle it over any object you wish to change back into
its former substance."

You may be sure that Midas lost no time in snatching up a large
pitcher and running down to the river where he plunged in headlong, without waiting so much as to pull off his shoes. Then noticing a violet that grew on the bank of the river, he touched it
with his finger, and was overjoyed to find that the delicate flower
kept its color instead of undergoing a yellow blight.

He hastened back to the palace and the first thing he did was
to sprinkle the river water over the golden figure of his little daughter. No sooner did it fall on her, than her rosy color came back,
and she began to sputter as her father threw still more water over
her. "Pray stop," she cried, "you are wetting my nice frock!"

The little girl did not know that she had been a golden statue,
and her father did not want to tell his beloved child how foolish
he had been. He contented himself with showing how much
wiser he had grown. Leading the little girl into the garden, he
sprinkled the remainder of the water over the rose bushes, so that
they all recovered their beautiful bloom.

Later he could not rest until everything around the palace that
had been transformed by the Golden Touch had been sprinkled
with the river water and restored to its original state. For ever
since that morning, more than anything in the world, King Midas
hated the sight of gold.

Adapted from *The Golden Touch* by Nathaniel Hawthorne.

PERSEUS AND THE GORGON HEAD

Perseus was the son of the great god Zeus (Jupiter) and Danae.
The father of Danae had consulted an oracle at his birth and was
alarmed to learn that the infant would one day be the cause of
his death. So he had Danae and her child shut up in a chest and
set adrift on the sea, thinking that they might thus be drowned.
But after drifting about for many days, the chest finally floated

to the shores of Seriphus where it was found by a fisherman. He brought the mother and child to Polydectes, the king of the country, who treated them kindly, offering them the hospitality of his own home.

When Perseus had grown to manhood, Polydectes called him to him and asked if he would be brave enough to try and rid his country of the terrible monster Medusa who was laying waste the kingdom. She was one of the Gorgons, monstrous females having huge tusks instead of teeth, claws made of brass, and on their heads instead of hair, hundreds of live, twisting, hissing snakes. Medusa had once been a beautiful maiden whose hair was her chief glory, but she had dared to compete in beauty with the goddesses. So her beautiful ringlets had been changed into hissing serpents and she herself into a cruel monster, so horrible to behold that no living thing could gaze at her frightful head without being turned at once into stone. All around the cave where she dwelt could be seen the petrified figures of people who had happened to catch a glimpse of her and had been turned to stone on the spot.

Perseus consented to try to conquer the Gorgon, but first, being the son of Zeus, he sought the help of the gods. Athena (Minerva) was kind to Perseus, and lent him her bright shield to protect him from the monster. Hermes (Mercury) lent him his wingèd shoes and told him to fly over Medusa while she slept and to remember that he must never look directly at the snaky head. Holding up his shield like a mirror, and guided only by the image as it was reflected in its bright surface, Perseus succeeded in cutting off the head of Medusa.

Bearing the Gorgon's head with him, Perseus continued on his flight until he arrived at the country of the Aethiopians of which Cepheus was the king. His queen, Cassiopeia, had been so proud of her beauty that she had dared to compare herself to the sea nymphs. This made them so angry that they sent a horrible sea-monster to ravage the coast. It roamed up and down the shore, destroying ships and killing everyone in its path. King Cepheus was in despair, and when he consulted an oracle, he was told that the only thing that could save the country was to allow his daughter Andromeda to be sacrificed to the sea-monster. So the poor girl was chained to a rock and left for the monster to devour.

As Perseus looked down from his aerial height, he beheld the beautiful maiden helpless on the rock, awaiting the moment of her death. She was so pale and motionless that if it had not been for her flowing tears and her hair that moved in the breeze, he would have taken her for a marble statue. He was so startled at the sight that he forgot to move his wings and almost tumbled into the water. Recovering his balance, and hovering over her, he said, "O maiden, undeserving of these chains, tell me, I beseech you, your name and the name of your country, and why you are thus bound."

At first she was silent from modesty. But when he gently repeated his questions, she grew less afraid, and told him her name and that of her country, and how her mother's pride had brought a punishment to the land. Before she had done speaking, a sound was heard in the water, and there came the sea-monster with his head raised above the surface, and his broad breast parting the waves. Andromeda shrieked, and her father and mother who had been standing on the shore in utter misery, rushed up to the rock and stood by, helpless, and sobbing for the poor victim.

Then Perseus said, "There will be time enough for tears. This hour is all we have for rescue. My rank as the son of Zeus, and my renown as the slayer of the Gorgon might make me acceptable as a suitor. But I will try to win her by the services I now hope to render, if the gods will favor me. If I succeed in rescuing her, I demand, as a reward, that she be my bride."

The parents swiftly gave their consent—how could they hesitate?—and promised a royal dowry as well.

Now, when the monster was within a stone's throw of the maiden, Perseus with a sudden bound, soared up into the air. As an eagle in his lofty flight sees a serpent basking in the sun and pounces upon him, seizing him by the neck to prevent him from turning his head around and using his fangs, so did the brave youth dart down upon the back of the monster. Then he plunged

his sword into his shoulder. Irritated by the wound, the monster
raised himself in the air, then dived back into the water. Then,
like a wild boar surrounded by a pack of barking dogs, he turned
swiftly from side to side, while Perseus escaped his attacks by
means of his wings. Wherever he could strike, Perseus plunged
his sword—wounding now between the scales, now on the flank.
From his nostrils the brute spouted water mixed with blood. Soon
the wings of the hero were wet with blood so that he dared no

longer trust them to hold him up. Alighting on a rock which rose above the waves, he caught the monster as he floated near, and gave him the death blow.

The people who had gathered on the shore meanwhile let out a great shout of rejoicing so that the hills re-echoed the sound. The parents, overcome with joy, embraced their future son-in-law, calling him their deliverer and the savior of their country. Andromeda descended from the rock and was embraced by Perseus.

They all went to the palace where a great wedding feast was spread for them, and all was joy and festivity. But suddenly, a loud warlike noise was heard, and Phineus, who had been betrothed to Andromeda, burst into the room with a large band of his followers and demanded the maiden as his own. It was in vain that King Cepheus reminded him, "You should have claimed her when she lay bound to the rock, the monster's victim. The sentence of the gods dooming her to such a fate dissolved the engagement, as death itself would have done."

Phineus made no reply, but hurled his javelin at Perseus. It missed its mark, however, and fell harmless. Perseus would have thrown his in return, but his cowardly assailant ran and took shelter behind the altar. This act was a signal to his band to attack the guests. They defended themselves and soon a general conflict began.

Perseus and his friends kept up the unequal contest for some time, but the numbers of their assailants were too great for them, and defeat seemed inevitable. Then a sudden thought struck Perseus—"I will make my enemy defend me." He called out in a loud voice, "If I have any friends here, let them turn away their eyes!" And he held up the Gorgon's head.

"Seek not to frighten us with your juggling," said one of the band of Cepheus, and he raised his javelin to throw it. Immediately he turned to stone in that very attitude. Another was about to plunge his sword into the fallen body of one of Perseus' friends —when his arm stiffened so that he could neither thrust forward nor withdraw. All around Phineus' men stood petrified with their mouths open in the midst of a challenge; but no sound came forth.

Phineus beheld the dreadful result of his unjust demands and knew that he must pay for it. He called aloud to his friends, but got no answer. He touched them and found them stone. Falling on his knees, he stretched out his hands to Perseus, begging for mercy, but he took care to turn his head away from the sight of Medusa. "Take all," he cried, "spare me but my life."

"Base coward," answered Perseus, "this much I will grant you, no weapon shall touch you. Instead, you shall be preserved in my house forever as a memorial of these events."

So saying, he held the Gorgon's head to the side where Phineus was looking. And then in the very form in which he knelt, with his arms outstretched and face averted, Phineus became fixed immovably, a statue of stone!

Based on *The Age of Fable* by Thomas Bulfinch.

ATALANTA'S RACE

Atalanta was a beautiful maiden who was resolved to live unwed, and at last she devised a plan to be rid of all her suitors. She was known far and wide as the swiftest runner of her time; and so she said that she would marry only that man who could outstrip her in a race, but that all who dared to try and failed would be put to death.

This threat did not dishearten all of the suitors, however, and to her grief, for she was not cruel, they held her to her promise. On a certain day the few bold men who were to try their fortune made ready, and chose young Hippomenes as judge. He sat watching them before the word was given, and sadly wondered why any brave man should risk his life merely to win a bride. But when Atalanta stood ready for the contest, he was amazed by her beauty. She looked like Hebe, the goddess of young health, and glad serving-maiden to the gods when they sit at feast.

The signal was given, and, as the fair Atalanta darted away, flight made her more enchanting than ever. Just as a wind brings sparkles to the water and laughter to the trees, speed fanned her loveliness to a glow.

Alas for the suitors! The girl ran as if Hermes had lent her his wingèd sandals. The young men, skilled as they were, grew heavy with weariness and despair. For all their efforts, it seemed as if they lagged like ships in a calm, while Atalanta flew before them in a favoring breeze—and reached the goal!

To the sorrow of all on-lookers, the suitors were led away. And the judge himself, Hippomenes, rose and begged leave to try his fortune. As Atalanta listened, and looked at him, her heart was filled with pity. She would willingly have let him win the race to save him from defeat and death, for he was comely and younger than the others. But her friends urged her to rest and make ready, and she consented, with an unwilling heart.

Meanwhile Hippomenes prayed within himself to Aphrodite (Venus): "Goddess of Love, give ear, and send me good speed. Let me be swift to win as I have been swift to love her."

Now Aphrodite who was not far off—for it was she who had moved the heart of Hippomenes to love—came to his side invisibly, slipped into his hand three wondrous golden apples, and whispered a word of counsel in his ear.

The signal was given; youth and maiden started over the course. They went so like the wind that they left not a footprint. The people cheered on Hippomenes, eager that such valor should win. But the course was long, and soon fatigue seemed to clutch at his throat, the light shook before his eyes, and, even as he pressed on, the maiden passed him by.

At that instant Hippomenes tossed ahead one of the golden apples. The rolling bright thing caught Atalanta's eye, and full of wonder she stooped to pick it up. Hippomenes ran on. As he heard the flutter of her tunic close behind him, he flung aside another golden apple, and another moment was lost to the girl. Who could pass by such a marvel? The goal was near and Hippomenes was ahead, but once again Atalanta caught up with him, and they sped side by side like two dragon-flies. For an instant his heart failed him; then, with a last prayer to Aphrodite, he flung down

the last apple. The maiden glanced at it, wavered, and would have left it where it had fallen, had not Aphrodite turned her head for a second and given her a sudden wish to possess it. Against her will she turned to pick up the golden apple, and Hippomenes touched the goal.

So he won that perilous maiden; and as for Atalanta, she was glad to have found such a valorous man.

From *Old Greek Folk Stories Told Anew* by Josephine P. Peabody.

PERSEPHONE

On the island of Sicily, in the valley of Enna, there is a lovely woodland lake screened from the hot sun, where the rich moist ground is covered with flowers and it is always springtime. Here Persephone (Proserpine), daughter of Demeter (Ceres), the goddess of the harvest, was playing with her friends one day gathering lilies and violets. As she filled her basket and apron with flowers, she strayed too far from her companions and wandered off alone in the woodland. There she was seen by Pluto, the king of the underworld, who fell in love with her and carried her off in his chariot.

Persephone screamed for help, but Pluto urged his coal-black steeds on fiercely, calling them by name and throwing loose over their heads his iron-colored reins. When he reached the River Cyane and it tried to stop him, he struck the river bank with his trident and the earth opened and gave him passage down to Hades. Thus he bore Persephone away, weeping, down to his underground kingdom.

Her mother Demeter searched for her daughter the whole world over. In her great grief, the goddess left Olympus and dwelt on earth, disguised so that no mortal could recognize her. Bright-haired Aurora when she came forth with the dawn, and Hesperus when he led the stars out in the evening, found her still busy with her search. But it was to no avail. At length, weary and sad, she sat down upon a stone and continued sitting there for nine days and nine nights in the open fields, under the sunlight and moonlight and falling showers.

As she sat there an old man named Celeus was working in the fields, gathering herbs and berries and wood for his fire. His little daughter was driving home their two goats, and as she passed

the goddess, who was disguised as an old woman, she said to her, "Mother,"—and the name was sweet to the ears of Demeter —"why do you sit there alone on these rocks?" The old man stopped in pity too, though the load on his back was heavy, and he begged her to come to their cottage, poor as it was. She thanked them, but declined, and he urged her again.

"Go in peace," she replied, "and be happy in your daughter. I have lost mine." As she spoke, tears fell down her cheeks and upon her bosom. The kind old man and his daughter wept with her.

Then he said, "Come with us, and spurn not our humble roof; so may your daughter be restored to you in safety."

"Lead on," said Demeter, "that is an appeal I cannot resist." So she rose from the stone and went with them. As they walked along, he told her that his little boy, his only son, lay sleepless and very sick with fever. Hearing this, she stooped down and gathered some poppies. When they entered the cottage, they found the boy's mother in great distress, for he had grown worse and now seemed past hope of recovery. Yet the mother received Demeter kindly and made her welcome. The goddess went over to where the boy lay and bent over and kissed the lips of the sick child. Instantly, the paleness left his face and he became strong and healthy again.

The family was overjoyed, and they spread the table, putting on it curds and cream, apples, and honey in the comb. While they ate Demeter sprinkled some poppy juice in the boy's milk. When night came and everything was quiet, she arose, and taking up the sleeping boy, she moulded his limbs gently with her hands, chanting a solemn charm over him three times, then went and laid him in the ashes. His mother, who had awakened and was watching what her guest was doing, sprang forward with a scream and snatched the child from the ashes.

Now Demeter dropped her disguise and stood forth in her own goddess form, while a divine brightness shone all around her. To the family overcome with surprise and awe she said, "Mother, you have been foolish in your concern for your son. I would have made him immortal, but now you have spoiled my attempt. Nevertheless he shall be great and useful to the world. He shall teach mankind how to use the plough, and how to cultivate the soil so as to bring forth new abundance." So saying, she wrapped a cloud about her, and mounting her chariot, disappeared into the air.

Demeter continued her search for her daughter, passing from one land to another, and across the rivers and the seas, till at last she returned to Sicily where she had begun her search. She stood by the banks of the River Cyane, at the very spot where Pluto had made himself a passage to carry Persephone down to the underworld. The river nymph wanted to tell the goddess what she had seen here, but she dared not, for fear of Pluto. All she could venture to do was to take the girdle which Persephone had dropped in her flight and let the river float it to the feet of the mother.

When she saw this, Demeter was no longer in doubt about her loss. But still she did not know the cause, and she blamed it on the innocent land. "Ungrateful soil," said she, "which I have made fertile and clothed in green grass and nourishing grain, no longer shall you enjoy my favors." Then there followed a most dreadful time on earth when nothing would grow. The seed failed to come up; there was too much sun; there was too much rain; thistles and brambles were the only things that grew, and the cattle died.

The fountain Arethusa begged Demeter to have mercy. "Goddess," she said, "do not blame the land. It opened unwillingly to yield a passage to your daughter. I can tell you what has become of Persephone because I have seen her when I passed through the lower parts of the earth. She looked sad, but no longer fearful. Her look was such as became a queen—which she now is—the queen of the powerful monarch of the kingdom of the dead."

Demeter stood for a while like one stupefied. Then she sprang into her chariot and turned it towards heaven, where she hastened to present herself before the throne of Zeus (Jupiter). She told him her story and begged him to restore her daughter to her. Zeus agreed to do so on one condition—that Persephone should not have eaten any food during her stay in the lower world. Otherwise the Fates forbade her release.

The messenger god Hermes (Mercury) was sent down to Hades to demand Persephone of Pluto. But alas, although the maiden in her great longing for her mother had refused all food, she had taken a single pomegranate which Pluto had urged on her, and sucked the sweet pulp from a few of the seeds. This was enough to prevent her complete release. But a compromise was made—

Persephone was to spend half the time with her mother in the upper world, and the other half with her husband in Hades. Demeter was pacified with this arrangement and restored the earth to her favor.

So during the time that her daughter comes back to her in the upper world, the earth goddess makes the land rich with grain and fruit and bright with green fields and with flowers. When her daughter has to go back to the underworld in the winter, she withholds her gifts. And whenever springtime comes, and Persephone with it, the earth blooms anew.

Based on *The Age of Fable* by Thomas Bulfinch.

PANDORA'S CURIOSITY

Even though mighty Zeus (Jupiter) had already inflicted a terrible punishment on Prometheus for having stolen fire from heaven to give to mankind, he was still angry with him. He decided to send a gift to Epimetheus, the brother of Prometheus, which would plague mankind still further.

So Zeus had the first woman fashioned on Olympus out of clay brought from the earth. When she emerged, she was as radiant as any goddess, and all the gods and goddesses stood around admiring her. Then they all contributed something to make her more perfect—Aphrodite (Venus) gave her beauty, Apollo the gift of music, Hermes (Mercury) the art of persuasion, the Three Graces bestowed upon her every social charm. And the first woman was called Pandora, which means "all-gifted." As a special dowry, Zeus also presented her with a golden box of marvellous beauty that he warned her, however, never to open.

Then Zeus sent this lovely creature down to earth to be the wife of Epimetheus. And he was so enchanted with her beauty and grace that he completely forgot that his brother Prometheus had warned him to beware of accepting any gift from the hand of

Zeus. When he saw the golden box, however, he remembered his brother's warning. "What is in this box?" he asked Pandora.

"I do not know, dear husband," she answered. "I was told not to open it. But it is so beautiful that I am sure it must contain some equally lovely gift from the gods. Let us open it together."

Now Epimetheus was certain that it contained something evil and had been sent to do him harm. He decided to do away with it, but Pandora pleaded with him, saying that she would be con-

tent only to look at its marvellous beauty, and would never open it. Thinking it could do no harm as long as it was kept shut, Epimetheus finally consented to let her keep it, on her solemn promise never to look inside.

For a long time Pandora kept the box in her chamber, admiring its golden loveliness and wondering what it might possibly contain. Her curiosity to learn its secret grew stronger and stronger, until one day she could no longer resist the temptation. "I shall open it just the merest crack," she reasoned to herself, "then shut it at once. Surely that can do no harm."

She gently raised the lid, and immediately out rushed a thick dark cloud from which escaped a horde of hideous, buzzing, little insects that spread out in all directions. What Pandora had let loose over the earth were the spirits of hatred, envy, pain, disease, war, famine—all the evils which have plagued mankind from that hour. She hastened to shut the box, but it was too late. All the evils had already escaped. There was one thing, however, that still lay at the bottom of the box, and that last thing was *Hope*.

That is why, to this day, no matter what evils are abroad, hope never leaves us. And while we have that, no amount of ills can completely defeat us.

Based on *The Age of Fable* by Thomas Bulfinch.

A Norse Myth

In contrast to the graceful beauty and balance of the Greek myths, the Norse stories seem much more terse and grim. Nature is more rigorous in the north and man's struggle against natural forces much harder. Most of the Norse myths are told with a grand sweep that shows great strength and heroic courage. The continual warfare between the forces of the good gods and the forces of evil, such as the frost giants, give these stories a special spiritual quality. This story of how Thor loses and finds his hammer is unusual in that the mighty Thor pretending to be a woman is a rather ridiculous situation, quite different from the serious and even somber tone of most of the Norse myths.

The frost-giants were always trying to get into Asgard. For more than half the year they held the world in their grasp, locking up the streams in their rocky beds, hushing their music and the music of the birds as well, and leaving nothing but a wild waste of desolation under the cold sky. They hated the warm sunshine which stirred the wild flowers out of their sleep, and clothed the steep mountains with verdure, and set all the birds a-singing in the swaying tree-tops. They hated the beautiful god Balder, whose presence brought summer back to the ice-bound earth, and, above all, they hated Thor, whose flashing hammer drove them back into Jotunheim, and guarded the summer sky with its sudden

gleamings of power. So long as Thor had his hammer Asgard was safe against the giants.

One morning Thor started up out of a long, deep sleep, and put out his hand for the hammer; but no hammer was there. Not a sign of it could be found anywhere, although Thor anxiously searched for it. Then a thought of the giants came suddenly in his mind; and his anger rose till his eyes flashed like great fires, and his red beard trembled with wrath.

"Look, now, Loki," he shouted, "they have stolen Mjolner by enchantment, and no one on earth or in heaven knows where they have hidden it."

"We will get Freyja's falcon-guise and search for it," answered Loki, who was always quick to get into trouble or to get out of it again. So they went quickly to Folkvang and found Freyja surrounded by her maidens and weeping tears of pure gold, as she had always done since her husband went on his long journey.

"The hammer has been stolen by enchantment," said Thor. "Will you lend me the falcon-guise that I may search for it?"

"If it were silver, or even gold, you should have it and welcome," answered Freyja, glad to help Thor find the wonderful hammer that kept them all safe from the hands of the frost-giants.

So the falcon-guise was brought, and Loki put it on and flew swiftly out of Asgard to the home of the giants. His great wings made broad shadows over the ripe fields as he swept along, and the reapers, looking up from their work, wondered what mighty bird was flying seaward. At last he reached Jotunheim, and no sooner had he touched ground and taken off the falcon-guise than he came upon the giant Thrym, sitting on a hill twisting golden collars for his dogs and stroking the long manes of his horses.

"Welcome, Loki," said the giant. "How fares it with the gods and the elves, and what has brought you to Jotunheim?"

"It fares ill with both gods and elves since you stole Thor's hammer," replied Loki, guessing quickly that Thrym was the thief; "and I have come to find where you have hidden it."

Thrym laughed as only a giant can when he knows he has made trouble for somebody.

"You won't find it," he said at last. "I have buried it eight miles underground, and no one shall take it away unless he gets Freyja for me as my wife."

The giant looked as if he meant what he said, and Loki, seeing no other way of finding the hammer, put on his falcon-guise and flew back to Asgard. Thor was waiting to hear what news he brought, and both were soon at the great doors of Folkvang.

"Put on your bridal dress, Freyja," said Thor bluntly, after his fashion, "and we will ride swiftly to Jotunheim."

But Freyja had no idea of marrying a giant just to please Thor; and, in fact, that Thor should ask her to do such a thing threw her into such a rage that the floor shook under her angry tread, and her necklace snapped in pieces.

"Do you think I am a weak lovesick girl, to follow you to Jotunheim and marry Thrym?" she cried indignantly.

Finding they could do nothing with Freyja, Thor and Loki called all the gods together to talk over the matter and decide what should be done to get back the hammer. The gods were very much alarmed, because they knew the frost-giants would come upon Asgard as soon as they knew the hammer was gone. They said little, for they did not waste time with idle words, but they thought long and earnestly, and still they could find no way of getting hold of Mjolner once more. At last Heimdal, who had once been a Var, and could therefore look into the future, said: "We must have the hammer at once or Asgard will be in danger. If Freyja will not go, let Thor be dressed up and go in her place. Let keys jingle from his waist and a woman's dress fall about his feet. Put precious stones upon his breast, braid his hair like a woman's, hang the necklace around his neck, and bind the bridal veil around his head."

Thor frowned angrily. "If I dress like a woman," he said, "you will jeer at me."

"Don't talk of jeers," retorted Loki; "unless that hammer is brought back quickly, the giants will rule in our places."

Thor said no more, but allowed himself to be dressed like a bride, and soon drove off to Jotunheim with Loki beside him disguised as a servant-maid. There was never such a wedding journey before. They rode in Thor's chariot and the goats drew them, plunging swiftly along the way, thunder pealing through the mountains and the frightened earth blazing and smoking as they passed. When Thrym saw the bridal party coming he was filled with delight.

"Stand up, you giants," he shouted to his companions; "spread cushions upon the benches and bring in Freyja, my bride. My yards are full of golden-horned cows, black oxen please my gaze whichever way I look, great wealth and many treasures are mine, and Freyja is all I lack."

It was evening when the bride came driving into the giant's court in her blazing chariot. The feast was already spread against her coming, and with her veil modestly covering her face she was seated at the great table, Thrym fairly beside himself with delight. It wasn't every giant who could marry a goddess!

If the bridal journey had been so strange that any one but a foolish giant would have hesitated to marry a wife who came in such a turmoil of fire and storm, her conduct at the table ought certainly to have put Thrym on his guard; for never had a bride such an appetite before. The great tables groaned under the load of good things, but they were quickly relieved of their burden by the voracious bride. She ate a whole ox before the astonished giant had fairly begun to enjoy his meal. Then she devoured eight large salmon, one after the other, without stopping to take breath; and having eaten up the part of the feast specially prepared for the hungry men, she turned upon the delicacies which had been made for the women, and especially for Freyja's fastidious appetite.

Thrym looked on with wondering eyes, and at last, when she had added to these solid foods three whole barrels of mead, his amazement was so great that, his astonishment getting the better of his politeness, he called out, "Did any one ever see such an appetite in a bride before, or know a maid who could drink so much mead?"

Then Loki, who was playing the part of a serving-maid, thinking that the giant might have some suspicions, whispered to him, "Freyja was so happy in the thought of coming here that she has eaten nothing for eight whole days."

Thrym was so pleased at this evidence of affection that he leaned forward and raised the veil as gently as a giant could, but he instantly dropped it and sprang back the whole length of the hall before the bride's terrible eyes.

"Why are Freyja's eyes so sharp?" he called to Loki. "They burn me like fire."

"Oh," said the cunning serving-maid, "she has not slept for a week, so anxious has she been to come here, and that is why her eyes are so fiery."

Everybody looked at the bride and nobody envied Thrym. They thought it was too much like marrying a thunder-storm.

The giant's sister came into the hall just then, and seeing the veiled form of the bride sitting there went up to her and asked for a bridal gift. "If you would have my love and friendship give me those rings of gold upon your fingers."

But the bride sat perfectly silent. No one had yet seen her face or heard her voice.

Thrym became very impatient. "Bring in the hammer," he shouted, "that the bride may be consecrated, and wed us in the name of Var."

If the giant could have seen the bride's eyes when she heard these words he would have sent her home as quickly as possible, and looked somewhere else for a wife.

The hammer was brought and placed in the bride's lap, and everybody looked to see the marriage ceremony; but the wedding was more strange and terrible than the bridal journey had been. No sooner did the bride's fingers close round the handle of Mjolner than the veil which covered her face was torn off and there stood Thor, the giant-queller, his terrible eyes blazing with wrath.

The giants shuddered and shrank away from those flaming eyes, the sight of which they dreaded more than anything else in all the world. But there was no chance of escape. Thor swung the hammer round his head and the great house rocked on its foundations. There was a vivid flash of lightning, an awful crash of thunder, and the burning roof and walls buried the whole company in one common ruin.

Thrym was punished for stealing the hammer, his wedding guests got crushing blows instead of bridal gifts, and Thor and Loki went back to Asgard, where the presence of Mjolner made the gods safe once more.

From *Norse Stories* by Hamilton Wright Mabie.

More Good Reading

FAIRY TALES AND FOLK TALES

MANY MOONS by James Thurber. Illus. by Louis Slobodkin. Harcourt. Another fairy tale about a princess who wanted the moon, told with unusual humor.

ENGLISH FAIRY TALES edited by Joseph Jacobs. Illus. by J. D. Batten. Putnam. The richest source of favorite English folk tales, told in the traditional dialect. (Also *More English Fairy Tales* and *Celtic Fairy Tales*.)

CHARLES PERRAULT: ALL THE FRENCH FAIRY TALES retold by Louis Untermeyer. Illus. by Gustave Doré. Didier. Old favorites like *Cinderella, The White Cat,* etc. in a fine new translation, with reproductions of the superb Doré illustrations.

GRIMM'S FAIRY TALES. Illus. by Fritz Kredel. Grosset. A recent large, yet inexpensive, edition containing all the best known folk tales by the Grimm Brothers. For children of practically any age.

FAIRY TALES BY HANS CHRISTIAN ANDERSEN. Numerous editions since these fairy tale classics first appeared more than one hundred years ago. Children just learning to read love them, and young people in college appreciate them too.

THE BLUE, RED, GREEN FAIRY BOOKS by Andrew Lang. Longmans. Famous traditional fairy tales from many lands, each volume named after a color. Not to be missed by any child who likes fairy tales. (Also *Brown, Yellow, Crimson* and other colors.)

POPULAR TALES FROM THE NORSE by Peter C. Asbjörnsen and Jörgen Moe. Putnam. The finest treasure store of old Norwegian tales, containing such favorite stories as *East o' the Sun and West o' the Moon.*

THE ARABIAN NIGHTS. Many excellent editions of these old, yet ever fresh, stories of fabulous adventure and magic like *Sinbad the Sailor, Aladdin and the Wonderful Lamp.*

THE JACK TALES edited by Richard Chase. Illus. by Berkeley Williams. Houghton Mifflin. Vigorous and authentic folk tales of the Appalachian Mountain people, told in their humorous country dialect.

THE RED INDIAN FAIRY BOOK by Frances J. Olcott. Illus. by Frederick Richardson. Houghton Mifflin. Folk tales of the North American Indians, with stories from all the main tribes.

THE KING OF THE GOLDEN RIVER by John Ruskin. Illus. by Arthur Rackham. Lippincott. A strong and beautifully told tale of the triumph of kindness over cruelty.

BOYS AND GIRLS, TODAY AND YESTERDAY

UNDERSTOOD BETSY by Dorothy Canfield Fisher. Holt. How a spoiled and timid city girl learns independence and courage on a Vermont farm. Boys as well as girls will like this fine story.

RED SAILS TO CAPRI by Ann Weil. Illus. by C. B. Falls. Viking. A delightful tale about a delightful Italian mother and her family, and the dramatic story of the discovery of the Blue Grotto in Capri.

THE MATCHLOCK GUN by Walter D. Edmonds. Illus. by Paul Lantz. Dodd, Mead. A thrilling story of how a brave young boy in Colonial days repels an Indian attack with his father's gun.

IN MY MOTHER'S HOUSE by Ann Nolan Clark. Illus. by Velino Herrera. Viking. A beautifully told and illustrated story about Pueblo Indian children, written with deep understanding and sympathy for Indian life.

THE COTTAGE AT BANTRY BAY by Hilda Van Stockum. Viking. The lively story of the mischievious O'Sullivan children against a vivid background of Ireland today. Packed with humor.

AT THE PALACE GATES by Helen Rand Parish. Illus. by Leo Politi. Viking. A charming story of the adventures of an orphan Peruvian boy, a sort of "hillbilly" who comes down from the mountains to live on his own in Lima, and of how he saves the life of the president there.

SWALLOWS AND AMAZONS by Arthur Ransome. Illus. by Helene Carter. Lippincott. Outstandingly good stories about some imaginative and resourceful children, in the Lake Country of England, who have believable and exciting adventures with boats and other outdoor things.

LITTLE WOMEN by Louisa May Alcott. This warm family story has been a favorite with most American girls for many years, and it still is. (Also *Little Men* and *Jo's Boys*.)

CALL IT COURAGE by Armstrong Sperry. Macmillan. An exciting tale of adventure and also a good story of how a Polynesian boy conquered his fear of the sea.

THE HUNDRED DRESSES by Eleanor Estes. Illus. by Louis Slobodkin. Harcourt. An unforgettable story about a little Polish girl who was rejected by her American classmates until they understood her fantasy about her hundred dresses. By the author of the delightful *Moffat* books.

THE MELENDY FAMILY by Elizabeth Enright. Rinehart. Three favorite books about the lively Melendy children brought together in one volume: *The Saturdays, The Four-Story Mistake,* and *Then There Were Five.*

Index